LIFE
CONTINGENCIES

The Prentice Hall Series in Security and Insurance

Consulting Editor: *Kenneth Black, Jr.*

Batten	*Life Contingencies: A Guide for the Actuarial Student*
Batten	*Mortality Table Construction*
Berliner	*Limits of Insurability of Risks*
Black and Skipper	*Life Insurance,* 11th ed. (revised)
Dorfman	*Introduction to Insurance,* 4th ed.
Huebner, Black, and Cline	*Property and Liability Insurance,* 3rd ed.
Rejda	*Social Insurance and Economic Security,* 4th ed.
Riegel, Miller, and Williams	*Insurance Principles and Practices,* 6th ed.
Rosenbloom and Hallman	*Employee Benefit Planning,* 3rd ed.
Salzman	*Estimated Liabilities for Losses and Loss Adjustment Expenses*

LIFE CONTINGENCIES

A Guide for the Actuarial Student

ROBERT W. BATTEN
Georgia State University
Fellow of the Society of Actuaries

PRENTICE HALL, Englewood Cliffs, New Jersey 07632

Cover design: Jayne Conte
Manufacturing buyer: Peter Havens

This publication was typeset using AMS-TeX,
the American Mathematical Society's
TeX macro system.

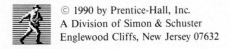 © 1990 by Prentice-Hall, Inc.
A Division of Simon & Schuster
Englewood Cliffs, New Jersey 07632

Printed in the United States of America

10 9 8 7 6 5 4 3 2 1

ISBN 0-13-539859-2   01

Prentice-Hall International (UK) Limited, *London*
Prentice-Hall of Australia Pty. Limited, *Sydney*
Prentice-Hall Canada Inc., *Toronto*
Prentice-Hall Hispanoamericana, S.A., *Mexico*
Prentice-Hall of India Private Limited, *New Delhi*
Prentice-Hall of Japan, Inc., *Tokyo*
Simon & Schuster Asia Pte. Ltd., *Singapore*
Editora Prentice-Hall do Brasil, Ltda., *Rio de Janeiro*

Contents

*This book is designed to parallel the life contingencies portion of *Actuarial Mathematics* by Newton L. Bowers *et al.* Therefore it does not cover Chapters 1, 2, 11, 12, and 13 of that text, which are devoted solely to the mathematical aspects of risk theory.

Chapter Seven

Chapter Eight

Chapter Nine

Chapter Ten

Chapter Fourteen

Chapter Fifteen

Preface

The Society of Actuaries' examination in life contingencies historically has been considered by the majority of actuarial students to be the most challenging and difficult of the Society's exams. Many students have continued to experience difficulties in grasping the relevant concepts necessary to be successful on this rigorous examination, even with the introduction of the excellent textbook *Actuarial Mathematics*. To aid in the understanding of the material and to maximize the chances of success on the examination, the student needs a sufficient quantity of illustrative examples and exercises to drive home the myriad of detailed concepts in this vital subject. Because most students of mathematics feel that the experience gained from solving large numbers of problems is invaluable, this book is designed to assist students of life contingencies to that end.

Each chapter of this manual begins with selected "Supplementary Concepts," designed in some cases to elaborate on material in *Actuarial Mathematics* and, in other cases, to introduce new approaches to replace traditional rote techniques. While some readers may categorize these techniques as "tricks," they should not be considered as such because they serve to clarify or improve upon more tedious methods, while still being solidly grounded in the underlying theory.

Included are numerous multiple choice problems from each of the ten chapters currently on the syllabus for the life contingencies examination, Course 150. Solutions, some detailed and some sketchy, are given. It is strongly recommended, however, that students refer to the solutions only after having explored all avenues on their own.

It is important that the student realize that these questions are not designed specifically for exam preparation. Rather, their purpose is to help the student with the intricacies of the subject matter, chapter by chapter, illustrating numerous logical insights along the way. This book should be considered a companion source which, along with *Actuarial Mathematics* itself, should provide the highly motivated student with a very realistic chance of passing the examination on the first attempt. More important, this book should facilitate the student's grasp of the subject, which will be the foundation for much of the practical actuarial work to be encountered in his or her professional career. The problem set for each chapter should be completed and thoroughly understood before the next chapter is begun.

The problems included are not designed to be typical actuarial examination questions, as many are either significantly easier or significantly harder than such questions. It is not recommended that these problems be used as dry-run exams under simulated test conditions; they should be considered slowly and deliberately with the text and other study materials available for reference.

Students will note that a disproportionate number of these questions involve the assumption that the random variable T is distributed either uniformly or exponentially; in other words, either De Moivre's Law or a constant force of mortality is assumed. Heavy use of these assumptions is not intended to give credibility to these unrealistic patterns of mortality. They are used, for the most part, to avoid an undue amount of arithmetic, which often serves to cloud the underlying principles. In other cases they are used to illustrate relationships between life contingencies and basic knowledge that the student should have gained from the earlier study of probability and statistics.

Notation used in this manual corresponds very closely with that of *Actuarial Mathematics*. One minor exception is the use of the superscript (T) rather than the

Greek letter tau (τ) to represent the lives in a multiple decrement table subject to all causes of decrement. The symbol $l_x^{(\tau)}$, for example, should be read "l_x total."

The exercises contained herein were developed in the course of teaching life contingencies at Georgia State University over the last five years. Many students in these courses have made contributions to their development and to their critical evaluation. Thanks go to Julie A. Pomroy and the staff of the Composition Services department of the American Mathematical Society for their assistance in the design and production of this book. Special thanks go to Wendy J. Engel and Deborah A. Kroll, graduate research assistants, for their painstaking review of the contents of this book. Mistakes, however, surely remain and are the sole responsibility of the author; readers who uncover errors of any kind are encouraged to bring them to his attention.

It is the author's sincere hope that the contents of this book will bring a new level of comprehension to students of life contingencies, accompanied by an increased appreciation for the mathematical and logical beauty of the subject. Many students have previously considered life contingencies as an uninteresting mass of formulas which, as a last resort or often out of frustration, are committed to memory with a generally low degree of success. As the serious student will rapidly learn, the degree of progress in the understanding of life contingencies is inversely proportional to the number of formulas he or she consciously puts to memory. A parallel study of the primary text and this book should allow the student to replace the necessity to memorize with an intuitive understanding of the basic concepts.

*LIFE
CONTINGENCIES*

Chapter Three

Supplementary Concepts

1. The force of mortality, μ_x, which is of vital importance in life contingencies, may be defined in several ways. The most common is

$$\mu_x = \frac{-\frac{d}{dx}l_x}{l_x}.$$

The student's grasp of the concept should be enhanced by the following:

$$\mu_x \doteq 2(_{1/2}q_x) \doteq 4(_{1/4}q_x) \doteq 365(_{1/365}q_x) \doteq 1000(_{.001}q_x)$$

$$\mu_x = \lim_{h \to o} \frac{_h q_x}{h}$$

This point of view emphasizes both the *annualized* and *instantaneous* nature of the force of mortality, as well as the conceptual relationship between μ_x and q_x.

2. Although it should be evident, it must be observed that the probability that (x) will survive to age $x + n$ is the same as the probability that (x) will die *after* age $x + n$, i.e.,

$$_n p_x = \int_n^\infty {}_t p_x \mu_{x+t} \, dt.$$

3. The mode of the distribution of X is found at the maximum of the curve of deaths $l_x \mu_x$, an age at which $\frac{d}{dx}\mu_x = (\mu_x)^2$.

4. The adjustment of a force of mortality by a multiplicative constant has a simple effect on probabilities of survival. Specifically,

$$\mu'_x = k\mu_x \text{ for all } x \Rightarrow {}_t p'_x = ({}_t p_x)^k \text{ for all } x, t.$$

In addition, if $\mu'_x = \frac{k}{\omega - x}$, $0 \le x < \omega$, then

$$\overset{\circ}{e}'_x = \frac{\omega - x}{k + 1}.$$

5. The following facts from elementary population theory should facilitate the understanding of relationships between T_x, L_x, l_x, and $a(x)$.

Consider those l_x persons who survive to age x from an initial survivorship group of l_0 births:

Total lifetime after age x: T_x
Total lifetime after age $x+1$: T_{x+1}
Average lifetime after age x: $\frac{T_x}{l_x} = \overset{\circ}{e}_x$
Average lifetime between ages x and $x+1$: $\frac{L_x}{l_x}$

Similarly, consider those $l_x - l_{x+1} = d_x$ persons who survive to age x but not to age $x+1$:

Total lifetime after age $x \equiv$ Total lifetime between ages x and $x+1$
$$= T_x - T_{x+1} - l_{x+1} = L_x - l_{x+1}$$
Average lifetime after age $x = \dfrac{L_x - l_{x+1}}{l_x - l_{x+1}} = a(x)$.

6.   Valuable and logically-evident recursion formulas for expectations of life include

$$e_x = p_x(1 + e_{x+1})$$
$$\overset{\circ}{e}_x = p_x(1 + \overset{\circ}{e}_{x+1}) + q_x a(x)$$
$$e_x = e_{x:\overline{m|}} + {}_np_x e_{x+n}$$
$$\overset{\circ}{e}_x = \overset{\circ}{e}_{x:\overline{m|}} + {}_np_x \overset{\circ}{e}_{x+n}$$

7.   The geometric distribution of the random variable K, for which all values of q_x are equal at integral ages x, is easily confused with the assumption of a constant force of mortality.

If a constant force of mortality is assumed, all values of q_x are necessarily equal. Accordingly, an assumption that T is exponentially distributed implies that K is geometrically distributed. For example, if T is exponential, we have $\overset{\circ}{e}_x = \dfrac{1}{\mu}$ and $e_x = \dfrac{p_x}{q_x}$.

However, if the values of q_x at integral ages are assumed to be constant, it cannot be inferred that the force of mortality is constant. For example, if K is geometric, we have $e_x = \dfrac{p_x}{q_x}$. It cannot be assumed that $\overset{\circ}{e}_x = \dfrac{-1}{ln\,p_x}$ as if μ were constant.

8.   The distinction between de Moivre's Law and "uniform distribution of deaths over the year of age" has not always been clearly understood. The latter assumption, which we shall simply represent by "UDD," is that the values of l_{x+t}, $0 \le t \le 1$, fall on a straight line. In a much more restrictive (and unlikely) sense, de Moivre's Law assumes that l_x is a linear function over the entire age continuum, $0 \le x \le \omega$.

In other words, the UDD assumption hypothesizes a sequence of straight lines, with (generally) different slopes, connecting the values of l_x and l_{x+1}. De Moivre's Law hypothesizes a single straight line, connecting the points $(0, l_0)$ and $(\omega, 0)$.

9.   A commonly-encountered survival function is $s(x) = \dfrac{a}{a+x}$, for some $a > 0$. Although it is easily derived, it is efficient to memorize that this survival function implies that the force of mortality μ_x equals $\dfrac{1}{a+x}$, and vice versa.

Special Mortality Laws

I. de Moivre's Law (DML)

$$s(x) = \frac{\omega - x}{\omega}, \ 0 \le x \le \omega$$

$$l_x = l_0 \frac{\omega - x}{\omega}$$

$$q_x = \mu_x = \frac{1}{\omega - x}$$

$$_{n|m}q_x = \frac{m}{\omega - x}$$

$$_np_x = \frac{\omega - x - n}{\omega - x}$$

$$_tp_x\mu_{x+t} = q_x = f(t)$$

$$L_x = \frac{1}{2}(l_x + l_{x+1})$$

$$T_x = \frac{1}{2}l_x + \sum_{k=1}^{\omega - x - 1} l_{x+k} = \frac{l_0(\omega - x)^2}{2\omega}$$

$$\mathring{e}_x = \frac{\omega - x}{2} = E[T] = \text{MEDIAN}[T]$$

$$e_x = \frac{\omega - x - 1}{2} = E[K]$$

$$\text{VAR}[T] = \frac{(\omega - x)^2}{12}$$

$$\text{VAR}[K] = \frac{(\omega - x)^2 - 1}{12}$$

$$m_x = \frac{q_x}{1 - \frac{1}{2}q_x} = \frac{2d_x}{l_x + l_{x+1}}$$

$$E[S] = \frac{1}{2} = a(x)$$

$$\mathring{e}_{x:\overline{n}|} = n \cdot {}_np_x + \frac{n}{2} \cdot {}_nq_x$$

II. Constant Force of Mortality (CF)

$$\mu_x = \mu > 0 \text{ for all } x$$

$$s(x) = e^{-\mu x}$$

$$l_x = l_0 e^{-\mu x}$$

$$_np_x = e^{-n\mu} = (p_x)^n$$

$$T_x = \frac{l_0}{\mu} e^{-\mu x}$$

$$\overset{\circ}{e}_x = \frac{1}{\mu} = E[T] = E[X]$$

$$VAR[T] = VAR[X] = \frac{1}{\mu^2}$$

$$a(x) = \frac{1}{\mu} - \frac{p_x}{q_x} < \frac{1}{2}$$

$$m_x = \mu$$

$$\text{Mode}[T] = 0 = \text{Mode}[X]$$

$$\text{Median}[T] = \frac{1}{\mu} ln2 = \text{Median}[X]$$

$$e_x = \frac{p_x}{q_x} = E[K] = \frac{1}{e^\mu - 1}$$

$$VAR[K] = \frac{p_x}{(q_x)^2}$$

Mortality is independent of age.

S and K are independent.

III. Balducci Hypothesis (BAL)

$$_{1-t}q_{x+t} = (1 - t)q_x, \ 0 \le t \le 1$$

$$\mu_{x+t} = \frac{q_x}{1 - (1 - t)q_x}, \ 0 \le t \le 1$$

$$_tq_x = \frac{tq_x}{1 - (1 - t)q_x} = t\mu_{x+t}, \ 0 \le t \le 1$$

$$_tp_x = \frac{p_x}{1 - (1 - t)q_x}, \ 0 \le t \le 1$$

$$_sq_{x+t} = \frac{sq_x}{1 - (1 - t - s)q_x} = s\mu_{x+t+s}, 0 \le s + t \le 1$$

IV. Uniform Distribution of Deaths (UDD)

$$_tq_x = t \cdot q_x, \ 0 \le t \le 1$$

$$\mu_{x+t} = \frac{q_x}{1 - tq_x}, \ 0 \le t \le 1$$

$$_sq_{x+t} = \frac{sq_x}{1 - tq_x}, \ 0 \le s + t \le 1$$

S and K are independent.

$$VAR[T] = VAR[K] + \frac{1}{12}$$

$$m_x = \mu_{x+(1/2)} = \frac{q_x}{1 - \frac{1}{2}q_x} = \frac{2d_x}{l_x + l_{x+1}}$$

$$L_x = l_x - \frac{1}{2}d_x$$

$$_tp_x\mu_{x+t} = q_x, \ 0 \le t \le 1$$

V. Gompertz' Law (GL)

$$\mu_x = Bc^x$$

$$_np_x = g^{c^x(c^n - 1)}, \text{ where } g = e^{-B/ln\,c}$$

$$s(x) = g^{c^x - 1}$$

VI. Makeham's Law (ML)

$$\mu_x = A + Bc^x$$

$$_np_x = s^n g^{c^x(c^n - 1)}, \text{ where } g = e^{-B/ln\,c} \text{ and } s = e^{-A}$$

$$s(x) = s^x g^{c^x - 1}$$

VII. Weibull's Law (WL)

$$\mu_x = kx^n$$

$$s(x) = e^{-\frac{k}{n+1}x^{n+1}}$$

Derivatives

$$\frac{\partial}{\partial x}\,_tp_x = {}_tp_x(\mu_x - \mu_{x+t})$$

$$\frac{\partial}{\partial t}\,_tp_x = -{}_tp_x\mu_{x+t}$$

$$\frac{\partial}{\partial x}l_{x+t} = \frac{\partial}{\partial t}l_{x+t} = -l_{x+t}\mu_{x+t}$$

$$\frac{d}{dx}\ln s(x) = -\mu_x$$

$$\frac{\partial}{\partial t}\,_{1-t}p_{x+t} = {}_{1-t}p_{x+t}\mu_{x+t}$$

$$\frac{d}{dx}T_x = -l_x$$

$$\frac{d}{dx}L_x = -d_x$$

$$\frac{d}{dx}\mathring{e}_x = \mu_x\mathring{e}_x - 1$$

Exercises

3-1   Define $z(w) = e^{-\int_x^{x+w}\mu_y\,dy} - 1$.

In terms of $z(w)$, indicate the probability that (x) will die between age n and age m, $x < n < m$.

A) $z(m - x) - z(n - x)$ B) $z(n + m - x) - z(n - x)$

C) $z(n - x) - z(m - x)$ D) $z(n - x) - z(n + m - x)$ E) $z(n) - z(m)$

3-2   The mortality pattern of 50,000 newborns in such that $l_x\mu_x$ is constant, $0 \le x < \omega$.

If $\dfrac{d^6}{dx^6}\mu_x = \dfrac{45}{8}$ at $x = 58$, find the expected number alive at age 42.

A) 15,000   B) 16,000   C) 17,000   D) 18,000   E) 19,000

3-3   If $\dfrac{\ln(\frac{1}{\mathring{e}_x} + 1)}{6} = 1$ for all x, find $_{10}p_x$.

A) e^{-12} B) e^{-30} C) e^{-60} D) e^{-6} E) Not enough information

3-4   If the survival function is given by $s(x) = \left(\dfrac{1}{1+x}\right)^4$, $x \geq 0$, how much longer can a forty-one year old "expect" to live?

A) 14 yrs.   B) $18\frac{1}{2}$ yrs.   C) 20 yrs.   D) 40 yrs.   E) 42 yrs.

3-5   Suppose $l_x = 1000 - 2x$, $0 \leq x \leq 500$.

Find the variance of the integral number of years of future lifetime at age 497.

A) $\frac{2}{3}$ B) $\frac{3}{4}$ C) $\frac{4}{3}$ D) $\frac{5}{3}$ E) 2

3-6   If $\mu_x = \dfrac{2}{100 - x}$, $0 \leq x < 100$, find m_{95}.

A) $\frac{1}{5}$ B) $\frac{1}{4}$ C) $\frac{2}{9}$ D) $\frac{18}{41}$ E) $\frac{27}{61}$

3-7   If $s(x) = 1 - \dfrac{x}{200}$, $0 \leq x \leq 200$, find $\mathring{e}_{50:\overline{10|}}$.

A) 5   B) $5\frac{1}{2}$ C) 9   D) $9\frac{1}{3}$ E) $9\frac{2}{3}$

3-8   If $\mu_x = \dfrac{1}{4 + x}$, $x \geq 0$, what is the probability that the age of death of a newborn is greater than five?

A) $\frac{1}{6}$ B) $\frac{2}{7}$ C) $\frac{3}{8}$ D) $\frac{4}{9}$ E) $\frac{1}{2}$

3-9   Given:

$$\sum_{40}^{\infty} L_x = 5900 \qquad a(40) = .75 \qquad l_{42} = 360$$

$$\sum_{41}^{\infty} L_x = 5400 \qquad a(41) = .5 \qquad l_{43} = 240$$

$$\sum_{42}^{\infty} L_x = 5000 \qquad a(42) = .65 \qquad l_{44} = 150$$

Find $\mathring{e}_{40}$.

A) 10.95   B) 11.15   C) 11.35   D) 11.55   E) 11.75

3-10   If $\mu_x = \dfrac{3}{110 - x} + \dfrac{2}{150 - x}$, $0 \leq x < 110$, find $_{70}p_{10}$.

A) .00234   B) .00675   C) .01500   D) .02090   E) .22500

3–11   If $E[T|T < 1] = \frac{3}{4}$ for a life aged 7, and if $l_7 = 80$ and $q_7 = .2$, find the central death rate at age 7.

A) $\frac{4}{19}$ B) $\frac{1}{4}$ C) $\frac{5}{16}$ D) $\frac{3}{4}$ E) $\frac{5}{19}$

3–12   Which of the following is/are true?

   I. $VAR[K] + (E[K])^2 = \sum_{0}^{\infty}(k + 1)_{k+1}p_x$

   II. $\mathring{e}_{x:\overline{n}|} = n - \int_0^n \int_0^t {}_sp_x\mu_{x+t}\,ds\,dt$

   III. $\int_0^x \mu_y\,dy = ln\left[\dfrac{l_0}{\int_0^1 l_{x+t}\,dt - a(x)\,d_x}\right]$

   IV. If $\mu_k = k^2$, $0 \le x$, the mode of the distribution of X exceeds its median for all positive k.

A) None   B) I only   C) II only   D) III only   E) IV only

3–13   Given: $f(x) = \dfrac{1}{20\sqrt{100 - x}}$, $0 \le x < 100$.

Find the probability that (69.75) will die within the next ten years.

A) $\frac{20}{121}$ B) $\frac{40}{121}$ C) $\frac{2}{11}$ D) $\frac{4}{11}$ E) $\frac{5}{11}$

3–14   Assuming a constant force of mortality, the expected future lifetime of (x) is 2 years.

Find the 75th percentile of the distribution of T.

A) $\frac{1}{2}ln4$ B) $2ln4$ C) $\frac{1}{2}ln\frac{4}{3}$ D) $2ln\frac{4}{3}$ E) None of these

3–15   Given: $s(x) = e^{-2x}$, $x \ge 0$

Let A = mean of X
     B = median of X
     C = mode of X
     D = variance of X
Which of the following is true?

A) $B < D < C < A$ B) $C < D < A < B$
C) $C < A < D < B$ D) $C < D < B < A$
E) $B < A < C < D$

3–16 If $_{\frac{1}{k}}q_x = \dfrac{2}{1+4k}$ for $k > 100$, find μ_x.

    A) $\dfrac{1}{100}$ B) $\dfrac{1}{8}$ C) $\dfrac{1}{4}$ D) $\dfrac{1}{2}$ E) Cannot be determined

3–17 If $s(x) = e^{-ex}$, $x \geq 0$, find the average age of death of all those persons now aged e.

    A) $\dfrac{1}{e}$ B) $\dfrac{2}{e}$ C) $\dfrac{e+1}{e}$ D) $\dfrac{e^2+1}{e}$ E) $e^2 + 1$

3–18 If $l_x = (100 - x)^n$, $0 \leq x \leq 100$, which of the following is equal to $\frac{d}{dx} \ln \overset{\circ}{e}_x$?

    A) $\dfrac{1}{100-x}$ B) $\dfrac{2}{100-x}$ C) $\dfrac{n}{100-x}$ D) $\dfrac{1}{x-100}$ E) $\dfrac{2}{x-100}$

3–19 If $\int_{10}^{\infty} {}_tp_{50}\,dt = 15$ and $\int_0^{\infty} {}_tp_{60}\,dt = 20$, find $_{10}p_{50}$.

    A) $\dfrac{1}{4}$ B) $\dfrac{1}{2}$ C) $\dfrac{3}{4}$ D) 1   E) Not enough information

3–20 If $\mu_x = 1$ for all x, find $E[S]$.

    A) $\dfrac{e-2}{e-1}$ B) $\dfrac{e-1}{e}$ C) $\dfrac{1}{2}$ D) $\dfrac{e}{e+1}$ E) $\dfrac{e+1}{e+2}$

3–21 If $\mu_x = \dfrac{x}{100 - x^2}$, $0 \leq x < 10$, find $F(6)$.

    A) .2   B) .4   C) .5   D) .6   E) .8

3–22 Given: $s(x) = e^{-.2x} - e^{-.4x}$, $x > 5 \ln 2$.

Find the mode of the distribution of deaths among a group of lives now aged $5\ln 2$.

    A) $5\ln2$ B) $6\ln2$ C) $8\ln2$ D) $10\ln2$ E) $12\ln2$

3–23 Given: $_np_{20} = \dfrac{e_{20}}{5 \cdot 2^n}$, $n = 1, 2, 3, 4$.

Find e_{24}.

    A) 17   B) 33   C) 50   D) 65   E) 75

3-24   The Balducci hypothesis is applicable for the unit interval between ages 30 and 31; $q_{30} = .1$.

If $_{\frac{1}{n}}q_{30\frac{1}{2}} = \frac{1}{39}$, find n .

A) 2   B) 3   C) 4   D) 5   E) 6

3-25

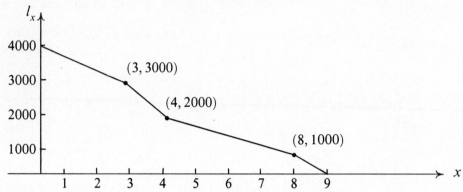

Based upon the accompanying graph, determine the expected age at death of a person now aged $1\frac{1}{2}$.

A) 4.0   B) 4.5   C) 5.0   D) 5.5   E) 6.0

3-26   Find $_9q_{15}$, if $\mu_x = \dfrac{1}{2+2x}$, $x \geq 0$.

A) .2   B) .4   C) .5   D) .6   E) .8

3-27   Given the following table, find the probability that (63) will not survive to age 65.

x	e_x
63	9.5
64	9.0
65	8.5

A) $\frac{1}{20}$ B) $\frac{2}{21}$ C) $\frac{1}{10}$ D) $\frac{1}{5}$ E) $\frac{13}{70}$

3-28   Given: μ_x is constant, $0 \leq x \leq 20$;
          μ_x follows de Moivre's Law, $x > 20$;
          μ_x is continuous.
          $\overset{\circ}{e}_{30} = 20$
          $ln2 = .7$; $ln3 = 1.1$

Find the 25th percentile of X .

A) 10   B) 15   C) 25   D) 40   E) 51

3–29   If $e_x = 5$, $x = 0, 1, 2, \ldots$, find $\text{VAR}[K]$ for a life aged 30.

A) 5   B) 15   C) 25   D) 30   E) 55

3–30   Given: $_tp_x = 1 - .6t + .12t^2 - .008t^3$, $0 \le t \le 5$.

Find μ_{x+3}.

A) .5   B) .75   C) 1.0   D) 1.25   E) 1.5

3–31   Given: $l_x = 100 - 15x - 6x^2 + x^3$, $0 \le x \le 5$.

Of 100 newborn lives, what is the maximum number expected to die within any one-year interval?

A) 26.00   B) 26.25   C) 26.50   D) 26.75   E) 27.00

3–32   Given: $\mu_x = \dfrac{3}{200 - 2x}$, $0 \le x < 100$.

Find $_{28|11}q_{36}$.

A) $\frac{91}{512}$ B) $\frac{8}{27}$ C) $\frac{11}{36}$ D) $\frac{27}{64}$ E) $\frac{4}{5}$

3–33   Given: $l_x = \dfrac{1}{(k + x)^3}$, $x \ge 10$.

The expected age of death of (40) is 63. Find k.

A) -4 B) 0   C) 3   D) 6   E) 23

3–34   Given: $l_x \mu_x = .01$ for all x, $0 \le x < \omega$

$$_5p_{25} = \tfrac{12}{13}$$

Find e_{31}.

A) 29   B) $29\tfrac{1}{2}$ C) 30   D) $30\tfrac{1}{2}$ E) 31

3–35   Find the probability that (25.3) will die at some age beyond 25.8. You are to assume the Balducci hypothesis over the unit interval from age 25 to age 26.

A) $\dfrac{3 + 3p_{25}}{8 - 2p_{25}}$ B) $\dfrac{3 + 7p_{25}}{8 + 2p_{25}}$ C) $\dfrac{2 + 8p_{25}}{7 + 3p_{25}}$ D) $\dfrac{1 + p_{25}}{2}$ E) $\dfrac{2p_{25}}{1 + p_{25}}$

3–36   Given: $\mu_x = \dfrac{3}{1+2x}$, $x \geq 0$.

Find $\overset{\circ}{e}_{12}$.

A) 15   B) 20   C) 25   D) 30   E) ∞

3–37   Given: $_tp_x = (\tfrac{1}{2})^t$, for all x and t.

Find the average lifetime lived between ages 10 and 11 by those who die during that year of age.

A) $\tfrac{1}{2}$ B) $\dfrac{1}{ln2} - 1$ C) $ln2 - \tfrac{1}{2}$ D) $\dfrac{1}{ln2} - \tfrac{1}{2}$ E) $ln2$

3–38   If $\mu_x = \dfrac{8}{100-x}$, $0 \leq x < 100$, find the standard deviation of the future lifetime random variable T for a life aged 90.

A) $\dfrac{2\sqrt5}{9}$ B) $\dfrac{\sqrt5}{3}$ C) $\dfrac{4\sqrt5}{9}$ D) $\dfrac{5\sqrt5}{9}$ E) $\dfrac{2\sqrt5}{3}$

3–39   Based upon de Moivre's Law, it is known that $\overset{\circ}{e}_{20:\overline{n}|} = \tfrac{n}{2}$ for some $n > 0$, and that $VAR[K] = 80$ for a life aged 20.

Find n.

A) 21   B) 31   C) 41   D) 51   E) Cannot be determined

3–40   The density for the "curve of deaths" is given by $h(x) = \frac{1}{(1+x)^2}$, $x \geq 0$.

Find the fraction of the total deaths in a population which occur between the ages y and $2y$.

A) $\dfrac{1}{y}$ B) $\dfrac{1}{2y}$ C) y D) $\dfrac{y}{1+2y}$ E) $\dfrac{y}{(1+y)(1+2y)}$

3–41   Given: $l_1 = 10,000$
$\qquad\qquad d_x = x(x+1)$, $x = 1, 2, 3, \ldots, 20$
Find $_{30}q_1$.

A) .632   B) .722   C) .812   D) .902   E) .992

3–42   If $L_x = (40-x)^2$, $(0 \leq x \leq 40)$, find the central death rate at age 35.

A) $\tfrac{1}{20}$ B) $\tfrac{3}{35}$ C) $\tfrac{2}{9}$ D) $\tfrac{2}{5}$ E) Cannot be determined

3-43 Given: $ln\dfrac{s(x)}{s(x+n)} = n\,ln2$, for all x and n.

Of 3200 infants born this year, what will be their expected aggregate future lifetime subsequent to attainment of age 5?

A) $\dfrac{100}{ln2}$ B) 100   C) $100ln2$ D) 3200   E) $3200ln2$

3-44 If $\mu_x = \tfrac{1}{2}x$, $x \ge 0$, find the 75th percentile of the distribution of X.

A) $ln2$ B) $2ln2$ C) $\sqrt{ln2}$ D) $\sqrt{2ln2}$ E) $2\sqrt{2ln2}$

3-45 Let $R(x,t) = \dfrac{\frac{\partial}{\partial x}\,{}_tp_x}{\frac{\partial}{\partial t}\,{}_tp_x}$. Which of the following is/are true?

    I. If T is exponentially distributed, $R(x,t) > 0$.
    II. If T is exponentially distributed, $R(x,t) < 0$.
    III. If T is uniformly distributed, $R(x,t) > 0$.

A) I only   B) II only   C) III only   D) I and III   E) II and III

3-46 Given: $l_{30+t}\mu_{30+t} = 20t^3$, $0 \le t \le 1$
              $m_{30} = .05$
Find l_{30}.

A) 98   B) 99   C) 100   D) 101   E) Cannot be determined

3-47 If $\mu_x = \mu$ for all x, find the probability that exactly one of two newborns will live at least their expected lifetime.

A) $e^{-1} - e^{-2}$ B) $2(e^{-1} - e^{-2})$ C) $2e^{-1} - e^{-2}$ D) $2e^{-1}$ E) The answer depends on the magnitude of μ.

3-48 Given: $\mu_x = \dfrac{2}{240 - 3x}$, $0 \le x < 80$

In which of the following ranges must $E[K]$ fall, where K refers to a life aged 50?

A) $(14, 15)$ B) $(16.5, 17]$ C) $(17, 17.5)$ D) $[17.5, 18]$ E) Cannot be determined

Answers to Chapter Three Exercises

3–1	C.	3–17	D.	3–33	D.
3–2	A.	3–18	D.	3–34	A.
3–3	C.	3–19	C.	3–35	B.
3–4	A.	3–20	A.	3–36	C.
3–5	A.	3–21	A.	3–37	B.
3–6	E.	3–22	D.	3–38	C.
3–7	E.	3–23	D.	3–39	B.
3–8	D.	3–24	C.	3–40	E.
3–9	C.	3–25	D.	3–41	E.
3–10	B.	3–26	A.	3–42	D.
3–11	A.	3–27	C.	3–43	A.
3–12	A.	3–28	B.	3–44	E.
3–13	C.	3–29	D.	3–45	C.
3–14	B.	3–30	E.	3–46	D.
3–15	D.	3–31	D.	3–47	B.
3–16	D.	3–32	A.	3–48	C.

Solutions

3–1.

Key Definition:
$$z(w) = {}_w p_x - 1$$

$$\therefore {}_w p_x = 1 + z(w)$$

Since the question is

$$_{n-x}p_x - {}_{m-x}p_x,$$

we have

$$1 + z(n - x) - 1 - z(m - x)$$
$$= \underline{\underline{z(n - x) - z(m - x)}}.$$

3–2.

Key Fact: If $l_x \mu_x$ is constant, deaths are uniform.   (DML)

Key Formula: $\mu_x = (\omega - x)^{-1}$ (DML)

Thus, $\mu_x^{'''''''} = 6!(\omega - x)^{-7}$

$\therefore$ at $x = 58$, $\dfrac{45}{8} = \dfrac{6!}{(\omega - 58)^7} \Rightarrow \omega = 60$

$\therefore s(42) = \dfrac{18}{60} = .3$

$\therefore l_{42} = \underline{15{,}000}$

3-3.

Key Observation: e_x is not a function of x; thus K follows a geometric distribution.

Key Formulas: Under the geometric distribution, $e_x = \dfrac{p_x}{q_x}$, and $_{10}p_x = (p_x)^{10}$.

Solving for e_x, $e_x = \dfrac{1}{e^6 - 1} = \dfrac{p_x}{1 - p_x}$

$\therefore p_x = e^{-6}$

$\therefore {}_{10}p_x = \underline{\underline{e^{-60}}}$

3-4.

$\mathring{e}_{41} = \displaystyle\int_0^\infty {}_t p_{41}\, dt$

$= \displaystyle\int_0^\infty \dfrac{s(41 + t)}{s(41)}\, dt$

$= \displaystyle\int_0^\infty \dfrac{(42)^4}{(42 + t)^4}\, dt$

$= \underline{14}$

Short-Cut Formula: $s(x) = \dfrac{1}{(1 + x)^n} \Rightarrow \mathring{e}_x = \dfrac{1 + x}{n - 1}$

$\therefore \mathring{e}_{41} = \dfrac{42}{3} = \underline{\underline{14}}$

3–5.

Method One

$$\Pr[K = 0] = \frac{1}{3}$$

$$\Pr[K = 1] = \frac{1}{3}$$

$$\Pr[K = 2] = \frac{1}{3}$$

$$E[K] = \frac{1}{3}(0 + 1 + 2) = 1$$

$$E[K^2] = \frac{1}{3}(0 + 1 + 4) = \frac{5}{3}$$

$$\mathrm{VAR}[K] = \frac{5}{3} - (1)^2 = \underline{\underline{\frac{2}{3}}}$$

Method Two

Key Formula: The variance of the uniform (discrete) distribution over $[a, b]$ is $\frac{(b-a)^2 - 1}{12}$.

$$\therefore \mathrm{VAR}[K] = \frac{(500 - 497)^2 - 1}{12} = \underline{\underline{\frac{2}{3}}}$$

Method Three

Key Formula: The variance of the uniform (continuous) distribution over $[a, b]$ is $\frac{(b - a)^2}{12}$.

$$\therefore \mathrm{VAR}[T] = \frac{(500 - 497)^2}{12} = \frac{3}{4}$$

$$\mathrm{But\ VAR}[T] = \mathrm{VAR}[K + S]$$

$$= \mathrm{VAR}[K] + \mathrm{VAR}[S] \quad (\mathrm{UDD})$$

$$\therefore \mathrm{VAR}[K] = \frac{3}{4} - \frac{1}{12} = \underline{\underline{\frac{2}{3}}}$$

3–6.

Key Fact:

$$\mu_x = \frac{k}{\omega - x} \Leftrightarrow s(x) = \left(\frac{\omega - x}{\omega}\right)^k$$

Let $l_x = (100 - x)^2$

$$L_{95} = \int_{95}^{96} (100 - x)^2 \, dx = \frac{61}{3}$$

$$l_{95} = 25$$

$$l_{96} = 16$$

$$\therefore m_{95} = \frac{d_{95}}{L_{95}} = \frac{27}{61}.$$

3–7.

Method One

Key Formulas:

$$\overset{\circ}{e}_x = \overset{\circ}{e}_{x:\overline{n}|} + {}_n p_x \overset{\circ}{e}_{x+n}$$

$$\overset{\circ}{e}_x = \frac{\omega - x}{2} \qquad \text{(DML)}$$

$$\therefore \overset{\circ}{e}_{50:\overline{10}|} = \overset{\circ}{e}_{50} - {}_{10} p_{50} \overset{\circ}{e}_{60}$$

$$= 75 - \frac{14}{15}(70) = 9\tfrac{2}{3}$$

Method Two

Key Formula:

$$\overset{\circ}{e}_{x:\overline{n}|} = \int_0^n {}_t p_x \, dt$$

$$\therefore \overset{\circ}{e}_{50:\overline{10}|} = \int_0^{10} \frac{150 - t}{150} \, dt$$

$$= 9\tfrac{2}{3}$$

Method Three

Key Formula:
$$\overset{\circ}{e}_{x:\,\overline{n}|} = \int_0^n t \cdot {}_tp_x\,\mu_{x+t}\,dt + n \cdot {}_np_x$$

$$\therefore \overset{\circ}{e}_{50:\,\overline{10}|} = \int_0^{10} \frac{t}{150}\,dt + 10 \cdot \frac{140}{150}$$
$$= 9\tfrac{2}{3}$$

Method Four

Intuitive Approach: Those who survive to age 60 are credited with 10 years.   (DML)
Those who die before age 60 are credited with 5 years.

$$\therefore \frac{14}{15}(10) + \frac{1}{15}(5) = 9\tfrac{2}{3}$$

3–8.

Key Fact:
$$\mu_x = \frac{1}{a+x} \Leftrightarrow s(x) = \frac{a}{a+x}$$

$$\therefore s(5) = \frac{4}{9}, \text{ since } a = 4.$$

3–9.

Key Formula:
$$a(x) = \frac{L_x - l_{x+1}}{l_x - l_{x+1}}$$

Let $x = 41$

$$.5 = \frac{400 - 360}{l_{41} - 360} \Rightarrow l_{41} = 440$$

Let $x = 40$

$$.75 = \frac{500 - 440}{l_{40} - 440} \Rightarrow l_{40} = 520$$

Now,

$$\overset{\circ}{e}_{40} = \frac{T_{40}}{l_{40}} = \frac{5900}{520} = \underline{\underline{11.35}}$$

3-10.

Method One (Inefficient)

$$_{70}p_{10} = e^{-\int_{10}^{80} \mu_y \, dy}$$

Perform the integration.

Method Two

Key Relationship: $$\mu'_x = k\mu_x \Rightarrow {}_np'_y = \left({}_np_y\right)^k$$

$$\text{If } \mu_x = \frac{3}{110 - x}, \text{ then } {}_{70}p_{10} = \left(\frac{30}{100}\right)^3$$

$$\text{If } \mu_x = \frac{2}{150 - x}, \text{ then } {}_{70}p_{10} = \left(\frac{70}{140}\right)^2$$

$$\therefore {}_{70}p_{10} = \left(\frac{3}{10}\right)^3 \left(\frac{1}{2}\right)^2 = \underline{\underline{.00675}}$$

3-11.

Key Definition: $$a(x) = E[T \mid T < 1] = \frac{L_x - l_{x+1}}{l_x - l_{x+1}}$$

$$\therefore \frac{3}{4} = \frac{L_7 - l_8}{l_7 - l_8} \Rightarrow L_7 = 76$$

$$\therefore m_7 = \frac{d_7}{L_7} = \frac{16}{76} = \underline{\underline{\frac{4}{19}}}$$

3–12.

    I. Key Formula:

$$E[K^2] = \sum_0^\infty (2k + 1)_{k+1}p_x$$

$$\therefore (k + 1) \text{ should be } (2k + 1).$$

    II. Key Formula:

$$\int_0^n {}_tq_x \, dt = \int_0^n (1 - {}_tp_x) \, dt = n - \overset{\circ}{e}_{x:\overline{n|}}$$

Therefore, this would be correct if the integrand had been ${}_sp_x\mu_{x+s}$.

    III. Key Formula:

$$a(x) = \frac{L_x - l_{x+1}}{d_x}$$

Bracketed quantity is $\dfrac{l_0}{L_x - (L_x - l_{x+1})} = \dfrac{l_0}{l_{x+1}}$.

Therefore, this would be correct if the upper limit of the integral had been $x + 1$.

    IV. Key Formula: At mode,

$$\mu'_x = (\mu_x)^2$$

$$\therefore 2kx = (kx^2)^2$$

$$\therefore \text{mode} = \left(\frac{2}{k}\right)^{1/3}$$

$$_np_0 = \frac{1}{2}, \text{ where } n \text{ is median}$$

$$\therefore \frac{1}{2} = e^{-\int_0^n kx^2 \, dx} = e^{-\frac{1}{3}kn^3}$$

$$\therefore \text{Median} = \left(\frac{3ln2}{k}\right)^{1/3} > \text{Mode}$$

$\therefore$ <u>All False</u>

3-13.

$$f(x) = \frac{1}{20}(100 - x)^{-1/2}$$

$$\therefore F(x) = -\frac{1}{10}(100 - x)^{1/2} + 1$$

$$\therefore s(x) = \left(\frac{100 - x}{100}\right)^{1/2}$$

$$\therefore {}_{10}p_{69.75} = \left(\frac{20.25}{30.25}\right)^{1/2} = \frac{9}{11}$$

$$\therefore {}_{10}q_{69.75} = \underline{\underline{\frac{2}{11}}}$$

3-14.

Key Formula:

$$\overset{\circ}{e}_x = \frac{1}{\mu} \qquad \text{(CF)}$$

Let h be that future duration of life which is exceeded by (x) 25% of the time, i.e., the 75th percentile of T. Thus, since $\mu = \frac{1}{2}$,

$$_h p_x = e^{-h\mu} = e^{-\frac{1}{2}h} = \frac{1}{4}$$

$$\therefore h = \underline{\underline{2ln4}}$$

3-15.

Key Observation: The force of mortality is constant and equal to 2.

$$\therefore A = \overset{\circ}{e}_0 = \frac{1}{\mu} = \frac{1}{2}$$

$$B = \frac{ln2}{\mu} = \frac{1}{2}ln2$$

$$C = 0$$

$$D = \frac{1}{\mu^2} = \frac{1}{4}$$

$$\therefore \underline{\underline{C < D < B < A}}$$

3–16.

Key Formula:
$$\mu_x = \lim_{h \to 0} \frac{{}_h q_x}{h} = \lim_{k \to \infty} \frac{{}_{1/k} q_x}{1/k}$$

$$\therefore \lim_{k \to \infty} \frac{2k}{1 + 4k} = \underline{\underline{\frac{1}{2}}}$$

3–17.

Key Observation: The force of mortality is constant and equal to e.

Key Formula:
$$\overset{\circ}{e}_x = \frac{1}{\mu} \qquad \text{(CF)}$$

The average age of death of those persons now exact age x equals their average past lifetime (x years apiece) plus their average future lifetime $(\overset{\circ}{e}_x)$.

Accordingly, we have

$$x + \overset{\circ}{e}_x, \text{ at age } e, \text{which equals}$$

$$e + \frac{1}{e} = \underline{\underline{\frac{e^2 + 1}{e}}}.$$

3–18.

Key Fact:
$$\mu_x = \frac{k}{\omega - x} \Rightarrow \overset{\circ}{e}_x = \frac{\omega - x}{k + 1}$$

$$\mu_x = \frac{n}{100 - x}$$
$$\therefore \overset{\circ}{e}_x = \frac{100 - x}{n + 1}$$
$$\therefore \ln \overset{\circ}{e}_x = \ln(100 - x) - \ln(n + 1)$$
$$\therefore \frac{d}{dx} \ln \overset{\circ}{e}_x = \frac{-1}{100 - x} = \underline{\underline{\frac{1}{x - 100}}}$$

NOTE: The answer, logically, must be negative since $\overset{\circ}{e}_x$ is a decreasing function.

3–19.

Key Formula:
$$\overset{\circ}{e}_x = \overset{\circ}{e}_{x:\overline{n}|} + {}_np_x\overset{\circ}{e}_{x+n}$$

Since it is immediate from the hypothesis that $\overset{\circ}{e}_{50} - \overset{\circ}{e}_{50:\overline{10}|} = 15$ and $\overset{\circ}{e}_{60} = 20$, we have

$$_{10}p_{50} = \frac{15}{20} = \underline{\underline{\frac{3}{4}}}.$$

3–20.

Key Formula:
$$E[S] = \overset{\circ}{e}_x - e_x$$

If the force of mortality is 1,

$$\overset{\circ}{e}_x = 1 \,; e_x = \frac{p}{q} = \frac{e^{-1}}{1-e^{-1}} = \frac{1}{e-1}$$

$$\therefore E[S] = 1 - \frac{1}{e-1} = \underline{\underline{\frac{e-2}{e-1}}}$$

NOTE: The answer must be less than $\frac{1}{2}$, since deaths are biased toward the beginning of the year of age. (Recall that the desired quantity is the average future lifetime *of those who die* within the next year.)

3–21.

$$s(x) = e^{-\int_0^x \frac{y}{100-y^2}\,dy}$$

$$= \left(\frac{100-x^2}{100}\right)^{1/2}$$

$$\therefore s(6) = .8$$

$$\therefore F(6) = \underline{\underline{.2}}$$

3–22.

Key Concept:
At the mode of the distribution of X, the curve of deaths has a maximum, i.e., $(l_x\mu_x)' = 0$.

$$\text{Let } l_x = e^{-.2x} - e^{-.4x}$$
$$\therefore l_x \mu_x = .2e^{-.2x} - .4e^{-.4x}$$
$$\therefore (l_x \mu_x)' = -.04e^{-.2x} + .16e^{-.4x} = 0$$
$$\therefore x = \underline{10ln2}$$

3–23.

Key Concept:
$$e_x = p_x(1 + e_{x+1})$$
$$= p_x + {}_2p_x(1 + e_{x+2})$$
$$= p_x + {}_2p_x + {}_3p_x(1 + e_{x+3})$$
$$\text{etc.}$$

$$\therefore p_{20} = \frac{1}{10}e_{20}$$
$${}_2p_{20} = \frac{1}{20}e_{20}$$
$${}_3p_{20} = \frac{1}{40}e_{20}$$
$${}_4p_{20} = \frac{1}{80}e_{20}$$
$$\therefore e_{20} = [p_{20} + {}_2p_{20} + {}_3p_{20} + {}_4p_{20}(1 + e_{24})]$$

Solving, $e_{24} = \underline{65}$.

Note the unusual, but mathematically acceptable, result that expectations increase with increasing age.

3–24.

Key Formula: If the Balducci hypothesis applies over $[y, y+1]$, then

$$_t q_{y+s} = \frac{t \cdot q_y}{1 - (1 - s - t)q_y}, \quad 0 \le s + t \le 1$$

$$\therefore {}_{1/n}q_{30+1/2} = \frac{\frac{1}{n}q_{30}}{1 - (1 - \frac{1}{2} - \frac{1}{n})q_{30}} = \frac{1}{39}$$

Letting $q_{30} = .1$, and solving,

$$n = \underline{\underline{4}}.$$

3–25.

Key Concept: The area under the l_x curve represents T_0, the total lifetime to be lived by l_0 newborns.

$$\text{Area from } x = 1\tfrac{1}{2} \text{ to } x = 3 : 4875$$
$$\text{Area from } x = 3 \text{ to } x = 4 : 2500$$
$$\text{Area from } x = 4 \text{ to } x = 8 : 6000$$
$$\text{Area from } x = 8 \text{ to } x = 9 : 500$$

$$\therefore T_{1.5} = 4875 + 2500 + 6000 + 500$$

Since $l_{1.5} = 3500$, we have

$$1.5 + \overset{\circ}{e}_{1.5} = 1.5 + \frac{13875}{3500} = \frac{153}{28} = \underline{\underline{5.5}}.$$

3–26.

Key Formulas: If $\mu_x = \frac{1}{1+x}$, then $s(x) = \frac{1}{1+x}$;
If $\mu_x = \frac{k}{1+x}$, then $s(x) = \left(\frac{1}{1+x}\right)^k$.

Key Approach: Determine the value of $_9p_{15}$ as if μ_x had been equal to $\frac{1}{1+x}$. Then, since μ_x is really only half as great, the preliminary answer must be adjusted by taking its square root.

Thus, if $\mu_x = \dfrac{1}{1+x}$, $_9p_{15} = \dfrac{s(24)}{s(15)} = \dfrac{16}{25}$. Finally, the true value of

$_9p_{15} = \left(\dfrac{16}{25}\right)^{1/2} = \dfrac{4}{5}$, and $_9q_{15} = \underline{\underline{\dfrac{1}{5}}}$.

NOTE: A somewhat less efficient method, requiring integration, should be performed by the student, using

$$_9p_{15} = e^{-\displaystyle\int_{15}^{24} \frac{1}{2+2x}\, dx}.$$

3–27.

Key Formula:
$$e_x = p_x(1 + e_{x+1})$$

$$\left. \begin{array}{l} \therefore p_{63} = \dfrac{9.5}{10} \\[2em] \therefore p_{64} = \dfrac{9}{9.5} \end{array} \right\} \Rightarrow {}_2p_{63} = \frac{9}{10} \Rightarrow {}_2q_{63} = \underline{\underline{\frac{1}{10}}}$$

3–28.

$$\overset{\circ}{e}_{30} = \frac{\omega - 30}{2} = 20 \Rightarrow \omega = 70$$

$$\therefore \mu_x = \frac{1}{70 - x}, \; x > 20 \qquad \text{(DML)}$$

$\therefore$ To produce continuity, μ_{20} must
equal .02.

$$\therefore \mu_x = .02, \; 0 \le x \le 20$$

Let h be that age which is attained by 75% of newborns, i.e.,
${}_hp_0 = .75$.

Assume $h < 20$.

$$\therefore {}_hp_0 = e^{-.02h} = 3/4$$
$$\therefore .02h = ln(4/3)$$
$$\therefore h = \underline{\underline{15}}$$

NOTE: If a value of h greater than 20 had been obtained, the problem would have involved the de Moivre portion of the curve and would have required considerably more effort.

3–29.

Key Concept: This is the geometric distribution of K, for which $e_x = \dfrac{p}{q}$ and
$\text{VAR}[K] = \dfrac{p}{q^2}$.

$$\frac{p}{1 - p} = 5 \Rightarrow p = 5/6$$

$$\therefore \text{VAR}[K] = \frac{5/6}{(1/6)^2} = \underline{\underline{30}}$$

3–30.

Key Formula:

$$\mu_{x+t} = \frac{-\frac{\partial}{\partial t}\,{}_t p_x}{{}_t p_x}$$

$$\therefore \mu_{x+t} = \frac{.6 - .24t + .024t^2}{1 - .6t + 12t^2 - .008t^3}$$

$$\therefore \mu_{x+3} = 1.5$$

Alternatively, note that ${}_t p_x = (1 - .2t)^3$

$$\therefore \mu_{x+t} = \frac{3(1 - .2t)^2(.2)}{(1 - .2t)^3}$$

$$= \frac{.6}{1 - .2t}$$

$$\therefore \mu_{x+3} = \underline{\underline{1.5}}$$

3–31.

$$d_x = l_x - l_{x+1} = 20 + 9x - 3x^2$$

To maximize d_x,

$$9 - 6x = 0$$

$$\therefore x = 3/2$$

$$\therefore d_{1.5} = 20 + 13.5 - 6.75 = \underline{26.75}$$

Note that the answer would have been different if it had been unjustifiably assumed that the desired interval must run from integer to integer.

3–32.

Key Fact:

$$\mu_x = \frac{k}{\omega - x} \Rightarrow {}_t p_x = \left(\frac{\omega - x - t}{\omega - x}\right)^k$$

Since $\mu_x = \dfrac{3/2}{100 - x}$, we have

$$_{28|11}q_{36} = {}_{28}p_{36} - {}_{39}p_{36}$$

$$= \left(\frac{36}{64}\right)^{3/2} - \left(\frac{25}{64}\right)^{3/2}$$

$$= \underline{\frac{91}{512}}$$

3–33.

$$l_x = (k + x)^{-3}$$

$$T_x = \int_x^\infty (k + y)^{-3}\, dy = \frac{(k + x)^{-2}}{2}$$

$$\therefore \overset{\circ}{e}_{40} = \frac{T_{40}}{l_{40}} = \frac{k + 40}{2} = 23$$

$$\therefore k = \underline{\underline{6}}$$

3–34.

Key Concept: If $l_x \mu_x$ is constant, then l_x is linear.   (DML)

$$\therefore l_x = k(\omega - x)$$

$$\therefore \frac{l_{30}}{l_{25}} = \frac{\omega - 30}{\omega - 25} = \frac{12}{13} \Rightarrow \omega = 90$$

$$\therefore e_{31} = \frac{90 - 31 - 1}{2} = \underline{\underline{29}}$$

3–35.

Key Formula: $$_s q_{x+t} = \frac{s \cdot q_x}{1 - (1 - t - s)q_x}$$ (BAL)

Thus,

$$_{1/2}p_{25\ 3/10} = 1 - {}_{1/2}q_{25\ 3/10}$$

$$= 1 - \frac{\frac{1}{2}q_{25}}{1 - \frac{1}{5}q_{25}}$$

$$= \frac{1 - \frac{7}{10}q_{25}}{1 - \frac{1}{5}q_{25}}$$

$$= \underline{\underline{\frac{3 + 7p_{25}}{8 + 2p_{25}}}}$$

3–36.

$$_tp_{12} = e^{-\int_{12}^{12+t} \frac{3}{1+2x} \, dx}$$

$$= \left(\frac{25}{25+2t}\right)^{3/2}$$

$$\therefore \overset{\circ}{e}_{12} = \int_0^\infty 125(25+2t)^{-3/2} \, dt$$

$$= \underline{\underline{25}}$$

3–37.

Method One

Key Formula:

$$a(10) = \frac{L_{10} - l_{11}}{l_{10} - l_{11}}$$

$$\text{Let } l_x = \left(\frac{1}{2}\right)^x$$

$$L_{10} = \int_{10}^{11} \left(\frac{1}{2}\right)^x \, dx = \frac{\left(\frac{1}{2}\right)^{11}}{ln2}$$

$$\therefore a(10) = \frac{\frac{\left(\frac{1}{2}\right)^{11}}{ln2} - \left(\frac{1}{2}\right)^{11}}{\left(\frac{1}{2}\right)^{10} - \left(\frac{1}{2}\right)^{11}} = \underline{\underline{\frac{1}{ln2} - 1}}$$

Method Two

Key Concept: Under constant force, $E[S] = a(x)$.

$$a(x) = \overset{\circ}{e}_x - e_x$$

$$= \frac{1}{\mu} - \frac{p}{q}$$

$$= \underline{\underline{\frac{1}{ln2} - 1}}$$

3–38.

Key Relationship:

$$\mu_x = \frac{8}{100-x} \quad \Rightarrow \quad \overset{\circ}{e}_x = \frac{100-x}{9}$$

Key Formula:
$$E[T^2] = \int_0^\infty t^2 \, _tp_x\mu_{x+t} \, dt = 2\int_0^\infty t \, _tp_x \, dt$$

$$\therefore E[T^2] = 2\int_0^{10} t\left(\frac{10-t}{10}\right)^8 dt$$
$$= \frac{20}{9} \qquad \text{(By parts)}$$
$$E[T] = \frac{10}{9}$$
$$\therefore \text{VAR}[T] = \frac{20}{9} - \frac{100}{81} = \frac{80}{81}$$
$$\therefore \sigma[T] = \frac{1}{9}\sqrt{80} = \underline{\underline{\frac{4\sqrt{5}}{9}}}$$

3–39.

Key Concept: Under de Moivre's Law,

$$\mathring{e}_{x:\overline{n}|} = n \cdot \, _np_x + \frac{n}{2}\, _nq_x$$

$$\therefore \mathring{e}_{20:\overline{n}|} = \frac{n}{2}(1 + \, _np_{20}) = \frac{n}{2}$$
$$\therefore \, _np_{20} = 0$$
$$\therefore \omega = 20 + n$$
$$\text{VAR}[K] = \frac{(\omega-20)^2 - 1}{12} = 80 \Rightarrow \omega = 51$$
$$\therefore n = \underline{\underline{31}}$$

Alternative Method: The formula

$$\mathring{e}_{20} = \mathring{e}_{20:\overline{n}|} + \, _np_{20}\mathring{e}_{20+n}$$

generates $\omega = 20 + n$, as above.

3–40.

$$\text{Find } \frac{\int_y^{2y}(1+x)^{-2}\,dx}{\int_0^\infty(1+x)^{-2}\,dx}$$
$$= \frac{\dfrac{1}{1+y} - \dfrac{1}{1+2y}}{1} = \underline{\underline{\frac{y}{(1+y)(1+2y)}}}$$

NOTE: If $y = 0$, the answer must be zero. If $y \to \infty$, the answer must be zero.

Thus, from these two observations, only answer E could possibly be correct.

3–41.

Key Formula:

$$l_x - l_{x+n} = \sum_{y=x}^{x+n-1} d_y$$

$$\therefore l_{31} = l_1 - \sum_{1}^{30} d_x$$

$$= 10,000 - \sum_{1}^{30}(x^2 + x)$$

$$= 10,000 - \frac{(30)(31)(61)}{6} - \frac{(30)(31)}{2} = 80$$

$$\therefore {}_{30}q_1 = \frac{10,000 - 80}{10,000} = \underline{\underline{.992}}$$

3–42.

Key Fact:

$$\frac{d}{dx}L_x = -d_x$$

$$\therefore d_x = 2(40 - x)$$

$$L_x = (40 - x)^2$$

$$\therefore m_x = \frac{2}{40 - x}$$

$$\therefore m_{35} = \underline{\underline{\frac{2}{5}}}$$

3–43.

Equivalent Statement $_np_x = (\frac{1}{2})^n$ for all x and n
of Hypothesis:

$$\therefore \, _np_x\mu_{x+n} = (\tfrac{1}{2})^n ln2$$
$$\therefore \mu_x = ln2$$
$$\text{Let } l_x = l_0(\tfrac{1}{2})^x = 3200(\tfrac{1}{2})^x$$
$$\therefore T_5 = \int_5^\infty 3200(\tfrac{1}{2})^x \, dx$$
$$= \underline{\frac{100}{ln2}}$$

3–44.

Let h be that age which 25% of the newborns attain, i.e., $_hp_0 = .25$.
Thus, h is the 75th percentile of X.

$$\therefore \, _hp_0 = e^{-\int_0^h \frac{1}{2}x \, dx} = e^{-\frac{1}{4}h^2} = \frac{1}{4}$$
$$\therefore \frac{h^2}{4} = ln4$$
$$\therefore h = \underline{2\sqrt{2ln2}}$$

3–45.

Key Formulas: $$\frac{\partial}{\partial x} \, _tp_x = \, _tp_x(\mu_x - \mu_{x+t})$$
$$\frac{\partial}{\partial t} \, _tp_x = - \, _tp_x\mu_{x+t}$$

$$\therefore R(x,t) = \frac{\mu_{x+t} - \mu_x}{\mu_{x+t}}$$

I, II. Under the constant force assumption, $R(x,t) = 0$.
   III. Under de Moivre's Law, μ_x is an increasing function.

$$\therefore \underline{\text{III only}}$$

3–46.

Key Formulas:

$$L_{30} = \int_0^1 t l_{30+t} \mu_{30+t}\, dt + l_{31}$$

$$d_{30} = \int_0^1 l_{30+t} \mu_{30+t}\, dt$$

$$\therefore L_{30} = \int_0^1 20t^4\, dt + l_{31} = 4 + l_{31}$$

$$d_{30} = \int_0^1 20t^3\, dt = 5$$

$$m_{30} = \frac{1}{20} = \frac{5}{4 + l_{31}} \Rightarrow l_{31} = 96$$

$$l_{30} = l_{31} + d_{30} = \underline{\underline{101}}$$

3–47.

Key Formulas:

$$\overset{\circ}{e}_x = \frac{1}{\mu} \qquad (\text{CF})$$

$$_t p_x = e^{-\mu t} \qquad (\text{CF})$$

$$\therefore \; _{\overset{\circ}{e}_0} p_0 = e^{-\mu \overset{\circ}{e}_0} = e^{-1}$$

The required probability, i.e., that one life will live $\overset{\circ}{e}_0$ years and one will not, is

$$2e^{-1}(1 - e^{-1}) = \underline{\underline{2(e^{-1} - e^{-2})}}.$$

3–48.

Key Relationship:

$$\mu_x = \frac{k}{\omega - x} \quad \Rightarrow \quad \overset{\circ}{e}_x = \frac{\omega - x}{k + 1}$$

Key Fact:

$$s(x) = \left(\frac{\omega - x}{\omega}\right)^r, \; 0 < r < 1 \Rightarrow s(x) \text{ is concave downward.}$$

Key Concept: If a survival function is concave downward, more deaths occur in the
                          second half of a year of age than in the first half, i.e., $\frac{1}{2} < \overset{\circ}{e}_x - e_x < 1$
                          and thus $\overset{\circ}{e}_x - 1 < e_x < \overset{\circ}{e}_x - \frac{1}{2}$.

$$\mu_x = \frac{2/3}{80 - x}$$

$$\therefore \overset{\circ}{e}_x = \frac{80 - x}{5/3}$$

$$\therefore \overset{\circ}{e}_{50} = 18$$

$$\therefore \underline{\underline{17 < e_{50} < 17.5}}$$

Chapter Four

Supplementary Concepts

1. Where net single premiums are to be evaluated at a doubled force of interest, one should isolate the interest component of the formula and then perform the doubling operation.

   Example 1.

   Under a constant force of mortality, $\bar{A}_x = \dfrac{\mu}{\mu + \delta}$.

   Therefore $^2\bar{A}_x = \dfrac{\mu}{\mu + 2\delta}$.

   Example 2.

   Under a constant force of mortality, $A_x = \dfrac{q}{q + i} = \dfrac{q}{q + e^\delta - 1}$.

   Therefore $^2A_x = \dfrac{q}{q + e^{2\delta} - 1} = \dfrac{q}{q + 2i + i^2} = \dfrac{q}{(1+i)^2 - p}$.

   Example 3.

   Under de Moivre's Law, $\bar{A}_x = \dfrac{\bar{a}_{\overline{\omega - x}|}}{\omega - x} = \dfrac{1 - v^{(\omega - x)}}{\delta(\omega - x)}$.

   Therefore $^2\bar{A}_x = \dfrac{1 - v^{2(\omega - x)}}{2\delta(\omega - x)} = \dfrac{\bar{a}_{\overline{2(\omega - x)}|}}{2(\omega - x)}$.

2. In solving for the median or another percentile of the distribution of a present value random variable, it is generally much more efficient to avoid the tedious step of solving for the duration h at which that percentile is located. Several problems later in this chapter illustrate this principle.

3. Since $_nE_x = e^{-\int_0^n (\mu_{x+t} + \delta)\, dt}$, a constant increase in the force of mortality will have the same effect on $_nE_x$ as that same constant increase in the force of interest. As life annuities are merely combinations of pure endowments, a similar situation exists with such annuities.

4. For insurance products whose face amounts vary, no simple formulas exist for the calculation of variances of the appropriate random variables. However, most such questions

are easily approached through a statement of the distribution of the random variable and a subsequent appeal to basic principles.

5.   If the interest rate i is assumed to be zero, insurance net single premiums become pure probabilities, e.g.,

$$A_x \xrightarrow{i=0} 1$$

$$A^1_{x:\overline{n}|} \xrightarrow{i=0} {}_nq_x$$

$$_{n|}A_x \xrightarrow{i=0} {}_np_x$$

$$A_{x:\overline{n}|} \xrightarrow{i=0} 1$$

$$_{m|n}A_x \xrightarrow{i=0} {}_{m|n}q_x$$

$$(IA)_x \xrightarrow{i=0} 1 + e_x$$

$$(\overline{I}\overline{A})_x \xrightarrow{i=0} \overset{\circ}{e}_x$$

6.   The quantity $\dfrac{i}{\delta}$, or $\overline{s}_{\overline{1}|}$, is used as an adjustment factor under the UDD assumption when single premiums for *pure* insurance protection payable at the instant of death are expressed in terms of single premiums for insurance protection payable at the end of the year of death. However, where pure endowments (or any other noninsurance product) are incorporated, the $\dfrac{i}{\delta}$ correction is improper. For example, under UDD,

$$\overline{A}^1_{x:\overline{n}|} = \frac{i}{\delta} A^1_{x:\overline{n}|}$$

and

$$(D\overline{A})^1_{x:\overline{n}|} = \frac{i}{\delta} (DA)^1_{x:\overline{n}|},$$

but

$$\overline{A}_{x:\overline{n}|} \neq \frac{i}{\delta} A_{x:\overline{n}|}$$

and

$$(I\overline{A})_{x:\overline{n}|} \neq \frac{i}{\delta} (IA)_{x:\overline{n}|}.$$

7.   The logical identities

$$(IA)^1_{x:\overline{n}|} + (DA)^1_{x:\overline{n}|} = (n+1)A^1_{x:\overline{n}|},$$

$$(I\overline{A})^1_{x:\overline{n}|} + (D\overline{A})^1_{x:\overline{n}|} = (n+1)\overline{A}^1_{x:\overline{n}|}, \text{ and}$$

$$(\overline{I}\overline{A})^1_{x:\overline{n}|} + (\overline{D}\,\overline{A})^1_{x:\overline{n}|} = n\overline{A}^1_{x:\overline{n}|}$$

may be used to obviate the memorization of more increasing/decreasing insurance formulas than are necessary.

Special Mortality Laws

I. de Moivre's Law (DML)

$$A_x = \frac{a_{\overline{\omega-x|}}}{\omega - x}$$

$$A^1_{x:\overline{n|}} = \frac{a_{\overline{n|}}}{\omega - x}$$

$$^2A_x = \frac{a_{\overline{2(\omega-x)|}}}{(\omega - x)s_{\overline{2|}}}$$

$$^2\overline{A}^1_{x:\overline{n|}} = \frac{a_{\overline{2n|}}}{(\omega - x)s_{\overline{2|}}}$$

$$\overline{A}_x = \frac{\overline{a}_{\overline{\omega-x|}}}{\omega - x}$$

$$\overline{A}^1_{x:\overline{n|}} = \frac{\overline{a}_{\overline{n|}}}{\omega - x}$$

$$^2\overline{A}_x = \frac{\overline{a}_{\overline{2(\omega-x)|}}}{2(\omega - x)}$$

$$^2\overline{A}^1_{x:\overline{n|}} = \frac{\overline{a}_{\overline{2n|}}}{2(\omega - x)}$$

II. Constant Force of Mortality (CF)

$$A_x = \frac{q}{q + i}$$

$$\overline{A}_x = \frac{\mu}{\mu + \delta}$$

$$^2A_x = \frac{q}{q + 2i + i^2}$$

$$^2\overline{A}_x = \frac{\mu}{\mu + 2\delta}$$

$$A^1_{x:\overline{n|}} = A_x(1 - {}_nE_x)$$

$$\overline{A}^1_{x:\overline{n|}} = \overline{A}_x(1 - {}_nE_x)$$

$$(IA)_x = \frac{q(1 + i)}{(q + i)^2}$$

$$(I\overline{A})_x = \frac{\mu}{\mu + \delta} \cdot \frac{1 + i}{q + i}$$

$$(\overline{I}\overline{A})_x = \frac{\mu}{(\mu + \delta)^2}$$

III. Uniform Distribution of Deaths (UDD)

$$\bar{A}_x = \frac{i}{\delta} A_x$$

$$\bar{A}^{\,1}_{x:\overline{n}|} = \frac{i}{\delta} A^{1}_{x:\overline{n}|}$$

$$\bar{A}_{x:\overline{n}|} = \frac{i}{\delta} A^{1}_{x:\overline{n}|} + {}_nE_x$$

$$A_x^{(m)} = \frac{i}{i^{(m)}} A_x$$

$$(I\bar{A})_x = \frac{i}{\delta}(IA)_x$$

$$(\bar{I}\bar{A})_x = \frac{i}{\delta}\left[(IA)_x - \left(\frac{1}{d} - \frac{1}{\delta}\right)A_x\right] \doteq \frac{i}{\delta}\left((IA)_x - \frac{1}{2}A_x\right)$$

$${}^2\bar{A}_x = \frac{2i + i^2}{2\delta} \cdot {}^2A_x$$

Derivatives

$$\frac{\partial}{\partial i} A_x = -v(IA)_x$$

$$\frac{\partial}{\partial x} \bar{A}_x = \bar{A}_x(\mu_x + \delta) - \mu_x$$

$$\frac{\partial}{\partial i} \bar{A}_x = -v(\bar{I}\bar{A})_x$$

$$\frac{\partial}{\partial x} \bar{A}^{\,1}_{x:\overline{n}|} = \bar{A}^{\,1}_{x:\overline{n}|}(\mu_x + \delta) - (\mu_x - {}_nE_x\mu_{x+n})$$

$$\frac{\partial}{\partial x} {}_{n|}\bar{A}_x = {}_{n|}\bar{A}_x(\mu_x + \delta) - {}_nE_x\mu_{x+n}$$

$$\frac{\partial}{\partial x} {}_nE_x = {}_nE_x(\mu_x - \mu_{x+n})$$

$$\frac{\partial}{\partial n} {}_nE_x = -{}_nE_x(\mu_{x+n} + \delta)$$

$$\frac{\partial}{\partial x} \bar{A}_{x:\overline{n}|} = \bar{A}^{\,1}_{x:\overline{n}|}(\mu_x + \delta) - \mu_x(1 - {}_nE_x)$$

$$= \bar{A}_{x:\overline{n}|} - \mu_x - \delta\,{}_nE_x$$

$$\frac{\partial}{\partial x} D_x = -D_x(\mu_x + \delta)$$

$$\frac{\partial}{\partial x} \bar{D}_x = D_{x+1} - D_x$$

$$\frac{\partial}{\partial x} \bar{C}_x = -D_x\mu_x + D_{x+1}\mu_{x+1}$$

$$\frac{\partial}{\partial x} \bar{M}_x = -D_x\mu_x$$

Exercises

4-1   Let $E[Z] = {}_{m|}\bar{A}_{26}$ and $i = .02$. Assuming de Moivre's law with $\omega = 96$, and given that the median of Z is .453, find the period of deferment to the nearest year.

A) 5   B) 6   C) 7   D) 8   E) 9

4-2   Assuming $\delta = 0$, and given that $\int_0^\infty l_{x+t}\,dt = 100$ and $l_x = 200$, find $\int_0^\infty {}_{m|}\bar{A}_x\,dm$.

A) .46   B) .48   C) .50   D) .52   E) .54

4-3   For a person now aged 95, the probability of dying in each of the next five years is as follows:
$$_{k|}q_{95} = 0.14 + 0.03k, \quad k = 0, 1, 2, 3, 4.$$
The force of interest δ_t is given by $\dfrac{1}{1+t}$. What is the net single premium for a $10,000 whole life insurance payable at the end of year of death?

A) $2600   B) $2620   C) $2640   D) $2660   E) $2680

4-4   If $ln\,{}_tp_x = -0.04t$, $t \geq 0$, and $\delta = 0.06$, find $\bar{A}_{x:\overline{10|}}$.

A) .25   B) .37   C) .38   D) .50   E) .62

4-5   Let $Z = 0$, $0 \leq T \leq 5$
             $= v^T$, $5 < T \leq 25$
             $= 0$, $25 < T$.

If $\delta = .06$ and $\mu_x = .04$ for all x, find the median of Z. Given: $e^{-.2} = .819$.

A) 0   B) .18   C) .36   D) .54   E) .70

4-6   Consider a 20-year term insurance with $\mu_x = .01$ for all x, and $\delta = .08$.

Find the 90th percentile of the distribution of the present value of the benefit payment, if claims are paid at the instant of death.

A) $(.8)^8$ B) $(.8)^9$ C) $(.9)^8$ D) $(.9)^9$ E) None of these

4-7   If $l_x = 100 - x$ and ${}^2\bar{A}{}^{\,1}_{20:\overline{30|}} = K$, find $\bar{A}_{40}$.

A) $\frac{3}{8}K$ B) K C) $2K$ D) $\frac{8}{3}K$ E) None of these

4-8   Given: $_{10}p_{20} = .75$ and $v^{10} = .6$

Find $^2A_{20:\overline{10}|}^{1}$.

A) .24   B) .27   C) .30   D) .33   E) .36

4-9   Assume deaths according to a de Moivre mortality law, with $\omega = 120$ and $\delta = .10$.

Find the variance of the random variable Z, where Z represents the present value random variable for a \$1 whole life insurance to a person aged 20, payable at the instant of death.

A) .005   B) .010   C) .040   D) .050   E) .067

4-10   Let $Z = 0,\quad 0 \le T < 5$
$= v^T,\quad 5 \le T < 20$
$= 0,\quad 20 \le T.$

If $\mu = .025$ and $\delta = .05$, find $f_Z(.64)$ and $f_Z(.25)$, respectively.

A) $(\frac{5}{8}, 1)$ B) $(\frac{5}{8}, 0)$ C) $(0,0)$ D) $(0,1)$ E) $(1,1)$

4-11   Let $Z = v^T,\quad 0 \le T < n$
$= 0,\quad n \le T.$

If the median of Z is $\frac{1}{32}$, and $\mu = .011$ for all ages, find δ.

A) .0022   B) .011   C) $(.011)^5$ D) .055   E) .5

4-12   Consider a life aged 5 who purchases an insurance policy whose present value random variable Z is defined as follows:

$$Z = 0,\quad 0 \le T < 5$$
$$= v^T,\quad 5 \le T < m + 5$$
$$= 0,\quad m + 5 \le T.$$

Assume de Moivre's Law with $\omega = 25$, $\delta = .05$, $v^5 = .779$, and $E[Z] = .306$.

Find m to the nearest integer.

A) 5   B) 6   C) 8   D) 10   E) 15

4–13 A man aged 42 has been selected to ride in the space shuttle when he is 45, involving an increase of .005 in his anticipated rate of mortality for that one year. Find the resulting increase in the net single premium for a $10,000 whole life policy with proceeds payable at the end of the year of death.

$$\text{Given:} \quad i = .06$$

$$D_{42} = 8000 \qquad M_{44} = 1350$$
$$D_{45} = 6650 \qquad M_{46} = 1315$$
$$D_{46} = 6250$$

A) $27 B) $29 C) $31 D) $33 E) $35

4–14 A 15-year single premium term insurance, with proceeds payable at the end of the year of death, is issued to (40). The first-year death protection is $1000, increasing by 6% in each succeeding year. If $i = .06$, find the net single premium to the nearest $5.

$$\text{Given:} \quad D_{40} = 2000 \qquad M_{40} = 300 \qquad (1.06)^{15} = 2.4$$
$$D_{55} = 400 \qquad M_{55} = 100$$

A) $430 B) $450 C) $470 D) $490 E) $510

4–15 The probability that (x) will live at least n more years is 1.1 times the probability that $(x + n)$ will live at least n more years.

Find $1000A\frac{1}{x+n:\,\overline{n|}}$.

Given: $_{n|}A_x = .24$, $_{n|}A_{x+n} = .192$, and $A_{x+2n} = .48$

A) 48 B) 288 C) 353 D) 440 E) 667

4–16 Assume de Moivre's Law with $e_{20} = 29$ and $i = .04$. Evaluate $\dfrac{^2A_{40}}{^2\overline{A}_{40}}$.

Use $ln1.04 = .0392$.

A) .500 B) .924 C) .943 D) .961 E) .981

4–17 Find $900(\overline{IA})_{40}$, given $\delta = 100\%$ and $\mu_x = \dfrac{2}{100 - x}$, $0 \le x < 100$.

A) 28 B) 29 C) 30 D) 31 E) 32

4–18   Let $Z = v^T$, $T \geq 0$, for $x = 40$

$\delta = .04$,

$s(x) = \dfrac{100 - x}{100}$, $0 \leq x \leq 100$.

If the K th percentile of Z is $e^{-.36}$, find K.

A) 9   B) 15   C) 50   D) 85   E) 91

4–19   Simplify $\dfrac{\frac{\partial}{\partial x}\overline{C}_x - \frac{\partial}{\partial x}\overline{M}_x}{l_{x+1}}$ at $x = 20$, given $\mu_x = (1 + i)^{21}$ for all x.

A) 1   B) $\dfrac{1}{e}$ C) e D) $\dfrac{1}{e^{21}}$ E) e^{21}

4–20   If $A_{x+1} = \dfrac{4.2A_x - 1}{3}$ and $q_x = \frac{1}{4}$, find i.

A) 2%   B) 5%   C) 10%   D) 20%   E) 40%

4–21   If $\mu_x = \delta = .05$, evaluate $(\overline{IA})^1_{30:\,\overline{10|}}$.

A) 5   B) $\dfrac{5e - 5}{e}$ C) $\dfrac{5e - 10}{e}$ D) $\dfrac{5e - 15}{e}$ E) $\dfrac{5e - 20}{e}$

4–22   If $d = \frac{1}{11}$ and the force of mortality is constant for all ages, find p_x if $^2A_x = \frac{10}{13}$.

A) .3   B) .4   C) .5   D) .6   E) .7

4–23   Calculate A_5 from the given table, using $A_3 = .75$ and $i = .10$.

x	l_x
2	65
3	50
4	32
5	27

A) .73   B) .74   C) .75   D) .76   E) .77

4-24 Let $Z = 0, \quad 0 \le T < 10$

$\qquad = v^T, \quad 10 \le T.$

Find the 95th percentile of the distribution of Z.

Let $\mu = \frac{1}{2}ln2$ and $\delta = .04$.

A) 0   B) .02   C) .04   D) .06   E) .08

4-25 An insurer issues \$10 five-year term life insurances to each of 100 lives aged 50, with claims payable at the instant of death. Find the required risk loading, as a percentage of the net single premium, if the insurer wishes to be 84% confident that claims may be paid when due.

Use the normal distribution; $^2\overline{A}\,^{1}_{50:\,\overline{5}|} = \frac{1}{8}$ and $\overline{A}\,^{1}_{50:\,\overline{5}|} = \frac{1}{4}$.

A) 5%   B) 10%   C) 15%   D) 20%   E) 25%

4-26 A \$1 single premium whole life policy is issued to (20), based upon $\mu = .02$ and $\delta = .08$. Find the probability that the present value of the claim will fall within one-half of a standard deviation of the mean of the distribution of the present value random variable.

A) .20   B) .25   C) .30   D) .35   E) .40

4-27 A \$50,000 whole life policy, payable at the instant of death, is issued to (25). The 90th percentile of the distribution of the present value of the claim is \$40,123. Assuming de Moivre's law with $\omega = 75$, find the assumed annual rate of interest.

A) .035   B) .040   C) .045   D) .050   E) .055

4-28 Let $Z = v^T, \quad 0 \le T < 10$

$\qquad = 0, \quad 10 \le T < 20$

$\qquad = v^T, \quad 20 \le T < 30$

$\qquad = 0, \quad 30 \le T.$

If $\mu_x = .1$ for all x and $\delta = .05$, find the 32nd percentile of the distribution of Z.

Given: $e^{-1} = .37$, $e^{-2} = .14$, $e^{-3} = .05$.

A) .25   B) .28   C) .30   D) .32   E) .35

4-29   Twins, aged 40, purchased insurance policies whose net single premiums were represented by $100(I^{(12)}A)_{40}$ and $100(\bar{I}\,\bar{A})_{40}$, respectively. Each died at exact age 63.70. What was the excess of the death claim of the first brother over that of the second?

A) −$5.00   B) −$3.33   C) $0   D) $3.33   E) $5.00

4-30   The expected value of the present value random variable Z is $(DA)^{1}_{[95]:\overline{3|}}$.

If $v = .9$ and the following table is used, find $VAR[Z]$.

$[x]$	$l_{[x]}$	$l_{[x]+1}$	l_{x+2}
95	300	60	15
96	175	10	0
97	15	0	0
98	1	0	0

A) .28   B) .30   C) .32   D) .34   E) .36

4-31   Given: $Z = v^{T}, \quad T \geq 0$

$$\delta_t = \frac{1}{1+t}, \quad t \geq 0$$

$$_tp_x = \frac{2}{2+t}, \quad t \geq 0.$$

Find the 90th percentile of the distribution of Z.

A) $\frac{9}{19}$ B) $\frac{10}{19}$ C) $\frac{9}{11}$ D) $\frac{9}{10}$ E) $\frac{10}{11}$

4-32   Given: $s(x) = \dfrac{100 - x}{100}, \quad 0 \leq x \leq 100,$

$i = 0,$

$Z = (K+1)v^{K+1}, \quad K = 0, 1, 2, \ldots,$

$VAR[\alpha Z] = 24.$

If the issue age is 97, find α.

A) 2   B) 3   C) 4   D) 5   E) 6

4-33   Given: $q_x = \dfrac{1}{80 - x}, \quad x = 0, 1, 2, \ldots, 79$

$A^1_{49:\,\overline{m}|} = \dfrac{1}{32}$

$i = 100\%$

Find $e_{20:\,\overline{m}|}$.

A) 4.10   B) 4.50   C) 4.70   D) 4.75   E) 4.79

4-34   A person aged 32 pays a net single premium of $5916 for death protection of $10,000 prior to age 40 and for a $10,000 pure endowment payable at age 64.

If both forces are constant and $\mu + \delta = .1$, find the probability that the insurer will ultimately pay out $10,000. Given: $e^{-.4} = .67$.

A) .50   B) .51   C) .55   D) .59   E) .60

4-35   An insurer issues $10 single premium two-year term policies to n lives aged x. It is known that $E[Z] = .4$ and $E[Z^2] = .2$, where $Z = v^T$, $0 \le T \le 2$. A risk loading of 3.29% of the net single premium is sufficient to ensure, with 95% confidence, that all claims will be paid as they are incurred. Find n. (Use the normal approximation.)

A) 25   B) 50   C) 625   D) 2500   E) Cannot be
                                                                                                determined

4-36   Given: $v^t = {}_t p_x$, for all $t \ge 0$, and $10,000 \;{}_{15|}\overline{A}_{20} = 1157$.

Find the constant force of interest δ .

A) .04849   B) .04879   C) .04909   D) .04939   E) .05000

4-37   Let $Z = Tv^T,$ $0 \le T < 10$

$\qquad = 10v^T,$ $10 \le T < 20$

$\qquad = (30 - T)v^T,$ $20 \le T < 30$

$\qquad = 0,$ $30 \le T.$

If $\mu = .08$ and $\delta = .02$, find $E[Z]$.

A) $.8(1 - e^{-1})(1 - e^{-2})$ B) $.8(1 - e^{-1})(1 + e^{-2})$
C) $8(1 - e^{-1})(1 - e^{-2})$ D) $8(1 - e^{-1})(1 + e^{-2})$
E) $.8(1 + e^{-1})(1 - e^{-2})$

4-38   Given: $\bar{A}_{20:\overline{10}|} = 1.05A_{20:\overline{10}|}$

$$l_x = 100 - x, \quad 0 \le x \le 100$$

Express $\bar{s}_{\overline{10}|}$ in terms of $s_{\overline{10}|}$.

A) $0.5 + 1.05s_{\overline{10}|}$ B) $1.5 + 1.05s_{\overline{10}|}$ C) $2.5 + 1.05s_{\overline{10}|}$

D) $3.5 + 1.05s_{\overline{10}|}$ E) $4.5 + 1.05s_{\overline{10}|}$

4-39   A fully discrete whole life policy to (30) has a death benefit of m for the first year and a death benefit of $10 - m$ for policy years beyond the first. Death benefits are always nonnegative.

If $q_x = .10$ for all x, and $i = 0$, find the minimum and maximum values, respectively, of the variance of the present value random variable Z.

A) (0,5)   B) (0,9)   C) (0,10)   D) (5,9)   E) (5,10)

4-40   A man aged x wishes to purchase a single premium \$1000 whole life policy payable at the end of the year of death. He has \$500, but that is deficient by \$10.54. However, if he waits one year, he will have the exact amount required to purchase the desired protection at that time. Assume $q_x = \frac{1}{40}$, find the assumed interest rate.

A) .085   B) .087   C) .089   D) .091   E) .093

4-41   Nine persons aged 65 contribute to a fund designed to pay each a death benefit of \$1000 at the end of the year of death. Their contributions are the net single premiums based upon $i = .04$ and $s(x) = \dfrac{80 - x}{80}, \quad 0 \le x \le 80$.

There were no deaths in the fourth year; one died in the fifth year. The rate of return on invested funds reflected the pricing assumptions.

As of the end of the fifth year, there had been an aggregate loss of \$458.60. Find the amount which was in the fund at the end of the third year.

A) \$3151   B) \$4075   C) \$4500   D) \$4750   E) \$5000

4–42   The net single premium for a $10,000 whole life policy to (50), with claims paid at the end of the year of death, is $4128. How much greater will the net single premium be three years later, assuming $v = .8$ and given the following table?

x	l_x
50	100
51	90
52	70
53	60
54	50

A) $256   B) $300   C) $500   D) $872   E) $1000

4–43   A policy to (x) pays $2 at the instant of death if death occurs before age $x + 10$. Upon survival to age $x + 10$, $1 is paid. Find the variance of the present value random variable for this benefit.

$$\text{Given}: \bar{A}_{x:\overline{10|}} = .60$$
$$\bar{A}^{\,1}_{x:\overline{10|}} = .20$$
$$^2\bar{A}_{x:\overline{10|}} = .45$$
$$^2\bar{A}^{\,1}_{x:\overline{10|}} = .15$$

A) .26   B) .30   C) .58   D) .82   E) .90

4–44   A company sells $10,000 single premium whole life policies, payable at the end of the year of death, to lives aged 40. Which of the following is the smallest single premium which may be charged if the company requires at least a 50% chance of making a profit?

Let $q_x = .0385$ for all x; $i = .03$.

A) $5537   B) $5703   C) $5875   D) $6050   E) $6232

4–45   Evaluate $\dfrac{\partial}{\partial x}\,_{n|}\bar{A}_x$, given the following:

$$D_x = 4000 \qquad \mu_x = .007$$
$$D_{x+n} = 200 \qquad \mu_{x+n} = .115$$
$$\bar{M}_{x+n} = 150 \qquad \delta = .093$$

A) −.002   B) −.001   C) 0   D) .001   E) .002

4–46 If $s(x) = \dfrac{\omega - x}{\omega}$, $0 \le x \le \omega$, and $Z = v^T$, $T \ge 0$, which of the following represents the variance of Z ?

A) $\bar{s}_{\overline{1}|} \cdot {}^2\bar{A}_x - (\bar{s}_{\overline{1}|})^2 (A_x)^2$

B) ${}^2A_x - A_x^2$

C) $\frac{1}{2}(s_{\overline{2}|})^2 \cdot {}^2A_x - \bar{s}_{\overline{1}|}(A_x)^2$

D) $\frac{1}{2}\bar{s}_{\overline{2}|} \cdot {}^2A_x - (\bar{s}_{\overline{1}|})^2 (A_x)^2$

E) None of these

Answers to Chapter Four Exercises

4–1	A.	4–17	B.	4–32	E.
4–2	C.	4–18	D.	4–33	D.
4–3	D.	4–19	A.	4–34	D.
4–4	E.	4–20	B.	4–35	C.
4–5	A.	4–21	C.	4–36	B.
4–6	C.	4–22	A.	4–37	C.
4–7	D.	4–23	D.	4–38	D.
4–8	B.	4–24	A.	4–39	B.
4–9	A.	4–25	B.	4–40	A.
4–10	B.	4–26	B.	4–41	E.
4–11	D.	4–27	B.	4–42	D.
4–12	D.	4–28	C.	4–43	A.
4–13	C.	4–29	E.	4–44	C.
4–14	D.	4–30	B.	4–45	A.
4–15	C.	4–31	C.	4–46	D.
4–16	D.				

Solutions

4–1.

By implication,

$$Z = 0, \qquad 0 \le T < m$$
$$= v^T, \qquad m \le T.$$

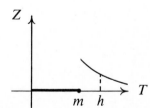

Let h be that time until death such that the present value of the associated claim will be exceeded 50% of the time, i.e.,

$$_m p_{26} - {}_h p_{26} = \tfrac{1}{2}.$$

Applying de Moivre's Law,

$$\frac{h - m}{70} = \frac{1}{2} \Rightarrow h - m = 35.$$

But $v_{.02}^h = .453$; from interest tables, h is found to be 40.

$$\therefore \underline{\underline{m = 5}}$$

4–2.

Key Formula:
$$\int_0^\infty {}_{m|}\overline{A}_x \, dm = (\overline{I}\overline{A})_x$$

Key Concept: When $i = 0$, $(\overline{I}\overline{A})_x = \overset{\circ}{e}_x$

$$\overset{\circ}{e}_x = \frac{T_x}{l_x} = \frac{100}{200} = \underline{\underline{\frac{1}{2}}}$$

4–3.

Key Compound
Interest Relationship:
$$a^{-1}(t) = e^{-\int_0^t \delta_s \, ds}$$

$\therefore$ Since $\delta_t = \dfrac{1}{1+t}$, $a^{-1}(t) = \dfrac{1}{1+t}$. From the basic definition of A_x,

$$A_{95} = \tfrac{1}{2}(.14) + \tfrac{1}{3}(.17) + \tfrac{1}{4}(.20) + \tfrac{1}{5}(.23) + \tfrac{1}{6}(.26) = .266$$

$$\therefore 10,000 A_{95} = \underline{\underline{2660}}$$

4–4.

Key Formulas:
$$\overline{A}_{x:\overline{n}|} = \overline{A}_x - {}_nE_x\overline{A}_{x+n} + {}_nE_x$$
$$= \overline{A}_x(1 - {}_nE_x) + {}_nE_x \qquad (CF)$$
$$\overline{A}_x = \frac{\mu}{\mu + \delta} \qquad\qquad (CF)$$
$$_nE_x = e^{-n(\mu+\delta)} \qquad\qquad (CF)$$

Since $\mu = .04$ and $\delta = .06$, we have

$$\overline{A}_x = .4 \text{ and } {}_{10}E_x = e^{-1}.$$

Finally,

$$\overline{A}_{x:\overline{10}|} = .4(1 - e^{-1}) + e^{-1}$$
$$= .4 + .6e^{-1}$$
$$\doteq \underline{\underline{.62}}$$

4–5.

$$Pr[Z = 0] = {}_5q_x + {}_{25}p_x$$
$$= 1 - e^{-.2} + e^{-1} > \tfrac{1}{2}$$

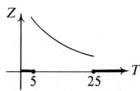

∴ By definition of median, the median of Z is <u>zero</u>.

4–6.

By implication,

$$Z = v^T,\ 0 \le T \le 20$$
$$= 0,\quad 20 < T$$

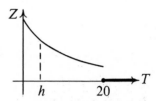

Let h be that time of death such that the present value of the associated claim will be exceeded 10% of the time.

Fact: ${}_hp_x = .9$

Question: v^h

$$\therefore\ .9 = e^{-.01h} \qquad\qquad (CF)$$
$$\therefore\ v^h = e^{-.08h} = \underline{\underline{(.9)^8}}$$

4–7.

Key Formulas:

$$\overset{2}{}\overline{A}{}^{\,1}_{x:\overline{n}|} = \frac{\overline{a}_{\overline{2n}|}}{2(\omega - x)} \qquad\qquad (DML)$$

$$\overline{A}_x = \frac{\overline{a}_{\overline{\omega-x}|}}{\omega - x} \qquad\qquad (DML)$$

$$\therefore\ \overset{2}{}\overline{A}{}^{\,1}_{20:\,\overline{30}|} = \frac{\overline{a}_{\overline{60}|}}{160} = k$$

$$\therefore\ \overline{A}_{40} = \frac{\overline{a}_{\overline{60}|}}{60} = \underline{\underline{\tfrac{8}{3}k}}$$

4–8.

Key Formula:

$$\overset{2}{}A{}^{\,1}_{x:\overline{n}|} = v^{2n}\,{}_np_x$$

$$\therefore {}^{2}A_{20:\overline{10}|}^{\;\;1} = v^{20}\,{}_{10}p_{20}$$
$$= (.36)(.75) = \underline{.27}$$

4-9.

Key Formulas: If $Z = v^{T}$, $T \geq 0$, then

$$\text{VAR}[Z] = {}^{2}\overline{A}_{x} - \overline{A}_{x}^{2}.$$

$$\overline{A}_{x} = \frac{\overline{a}\,_{\overline{\omega - x}|}}{\omega - x} \qquad (DML)$$

$$ {}^{2}\overline{A}_{x} = \frac{\overline{a}\,_{\overline{2(\omega - x)}|}}{2(\omega - x)} \qquad (DML)$$

$$\therefore \overline{A}_{20} = \frac{\overline{a}\,_{\overline{100}|}}{100} = \frac{1 - e^{-10}}{100} \doteq .01$$

$$ {}^{2}\overline{A}_{20} = \frac{\overline{a}\,_{\overline{200}|}}{200} = \frac{1 - e^{20}}{200} \doteq .005$$

$$\text{VAR}[Z] \doteq .005 - (.01)^{2} = \underline{.0049}$$

NOTE: The errors generated by assuming that e^{-10} and e^{-20} are zero are negligible. The answer to this question, to 8 decimals, is .00490001.

4-10.

Consider the distribution function $F_{z}(y)$, where $5 < h < 20$ and thus $y = v^{h} = e^{-.05h}$.

$$F_{z}(y) = {}_{5}q_{x} + {}_{h}p_{x}$$
$$= 1 - e^{-.125} + e^{-.025h} \qquad (CF)$$
$$= 1 - e^{-.125} + y^{1/2}, \quad v^{20} < y < v^{5}.$$
$$\therefore f_{Z}(y) = \tfrac{1}{2}y^{-1/2}, \quad v^{20} < y < v^{5}$$
$$= 0, \quad \text{otherwise.}$$

$$\text{NOTE}: v^{20} = e^{-1} \doteq .37$$
$$v^{5} = e^{-1/4} \doteq .78$$
$$\therefore f_{z}(.64) = \tfrac{1}{2}(.64)^{-1/2} = \underline{\underline{5/8}}$$
$$f_{z}(.25) = \underline{0}, \text{ since } .25 < v^{20}.$$

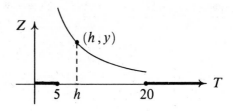

4–11.

Let h be that time of death such that the present value of the associated claim will be exceeded 50% of the time.

Facts : $v^h = \frac{1}{32}$

$_hp_x = \frac{1}{2}$

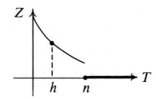

Using a constant force $\mu = .011$,

$\frac{1}{2} = e^{-.011h}$

$(\frac{1}{2})^5 = e^{-\delta h}$

$\therefore \delta = \underline{.055}$

4–12.

$$E[Z] = {}_5E_5\bar{A}^{\;1}_{10:\,\overline{m}|}$$

$$= (.779)(.75)\frac{\bar{a}_{\overline{m}|}}{15} = .306 \qquad\qquad (DML)$$

$$\therefore \bar{a}_{\overline{m}|} = 7.856 = \frac{1 - v^m}{.05}$$

$$\therefore v^m = .6072$$

But $v^5 = .779$

$$\therefore m \doteq \underline{\underline{10}}$$

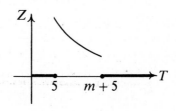

4-13.

Key Formula: If a new (primed) mortality basis is identical to an old (unprimed) basis at every age except at age $x + n$, where $q'_{x+n} = q_{x+n} + c$, then the net single premiums A_x are related as follows:

$$A'_x = A_x + cv_n E_x(1 - A_{x+n+1}).$$

$$\therefore \text{Increase} = .005v \cdot {}_3E_{42}(1 - A_{46})$$
$$= .003096$$
$$\therefore 10,000(.003096) \doteq \underline{\underline{31}}$$

4-14.

Death Benefit in year $(k + 1)$: $1000 (1.06)^k$
$\therefore$ Net Single Premium is

$$1000 \sum_{k=0}^{14} v_{.06}^{k+1}(1.06)^k \cdot {}_{k|}q_{40}$$
$$= 1000v \cdot {}_{15}q_{40}$$

NOTE: ${}_{15}p_{40} = (1 + i)^{15} {}_{15}E_{40} = .48$
$$\therefore NSP = 520v = \underline{\underline{490.57}}$$

4-15.

Key Formulas:
$$_{n|}A_{x+n} = {}_nE_{x+n}A_{x+2n}$$
$$_{n|}A_x = {}_nE_x\left[A^{\,1}_{\overline{x+n:\,\overline{m}|}} + {}_nE_{x+n}A_{x+2n}\right]$$

Given Fact:
$$_{n}p_x = 1.1\,{}_{n}p_{x+n}$$
$$\therefore {}_{n}E_x = 1.1\,{}_{n}E_{x+n}$$

From $_{n|}A_{x+n} = {}_nE_{x+n}A_{x+2n}$, ${}_nE_{x+n} = .4$.

From $_{n}E_x = 1.1\,{}_{n}E_{x+n}$, ${}_nE_x = .44$.

From $_{n|}A_x = {}_nE_x[A^{\,1}_{\overline{x+n:\,\overline{m}|}} + {}_nE_{x+n}A_{x+2n}]$, $A^{\,1}_{\overline{x+n:\,\overline{m}|}} = .35345$.

$$\therefore 1000(.35345) \doteq \underline{\underline{353}}$$

4–16.

Key Formulas:

$$\bar{A}_{40} = \frac{i}{\delta} A_{40} = \frac{e^{\delta} - 1}{\delta} A_{40} \qquad\qquad (UDD)$$

$$\therefore {}^{2}\bar{A}_{40} = \frac{e^{2\delta} - 1}{2\delta} \cdot {}^{2}A_{40} = \frac{2i + i^2}{2\delta} \cdot {}^{2}A_{40}$$

$$\therefore \frac{{}^{2}A_{40}}{{}^{2}\bar{A}_{40}} = \frac{2\delta}{2i + i^2} = \frac{2ln(1.04)}{.0816} \doteq \underline{\underline{.961}}$$

4–17.

Basic Formula:

$$(\bar{I}\,\bar{A})_x = \int_0^{\omega - x} t v^t \, {}_t p_x u_{x+t} \, dt$$

The interest/mortality assumptions generate

$$_t p_{40} = \left(\frac{60 - t}{60}\right)^2$$

$$v^t = e^{-t}$$

$$\therefore (\bar{I}\bar{A})_{40} = \int_0^{60} t e^{-t} \left(\frac{60 - t}{60}\right)^2 \frac{2}{60 - t} \, dt$$

$$= \frac{1}{1800} \int_0^{60} e^{-t}(60t - t^2) \, dt$$

$$= \frac{1}{1800}[58 + 62e^{-60}] \qquad\qquad \text{(By Parts)}$$

$$\therefore 900(\bar{I}\bar{A})_{40} = \underline{\underline{29}} \text{ (Ignoring } e^{-60} \doteq 10^{-26})$$

4–18.

Let h be that time of death such that the present value of the associated claim will be exceeded $(100 - k)\%$ of the time.

$$\text{Given}: v^h = e^{-.36} = e^{-.04h}$$

$$\therefore h = 9$$

$$\therefore {}_9p_{40} = \frac{k}{100} = \frac{51}{60}$$

$$\therefore k = \underline{\underline{85}}$$

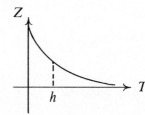

4–19.

Simplified Question:

$$\frac{1}{l_{x+1}}\frac{\partial}{\partial x}(-\overline{M}_{x+1})$$

$$= \frac{1}{l_{x+1}}D_{x+1}\mu_{x+1}$$

$$= v^{x+1}\mu_{x+1}$$

$$= \underline{1} \text{ (at } x = 20)$$

4–20.

Key Relationship:

$$A_x(1+i) = q_x + p_x A_{x+1}$$

$$\therefore A_x(1+i) = \frac{1}{4} + \frac{3}{4}\cdot\frac{4.2A_x - 1}{3}$$

$$\therefore A_x(1+i) = 1.05A_x$$

$$i = \underline{.05}$$

4–21.

Key Formula:

$$(\overline{I}\overline{A})_x = \frac{\mu}{(\mu + \delta)^2} \qquad\qquad (CF)$$

Key Relationship:

$$(\overline{I}\overline{A})_x = (\overline{I}\overline{A})^1_{x:\overline{n}|} + {}_nE_x(\overline{I}\overline{A})_{x+n} + n\,{}_nE_x\overline{A}_{x+n}$$

$$\therefore (\overline{I}\overline{A})_x = 5 \text{ for all ages}; \quad {}_{10}E_{30} = e^{-1}; \overline{A}_{40} = \tfrac{1}{2}$$

$$\therefore 5 = (\overline{I}\overline{A})^1_{30:\overline{10}|} + e^{-1}[5 + 5]$$

$$\therefore (\overline{I}\overline{A})^1_{30:\overline{10}|} = 5 - 10e^{-1}$$

$$= \underline{\underline{\frac{5e - 10}{e}}}$$

4–22.

Key Formula:

$${}^2A_x = \frac{q}{q + 2i + i^2} \qquad\qquad (CF)$$

$$\therefore \frac{10}{13} = \frac{q}{q + .21}$$
$$\therefore q = .7$$
$$\therefore p = \underline{\underline{.3}}$$

4–23.

Key Relationship: $A_x(1 + i)^2 = q_x(i + i) + {}_{1|}q_x + {}_2p_x A_{x+2}$

$$\therefore A_3(1.1)^2 = .36(1.1) + .1 + .54 A_5$$
$$\therefore A_5 \doteq \underline{\underline{.76}}$$

4–24.

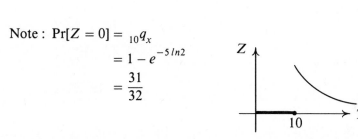

$$\text{Note}: \Pr[Z = 0] = {}_{10}q_x$$
$$= 1 - e^{-5\,ln2}$$
$$= \frac{31}{32}$$

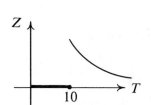

Since $\Pr[Z = 0] > .95$, the 95th percentile of Z is $\underline{\text{zero}}$, i.e., the only value of Z which is exceeded 5% of the time is zero.

4–25.

Consider a $10 policy to one life:

$$Z = 10v^T, \ 0 \le T \le 5$$
$$E[Z] = 10\overline{A}\,{}^1_{50:\,\overline{5|}} = 2.5$$
$$\text{VAR}[Z] = 100[{}^2\overline{A}\,{}^1_{50:\,\overline{5|}} - (\overline{A}\,{}^1_{50:\,\overline{5|}})^2] = 6.25$$

Let $S = \sum_{i=1}^{100} Z_i$, where the Z_i are independent.

$$E[S] = 100E[Z_i] = 250$$
$$\text{VAR}[S] = 100\text{VAR}[Z_i] = 625$$
$$\sigma[S] = 25$$

The normal curve representing claim densities leads to an immediate solution.

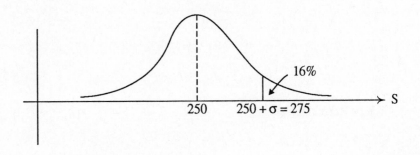

$\therefore$ Required Loading = \$25 per policy

= 10% of NSP

4–26.

Key Formulas:

$$\overline{A}_x = \frac{\mu}{\mu + \delta} \qquad (CF)$$

$$^2\overline{A}_x = \frac{\mu}{\mu + 2\delta} \qquad (CF)$$

$$\text{VAR}[Z] = {}^2\overline{A}_x - (\overline{A}_x)^2$$

$$\therefore \overline{A}_x = \frac{1}{5} = E[Z]$$

$$^2\overline{A}_x = \frac{1}{9}$$

$$\text{VAR}[Z] = \frac{16}{225}$$

$$\sigma[Z] = \frac{4}{15}$$

Thus, the question may be stated as

$$\Pr[\tfrac{1}{5} < Z < \tfrac{1}{3}].$$

Define h_1 and h_2 such that $v^{h_1} = \frac{1}{3}$ and $v^{h_2} = \frac{1}{15}$, i.e, $\frac{1}{3} = e^{-.08h_1}$ and $\frac{1}{15} = e^{-.08h_2}$.

Restated Question:

$$h_1 p_{20} - h_2 p_{20}$$
$$= e^{-.02h_1} - e^{-.02h_2}$$
$$= \left(\frac{1}{3}\right)^{1/4} - \left(\frac{1}{15}\right)^{1/4}$$
$$\doteq \underline{\underline{.25}}$$

4–27.

Let $Z = 50,000 \, v^T$, $T \geq 0$.

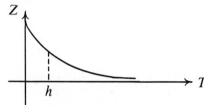

Let h be that time of death such that the present value of the associated claim will be exceeded 10% of the time, i.e., $_h p_{25} = .9 = \frac{50-h}{50}$.

$$\therefore h = 5$$
$$\therefore v^5 = \frac{41,095}{50,000} = .8219$$

From interest tables, $i = \underline{\underline{.04}}$.

4–28.

Constant Force
Probabilities:

$$_{10}q_x = 1 - e^{-1} = .63$$
$$_{10|10}q_x = e^{-1} - e^{-2} = .23$$
$$_{20|10}q_x = e^{-2} - e^{-3} = .09$$
$$_{30}p_x = e^{-3} = .05$$

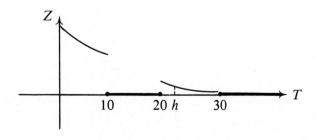

Let h be that time of death such that the present value of the associated claim is exceeded 68% of the time.

$$\therefore \text{Since } {}_{10}q_x = .63 \text{, we require that}$$
$$_{20}p_x - {}_hp_x = .05.$$
$$\therefore {}_hp_x = .09 = e^{-.1h}$$

$$\text{Question}: v^h = e^{-.05h}$$
$$= \sqrt{.09}$$
$$= \underline{\underline{.30}}$$

4-29.

Key Concept: The face amount available under the policy whose premium is $(I^{(12)}A)_{40}$ increases only once per month. For example, first-year death benefits, month-by-month, would be

$$\frac{1}{12}, \frac{2}{12}, \frac{3}{12}, \cdots, \frac{11}{12}, 1.$$

The face amount available under the other policy increases linearly and continuously. Accordingly, the face amount at time t is t.

$$\therefore 100[23.75] - 100[23.70] = \underline{5}$$

(Death occurs in the ninth month of the 24th policy year).

4-30.

NOTE: This problem illustrates the calculation of a variance of a random variable when the product in question does not suggest a simple formula. Thus, a basic principles approach is required.

z	$\Pr[Z = z]$
$3v = 2.7$	.80
$2v^2 = 1.62$	.15
$v^3 = .729$	.05

$$\therefore E[Z] = (2.7)(.8) + (1.62)(.15) + (.729)(.05) = 2.43945$$
$$E[Z^2] = (2.7)^2(.8) + (1.62)^2(.15) + (.729)^2(.05) = 6.25223205$$
$$\therefore \text{VAR}[Z] = 6.25223205 - (2.43945)^2$$
$$= \underline{\underline{.3013}}$$

4–31.

Let h be that time of death such that the present value of the associated claim will be exceeded 10% of the time.

$$\text{Given :} \qquad {}_hp_x = .9 = \frac{2}{2+h}$$

$$\therefore h = 2/9$$

$$\text{Question :} \quad a^{-1}(2/9) = e^{-\int_0^{2/9} \frac{dt}{1+t}}$$

$$= \underline{\underline{9/11}}$$

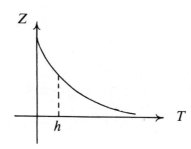

4–32.

$$Z = (K+1)v^{K+1} = K+1, \quad K = 0,1,2$$

z	$\Pr[Z=z]$
1	1/3
2	1/3
3	1/3

$$\therefore E[Z] = 2$$

$$E[Z^2] = 14/3$$

$$\therefore \text{VAR}[Z] = 14/3 - 4 = 2/3$$

$$\therefore \alpha^2 \text{VAR}[Z] = \frac{2}{3}\alpha^2 = 24$$

$$\therefore \alpha = \underline{\underline{6}}$$

4–33.

Key Formulas:

$$A^1_{x:\overline{n}|} = \frac{a_{\overline{n}|}}{\omega - x} \qquad\qquad (DML)$$

$$e_{x:\overline{n}|} = \sum_{t=1}^{n} {}_tp_x$$

$$\therefore A_{49:\,\overline{n}|}^{1} = \frac{a_{\overline{n}|}}{31} = \frac{1}{32}$$

$$\therefore a_{\overline{n}|} = \frac{1 - v^{n}}{i} = \frac{31}{32}$$

Since i=1,

$$1 - \left(\frac{1}{2}\right)^{n} = \frac{31}{32}$$

$$\therefore n = 5$$

$$\therefore e_{20:\,\overline{5}|} = \sum_{t=1}^{5} {}_{t}p_{20}$$

$$= \frac{59 + 58 + 57 + 56 + 55}{60}$$

$$= \underline{\underline{4.75}}$$

NOTE : $\overset{\circ}{e}_{20:\,\overline{5}|} = 4.7916$, because

$$\overset{\circ}{e}_{x:\,\overline{n}|} = e_{x:\,\overline{n}|} + \tfrac{1}{2} {}_{n}q_{x} \qquad (DML)$$

4–34.

Key Concept: The probability of a \$10,000 payout equals the probability that (32) will die before age 40 or after age 64. Accordingly, the desired probability is

$$_{8}q_{32} + {}_{32}p_{32}.$$

Key Formulas:

$$\overline{A}_{x:\,\overline{n}|}^{1} = \overline{A}_{x}(1 - {}_{n}E_{x}) \qquad (CF)$$

$$_{n}E_{x} = e^{-n(\mu + \delta)} \qquad (CF)$$

$$\overline{A}_{x} = \frac{\mu}{\mu + \delta} \qquad (CF)$$

Thus,

$$.5916 = \overline{A}_{32:\,\overline{8}|}^{1} + {}_{32}E_{32}$$

$$= \overline{A}_{32}(1 - {}_{8}E_{32}) + {}_{32}E_{32}$$

$$= 10\mu(1 - e^{-.8}) + e^{-3.2}$$

Solving,

$$\mu \doteq .1.$$

Finally,

$$_{8}q_{32} + {}_{32}p_{32} = 1 - e^{-.8} + e^{-3.2}$$

$$\doteq \underline{\underline{.59}}.$$

4–35.

$$Z = v^T, \quad 0 \le T \le 2$$
$$= 0, \quad 2 < T$$
$$E[Z] = \bar{A}^{\,1}_{x:\,\overline{2}|} = .4$$
$$E[Z^2] = {}^2\bar{A}^{\,1}_{x:\,\overline{2}|} = .2$$
$$\text{VAR}[Z] = .2 - (.4)^2 = .04$$
$$\therefore E[10Z] = 4$$
$$\text{VAR}[10Z] = 4$$

Letting $S = 10Z + 10Z_2 + \cdots + 10Z_n$,

$$E[S] = 4n$$
$$\text{VAR}[S] = 4n$$

$\therefore$ Aggregate premium income: $(4)(1.0329)$

Aggregate premium necessary to ensure 95% confidence is the mean plus 1.645 standard deviations of S, i.e., $4n + 1.645(2\sqrt{n})$.

Equating,

$$4(1.0329)n = 4n + 3.29\sqrt{n}$$
$$\therefore n = \underline{625}.$$

4–36.

Key Fact: If, for all x and t, ${}_t p_x = v^t$, then μ_x is constant and equals δ.

Key Formula:
$$_{n|}\bar{A}_x = {}_n E_x \bar{A}_{x+n}$$
$$= e^{-n(\mu+\delta)} \left(\frac{\mu}{\mu + \delta} \right) \qquad (CF)$$

$$\therefore {}_{15|}\bar{A}_{20} = e^{-30\delta} \left(\frac{1}{2} \right) = .1157$$
$$\therefore e^{-30\delta} = .2314 = v^{30}$$
$$\therefore i = .05, \text{ from interest tables}$$

To find the corresponding value of δ from interest tables, observe that $\bar{s}_{\overline{1}|} = \frac{i}{\delta}$ is given.

$$\therefore 1.0248 = \frac{.05}{\delta}$$

$$\therefore \delta = \underline{.04879}$$

4–37.

The determination of $E[Z]$ is facilitated by the graphical representation of the stipulated pattern of face amounts F.

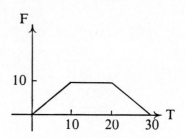

$$E[Z] = (\overline{I}\,\overline{A})^1_{x:\,\overline{10|}} + {}_{10}E_x \cdot 10\overline{A}^{\,1}_{x+10:\,\overline{20|}} - {}_{20}E_x(\overline{I}\,\overline{A})^{\,1}_{x+20:\,\overline{10|}}$$

Restating under the constant force assumption,

$$E[Z] = (\overline{I}\,\overline{A})^1_{x:\,\overline{10|}}(1 - {}_{20}E_x) + 10\,{}_{10}E_x\overline{A}_x(1 - {}_{20}E_x)$$
$$= (1 - {}_{20}E_x)[(\overline{I}\,\overline{A})_x - {}_{10}E_x(\overline{I}\,\overline{A})_x]$$
$$= (1 - {}_{20}E_x)(1 - {}_{10}E_x)(\overline{I}\,\overline{A})_x.$$

$$\text{Since } (\overline{I}\,\overline{A})_x = \frac{\mu}{(\mu + \delta)^2} \qquad (CF)$$
$$= 8,$$

we have

$$E[Z] = \underline{\underline{8(1 - e^{-2})(1 - e^{-1})}}.$$

4–38.

$$\overline{A}_{20:\,\overline{10|}} = \frac{i}{\delta}A^1_{20:\,\overline{10|}} + {}_{10}E_{20} \qquad (UDD)$$

$$= 1.05A^1_{20:\,\overline{10|}} + 1.05\,{}_{10}E_{20}$$

$$\therefore .05v^{10}\,{}_{10}p_{20} = \left(\frac{i}{\delta} - 1.05\right)A^1_{20:\,\overline{10|}}$$

$$\therefore \frac{7}{8}v^{10} = \left(20\frac{i}{\delta} - 21\right)\frac{a_{\overline{10|}}}{80} \qquad (DML)$$

$$\therefore 70 = \left(20\frac{i}{\delta} - 21\right)s_{\overline{10|}}$$

$$= 20\overline{s}_{\overline{10|}} - 21s_{\overline{10|}}$$

$$\therefore \overline{s}_{\overline{10|}} = \underline{\underline{3.5 + 1.05s_{\overline{10|}}}}$$

4-39.

z	$\Pr[Z = z]$
m	.1
$10 - m$	.9

$$\therefore E[Z] = .1m + .9(10 - m) = 9 - .8m$$
$$E[Z^2] = .1m^2 + .9(10 - m)^2 = 90 - 18m + m^2$$

$$\therefore \text{VAR}[Z] = E[Z^2] - (E[Z])^2 = 9 - 3.6m + .36m^2$$

Differentiating, in order to maximize,

$$-3.6 + .72m = 0$$

$$\therefore m = 5$$

But critical points also exist at the endpoints $m = 0$ and $m = 10$.

m	Corresponding Variance
0	9
5	0
10	9

$$\therefore \underline{\underline{(0, 9)}}$$

NOTE: It should be evident that the variance is minimized when $m = 5$ because in that case the random variable is a constant.

4-40.

Basic Relationship:
$$A_x = vq_x + vp_x A_{x+1}$$

Given:
$$A_x = .51054$$
$$A_{x+1} = .5(1 + i) \Rightarrow vA_{x+1} = \tfrac{1}{2}$$

Solving,
$$.51054 = \frac{1}{40}v + \frac{1}{2} \cdot \frac{39}{40}$$
$$v = .9216$$
$$i \doteq \underline{\underline{.085}}$$

4–41.

Let $(AF)_k$ and $(EF)_k$ represent the actual and expected sizes of the fund, respectively, at the end of the k th year.

$$(AF)_5 = (AF)_3(1.04)^2 - 1000$$
$$(EF)_5 = 9 \cdot {}_5p_{65}A_{70}(1000)$$
$$= 6000\frac{a_{\overline{10}|}}{10} = 600a_{\overline{10}|} \qquad (DML)$$

Given: $(EF)_5 - (AF)_5 = 458.60$

$$600a_{\overline{10}|} - (AF)_3(1.04)^2 + 1000 = 458.60$$
$$\therefore (AF)_3 = \underline{\underline{5000}}$$

4–42.

Basic Formula:
$$A_x = vq_x + v^2{}_{1|}q_x + v^3{}_{2|}q_x + v^3{}_3p_xA_{x+3}$$

From the given table, and using $A_{50} = .4128$,

$$.4128 = .8(.1) + (.8)^2(.2) + (.8)^3(.1) + (.8)^3(.6)A_{53}$$

$$\therefore A_{53} = .5000$$

Question: $(A_{53} - A_{50})10,000$

$$= \underline{\underline{872}}$$

4–43.

Key Formula:
$$\text{VAR}[Z_1 + Z_2] = \text{VAR}[Z_1] + \text{VAR}[Z_2] + 2\text{COV}[Z_1, Z_2]$$

Let $Z_1 = 2v^T$, $0 \le T \le 10$
$$= 0, \ 10 < T$$
Let $Z_2 = 0$, $0 \le T \le 10$
$$= v^{10}, \ 10 < T$$
$$\text{VAR}[Z_1] = 4[{}^2\overline{A}{}^{\ 1}_{x:\overline{10}|} - (\overline{A}{}^{\ 1}_{x:\overline{10}|})^2] = .44$$
$$\text{VAR}[Z_2] = {}^2A{}^{\ 1}_{x:\overline{10}|} - (A^{\ 1}_{x:\overline{10}|})^2 = .14$$

Since $Z_1Z_2 \equiv 0$, $\text{COV}[Z_1, Z_2] = -E[Z_1]E[Z_2]$
$$= -(.4)(.4) = -.16$$

$$\text{Finally, } \text{VAR}[Z_1 + Z_2] = \text{VAR}[Z_1] + \text{VAR}[Z_2] + 2\,\text{COV}[Z_1, Z_2]$$
$$= .44 + .14 + 2(-.16) = \underline{.26}$$

4-44.

The question poses the subquestion: "At what duration have exactly half the deaths occurred?" That is, find n such that

$$_np_{40} = \frac{1}{2}$$

$$\therefore (.9615)^n = \frac{1}{2} \qquad \text{(Geometric Distribution)}$$

NOTE: Since $.9615 = v_{.04}$, interest tables may be applied to restate the subquestion as

$$v_{.04}^n = \frac{1}{2}.$$

From interest tables, $17 < n < 18$.

Thus the insurer insists on making a profit if (40) survives as long as 17 years, i.e., if death occurs in the 18th year, or later, the insurer's fund must be more than sufficient to pay the claim.

$$\therefore \pi(1.03)^{18} > 10,000$$
$$\therefore \pi > 5874.06$$
$$\therefore \underline{5875}$$

4-45.

Key Formulas:

$$\frac{\partial}{\partial x}\overline{M}_x = -D_x\mu_x$$

$$\frac{\partial}{\partial x}D_x = -D_x(\mu_x + \delta)$$

$$\frac{\partial}{\partial x}\frac{\overline{M}_{x+n}}{D_x} = \frac{-D_xD_{x+n}\mu_{x+n} + \overline{M}_{x+n}D_x(\mu_x + \delta)}{D_xD_x}$$

$$= -\frac{D_{x+n}}{D_x}\mu_{x+n} + \frac{\overline{M}_{x+n}}{D_x}(\mu_x + \delta)$$

$$= \underline{\underline{-.002}}$$

4-46.

NOTE: The correct answer is easily seen to be ${}^2\overline{A}_x - \overline{A}_x^2$. However, since all of the choices involve A rather than $\overline{A}$, a relationship between ${}^2\overline{A}_x$ and ${}^2A_x$ must be found.

Key Formulas:

$$^2\overline{A}_x = \frac{\overline{a}_{\overline{2(\omega-x)|}}}{2(\omega - x)} \qquad (DML)$$

$$^2A_x = \frac{a_{\overline{2(\omega-x)|}}}{(\omega - x)s_{\overline{2|}}} \qquad (DML)$$

$$\therefore \frac{^2\overline{A}_x}{^2A_x} = \frac{i}{2\delta}s_{\overline{2|}} = \frac{1}{2}\overline{s}_{\overline{2|}}$$

Since $\dfrac{\overline{A}_x}{A_x} = \dfrac{i}{\delta} = \overline{s}_{\overline{1|}},$ $\qquad\qquad (UDD)$

$$^2\overline{A}_x - \overline{A}_x^2 = \underline{\underline{\frac{1}{2}\overline{s}_{\overline{2|}} \cdot {}^2A_x - (\overline{s}_{\overline{1|}})^2(A_x)^2}}$$

Chapter Five

Supplementary Concepts

1. The variances of annuity-related present value random variables are analogous to those of insurance-related present value random variables.

   Example 1

   If $Z = v^T$, $T \geq 0$, then $\text{VAR}[Z] = {}^2\bar{A}_x - \bar{A}_x^2$.

   If $Y = \bar{a}_{\overline{T}|}$, $T \geq 0$, then $\text{VAR}[Y] = \dfrac{{}^2\bar{A}_x - \bar{A}_x^2}{\delta^2}$.

   Example 2

   If $Z = v^{K+1}$, $K = 0, 1, 2, \ldots$, then $\text{VAR}[Z] = {}^2A_x - A_x^2$.

   If $Y = \ddot{a}_{\overline{K+1}|}$, $K = 0, 1, 2, \ldots$, then $\text{VAR}[Y] = \dfrac{{}^2A_x - A_x^2}{d^2}$.

   Example 3

   If $\left. \begin{array}{ll} Z = v^{K+1}, & K = 0, 1, 2, \ldots, n-1 \\ = v^n, & K = n, n+1, \ldots \end{array} \right\}$, then $\text{VAR}[Z] = {}^2A_{x:\overline{n}|} - A_{x:\overline{n}|}^2$.

   If $\left. \begin{array}{ll} Y = \ddot{a}_{\overline{K+1}|}, & K = 0, 1, 2, \ldots, n-1 \\ = \ddot{a}_{\overline{n}|}, & K = n, n+1, \ldots \end{array} \right\}$, then $\text{VAR}[Y] = \dfrac{{}^2A_{x:\overline{n}|} - A_{x:\overline{n}|}^2}{d^2}$.

   Similar results hold for term insurance/temporary annuities, but the "expected" relationship does not materialize in the case of deferred insurance/deferred annuities.

2. Expected values of annuity random variables which are somewhat unorthodox should be determined logically rather than mechanically.

   Example 1

   If $\left. \begin{array}{ll} Y = \bar{a}_{\overline{T}|}, & 0 \leq T < n \\ = \bar{a}_{\overline{n}|}, & T \geq n \end{array} \right\}$, then $E[Y] = \bar{a}_{x:\overline{n}|}$.

   Therefore, if $\left. \begin{array}{ll} Y = \bar{a}_{\overline{T}|}, & 0 \leq T < n \\ = 0, & T \geq n \end{array} \right\}$, then $E[Y] = \bar{a}_{x:\overline{n}|} - {}_n p_x \bar{a}_{\overline{n}|}$.

Example 2

$$\left. \begin{array}{l} \text{If } Y = a_{\overline{K}|}, \;\; K = 0, 1, \ldots, n \\ \phantom{\text{If } Y} = a_{\overline{n}|}, \;\; K = n+1, n+2, \ldots \end{array} \right\}, \;\; \text{then } E[Y] = a_{x:\overline{n}|}.$$

Therefore, if

$$\left. \begin{array}{l} Y = a_{\overline{K}|}, \;\; K = 0, 1, \ldots, n \\ = 0, \;\;\;\; K = n+1, n+2, \ldots \end{array} \right\}, \;\; \text{then } E[Y] = a_{x:\overline{n}|} - {}_{n+1}p_x a_{\overline{n}|}.$$

Further, if

$$\left. \begin{array}{l} Y = 0, \;\;\;\; K = 0, 1, \ldots, n \\ = a_{\overline{K}|}, \;\; K = n+1, n+2, \ldots \end{array} \right\}, \;\; \text{then } E[Y] = a_x - (a_{x:\overline{n}|} - {}_{n+1}p_x a_{\overline{n}|})$$

$$= {}_{n|}a_x + {}_{n+1}p_x a_{\overline{n}|}.$$

These results should be verified logically, diagrammatically, and algebraically.

3. Suppose a primed mortality table is identical to an unprimed table, with the single exception that $q'_{x+n} = q_{x+n} + c$, where n is a positive integer.

Then the values of a whole life annuity-due to (x), under the two bases, are related as follows:

$$\ddot{a}'_x = \ddot{a}_x - \frac{cd \cdot {}_{n|}a_x}{p_{x+n}}$$

4. Since $\overline{A}_x = 1 - \delta \bar{a}_x$,
    $${}^2\overline{A}_x = 1 - 2\delta \cdot {}^2\bar{a}_x .$$

Likewise, since $A_x = 1 - d\ddot{a}_x = 1 - (1 - e^{-\delta})\ddot{a}_x$, we have

$${}^2A_x = 1 - (1 - e^{-2\delta}) \cdot {}^2\ddot{a}_x$$

$$= 1 - (1 - v^2) \cdot {}^2\ddot{a}_x$$

$$= 1 - (2d - d^2) \cdot {}^2\ddot{a}_x$$

5. Commutation symbol and other relationships may be easily derived as follows, beginning with two elementary formulas relating insurances and annuities:

$$A_x = 1 - d\ddot{a}_x = v\ddot{a}_x - a_x$$

(Multiply by D_x) $\quad M_x = D_x - dN_x = vN_x - N_{x+1}$

(Sum to infinity) $\quad R_x = N_x - dS_x = vS_x - S_{x+1}$

(Divide by D_x) $\quad (IA)_x = \ddot{a}_x - d(I\ddot{a})_x = v(I\ddot{a})_x - (Ia)_x$

Similarly,

$$\overline{A}_x = 1 - \delta \ddot{a}_x$$
$$\overline{M}_x = D_x - \delta \overline{N}_x$$
$$\overline{R}_x = N_x - \delta \overline{S}_x$$
$$(I\,\overline{A})_x = \ddot{a}_x - \delta (I\bar{a})_x$$

6. In *Actuarial Mathematics*, the traditional actuarial approximations for m th-ly annuities, such as

$$\ddot{a}^{(m)}_{x:\overline{n}|} = \ddot{a}_{x:\overline{n}|} - \frac{m-1}{2m}(1 - {}_nE_x)$$

have been replaced by expressions involving $\alpha(m)$ and $\beta(m)$. In all such cases, the assumption of a uniform distribution of deaths over each year of age is imposed.

If $i = 0$, or if D_{x+t} is linear, $0 \le t \le 1$, then the traditional approximations remain valid, with $\alpha(m) = 1$ and $\beta(m) = \frac{m-1}{2m}$. For *any* interest rate, $\alpha(1) = 1$ and $\beta(1) = 0$.

The symbol $\beta(m)$ may be given a verbal interpretation which should help in the understanding of formulas in which it appears. If payments of $\frac{1}{m}$ are made to (x) at the beginning of each m th of a year, irrespective of the survival of (x), then $\beta(m)$ represents the expected *accumulated* value, at the end of the year of death, of those payments made subsequent to death.

For example, letting $m = 4$ and realizing that the probability of death (within the year of death) is $\frac{1}{4}$ for each quarter, we have

$$\beta(4) = \frac{1}{4}\left[\frac{1}{4}(1+i)^{3/4} + \frac{1}{4}(1+i)^{1/2} + \frac{1}{4}(1+i)^{1/4}\right]$$
$$+ \frac{1}{4}\left[\frac{1}{4}(1+i)^{1/2} + \frac{1}{4}(1+i)^{1/4}\right] + \frac{1}{4}\left[\frac{1}{4}(1+i)^{1/4}\right].$$

Several algebraic steps lead to the expression $\dfrac{i - i^{(4)}}{i^{(4)}d^{(4)}}$, as expected.

This verbal interpretation facilitates the understanding of such formulas as

$$\ddot{a}^{(m)}_x = \ddot{a}^{(m)}_{\overline{1}|}\ddot{a}_x - \beta(m)A_x,$$

in which the periodic payments for each year are discounted and made at the beginning of the year, thus requiring a "repayment" at the end of the year of death of that amount representing the accumulated value of those payments not "earned" by the annuitant. It also shows that $\beta(m) \ge \frac{m-1}{2m}$.

7. A thorough understanding of the relationship between complete and apportionable annuities facilitates comparison of the two. The primary point is that, even in the year of death, each annuity generates exactly the same *total* payment when the death benefit of the complete annuity and the refund feature of the apportionable annuity are taken into account. This fact correctly suggests that the two types of annuities are related by interest only, i.e., mortality is not a factor when the ratio of the two is analyzed.

> *Example*: If death occurs after the first three months of the contract year, the annual apportionable annuity pays \$1, reduced by a refund payment of $\frac{1}{a_{\overline{1}|}}\bar{a}_{\overline{3/4}|}$. The complete annuity provides only a death benefit of $\frac{1}{s_{\overline{1}|}}\bar{s}_{\overline{1/4}|}$. Since $1 - \frac{1}{a_{\overline{1}|}}\bar{a}_{\overline{3/4}|} = \frac{1}{s_{\overline{1}|}}\bar{s}_{\overline{1/4}|}$, the *total payment* for the year of death is the same.

8. If the interest rate i is assumed to be zero, annuity net single premiums simply become expectations of life, e.g.,

$$a_x \xrightarrow{i=0} e_x$$

$$\ddot{a}_x \xrightarrow{i=0} 1 + e_x$$

$$\bar{a}_x \xrightarrow{i=0} \overset{\circ}{e}_x$$

$$\ddot{a}_{x:\overline{n}|} \xrightarrow{i=0} 1 + e_{x:\overline{n-1}|}$$

$$a_{x:\overline{n}|} \xrightarrow{i=0} e_{x:\overline{n}|}$$

$$\bar{a}_{x:\overline{n}|} \xrightarrow{i=0} \overset{\circ}{e}_{x:\overline{n}|}$$

Special Mortality Laws

I. de Moivre's Law (DML)

No especially useful annuity formulas are available for de Moivre's Law. As a general approach, annuities should be evaluated by appealing to insurance/annuity relationships, such as $\ddot{a}_x = \dfrac{1 - A_x}{d}$. De Moivre insurance relationships are then applied.

II. Constant Force (CF)

$$\bar{a}_x = \frac{1}{\mu + \delta}$$

$$^2\bar{a}_x = \frac{1}{\mu + 2\delta}$$

$$\ddot{a}_x = \frac{1+i}{q+i} = \frac{1+i}{1+i-p}$$

$$^2\ddot{a}_x = \frac{(1+i)^2}{(1+i)^2 - p}$$

$$\bar{a}_{x:\overline{n}|} = \bar{a}_x(1 - {}_nE_x)$$

$$\ddot{a}_{x:\overline{n}|} = \ddot{a}_x(1 - {}_nE_x)$$

$$a_x = \frac{p}{q+i}$$

$$(\bar{I}\bar{a})_x = (\bar{a}_x)^2$$

$$(I\bar{a})_x = \ddot{a}_x\bar{a}_x$$

$$(I\ddot{a})_x = (\ddot{a}_x)^2$$

$$(Ia)_x = a_x\ddot{a}_x$$

III. Uniform Distribution of Deaths (UDD)

$$\alpha(m) = \frac{id}{i^{(m)}d^{(m)}} \doteq 1$$

$$\beta(m) = \frac{i - i^{(m)}}{i^{(m)}d^{(m)}} \doteq \frac{m-1}{2m}$$

$$\gamma(m) = \frac{d^{(m)} - d}{i^{(m)}d^{(m)}} = \alpha(m) - \beta(m) - \frac{1}{m} \doteq \frac{m-1}{2m}$$

$$\ddot{a}_x^{(m)} = \alpha(m)\ddot{a}_x - \beta(m) = \ddot{a}_{\overline{1}|}^{(m)}\ddot{a}_x - \beta(m)A_x$$

$$\ddot{a}_{x:\overline{n}|}^{(m)} = \alpha(m)\ddot{a}_{x:\overline{n}|} - \beta(m)(1 - {}_nE_x) = \ddot{a}_{\overline{1}|}^{(m)}\ddot{a}_{x:\overline{n}|} - \beta(m)A_{x:\overline{n}|}^1$$

$${}_{n|}\ddot{a}_x^{(m)} = \alpha(m)\,{}_{n|}\ddot{a}_x - \beta(m)\,{}_nE_x = \ddot{a}_{\overline{1}|}^{(m)}\,{}_{n|}\ddot{a}_x - \beta(m)\,{}_{n|}A_x$$

$$a_x^{(m)} = \alpha(m)a_x + \gamma(m) = s_{\overline{1}|}^{(m)}a_x + (1+i)\gamma(m)A_x$$

$$a_{x:\overline{n}|}^{(m)} = \alpha(m)a_{x:\overline{n}|} + \gamma(m)(1 - {}_nE_x) = s_{\overline{1}|}^{(m)}a_{x:\overline{n}|} + (1+i)\gamma(m)A_{x:\overline{n}|}^1$$

$${}_{n|}a_x^{(m)} = \alpha(m)\,{}_{n|}a_x + \gamma(m)\,{}_nE_x = s_{\overline{1}|}^{(m)}\,{}_{n|}a_x + (1+i)\gamma(m)\,{}_{n|}A_x$$

$$D_x^{(m)} = \alpha(m)D_x - \beta(m)(D_x - D_{x+1})$$

$$N_x^{(m)} = \alpha(m)N_x - \beta(m)D_x$$

$$S_x^{(m)} = \alpha(m)S_x - \beta(m)N_x$$

$$\tilde{D}_x^{(m)} = \alpha(m)D_x - (\alpha(m) - \gamma(m))(D_x - D_{x+1}) = \alpha(m)D_x - \left(\beta(m) + \frac{1}{m}\right)(D_x - D_{x+1})$$

$$\tilde{N}_x^{(m)} = \alpha(m)N_x - (\alpha(m) - \gamma(m))D_x$$

$$\overline{D}_x = \alpha(\infty)D_x - \beta(\infty)(D_x - D_{x+1})$$

$$\overline{N}_x = \alpha(\infty)N_x - \beta(\infty)D_x$$

Derivatives

$$\frac{\partial}{\partial x}\bar{a}_x = \bar{a}_x(\mu_x + \delta) - 1 = \mu_x\bar{a}_x - \overline{A}_x$$

$$\frac{\partial}{\partial x}\bar{a}_{x:\overline{n}|} = \bar{a}_{x:\overline{n}|}(\mu_x + \delta) - (1 - {}_nE_x) = \mu_x\bar{a}_{x:\overline{n}|} - \overline{A}_{x:\overline{n}|}^1$$

$$\frac{\partial}{\partial n}\bar{a}_{x:\overline{n}|} = {}_nE_x$$

$$\frac{\partial}{\partial x}\,{}_{n|}\bar{a}_x = {}_{n|}\bar{a}_x(\mu_x + \delta) - {}_nE_x$$

$$\frac{\partial}{\partial i}\ddot{a}_x = \frac{\partial}{\partial i}a_x = -v(Ia)_x$$

$$\frac{\partial}{\partial i}\bar{a}_x = -v(\overline{I}\bar{a})_x$$

$$\frac{\partial}{\partial x}\overline{N}_x = -D_x$$

$$\frac{\partial}{\partial x}\overline{S}_x = -N_x$$

$$\frac{\partial}{\partial x}(I\bar{a})_x = (I\bar{a})_x(\mu_x + \delta) - \ddot{a}_x$$

Exercises

5–1   Given: $\mu_{x+t} = \mu$ for $t \geq 0$. Which of the following is/are true?

     I. $\overline{A}_x < \dfrac{i}{\delta}A_x$

    II. $A_x = \dfrac{q_x}{q_x + i}$

    III. $\dfrac{a_x}{\ddot{a}_x} = {}_1E_x$

    A) I only   B) II only   C) III only   D) II, III only   E) All

5–2   Assuming $\mu_{x+t} = \mu$ for $t \geq 0$, and given $A_x = 2a_x$, find μ.

    A) 1   B) 2   C) 3   D) ln 3   E) Not enough
                                                                         information

5–3   If Jones, aged x, purchased an annuity with a net single premium of

$$\frac{40[100\tilde{N}_x^{(4)} + 10S_x^{(4)} - 40\tilde{S}_{x+1}^{(4)}]}{D_x}$$, and died in the second quarter of the second year, what

is the *sum* of the payments he received prior to death?

    A) 5400   B) 5560   C) 5600   D) 5660   E) 5760

5–4   Jones, aged 50, buys a complete life annuity with payments of one each quarter. If he
dies 19/3 years later, what is his death benefit?

    A) $\dfrac{\overline{s}_{\overline{1/3|}}}{\overline{s}_{\overline{1/4|}}}$ B) $\dfrac{\overline{s}_{\overline{1/12|}}}{\overline{s}_{\overline{1/4|}}}$ C) $\dfrac{\overline{s}_{\overline{1/3|}}}{4\overline{s}_{\overline{1/4|}}}$ D) $\dfrac{\overline{s}_{\overline{1/12|}}}{4\overline{s}_{\overline{1/4|}}}$ E) None of these

5-5   Which equations are true?

> I. $\alpha(m)a_{x:\overline{n}|} + \gamma(m)(1 - {}_nE_x) = a_{x:\overline{n}|} + \frac{m-1}{2m}(1 - {}_nE_x)$ (UDD)
>
> II. $\ddot{a}^{(m)}_{\overline{1}|}\ddot{a}_x + \beta(m) = \alpha(m)\ddot{a}_x + \frac{(A^{(m)}_x - A_x)}{d^{(m)}}$
>
> III. $a^{(6)}_{30:\overline{4}|} = \ddot{a}^{(6)}_{30:\overline{4}|} - \frac{5}{12}(1 - {}_4E_{30})$ (UDD and $i = 0$)

A) I, III only   B) II only   C) III only   D) II, III only   E) None

5-6   If $s(x) = 1 - \frac{x}{80}$, $0 \le x \le 80$, and $\delta = .1$, find $\Pr(\bar{a}_{\overline{T}|} < E(\bar{a}_{\overline{T}|}))$, for a life aged 40.

A) $\frac{1}{4}\ln\frac{4}{1 - e^{-4}}$ B) $\ln\frac{4}{1 - e^{-4}}$ C) $4\ln\frac{4}{1 - e^{-4}}$ D) $\ln\frac{1}{1 - e^{-4}}$ E) $\ln\frac{1}{4(1 - e^{-4})}$

5-7   Given: $\mu = .03$
             $\delta = .09$

Which of the following is/are true?

> I. $E(\bar{a}_{\overline{T}|}) = 25/3$
> II. ST. DEV. $(\bar{a}_{\overline{T}|}) = 9.92$
> III. $\Pr(2\bar{a}_{\overline{T}|} - \bar{a}_x < 0) = .855$

A) I only   B) I, III only   C) I, II only   D) II, III only   E) All

5-8   Find the expected value of the random variable Y for a person aged 25 (to the nearest .05).

$$s(x) = \frac{100 - x}{100}, \; 0 \le x \le 100$$

$$i = .05$$
$$Y = a_{\overline{K}|}, \qquad K = 0, 1, 2, 3, 4, 5$$
$$\quad = a_{\overline{3}|}, \qquad K = 6, 7, 8, \ldots$$

A) 3.85   B) 3.95   C) 4.05   D) 4.15   E) 4.25

5-9   Find the variance of the random variable in Question 5-8 for a person aged 25 (to the nearest .05).

A) .40   B) .45   C) .50   D) .55   E) .60

5-10   Under the assumptions of a constant force of mortality $\mu = .02$ and constant force of interest $\delta = .04$, find the probability that ${}_{10|}\bar{a}_{20}$ will be insufficient to provide the deferred life annuity of \$1 per year beginning at age 30. Let $e^{-.2} = .819$.

A) .50   B) .55   C) .60   D) .65   E) .70

5-11   Find $\Pr(\bar{a}_T > \bar{a}_x)$, given $\mu_x = .02$ for all x, and $\delta = .10$.

A) $\left(\dfrac{1}{5}\right)^6$ B) $\left(\dfrac{1}{5}\right)^{1/6}$ C) $\left(\dfrac{1}{6}\right)^5$ D) $\left(\dfrac{1}{6}\right)^{1/5}$ E) None of these

5-12   The net single premium for an apportionable annuity, purchased on February 1, is represented by $1200\ddot{a}_{30}^{\{2\}}$. Find the amount of the refund if death occurs on June 1.

A) $100\dfrac{d^{(12)}}{d^{(2)}}$ B) $200\dfrac{i^{(6)}}{d^{(2)}}$ C) $200\dfrac{d^{(6)}}{d^{(2)}}$ D) $200\dfrac{i^{(6)}}{i^{(2)}}$ E) $400\dfrac{i^{(3)}}{i^{(2)}}$

5-13   Ms. Johnson buys two annuities as of April 1, 1989 whose present values are represented by $100\ddot{a}_{25}^{\{2\}}$ and $100\,\mathring{a}_{25}^{(2)}$, respectively. If death occurs on August 1, 1991, what is the absolute difference in the sum received under the two annuities, after final adjustments are made for the refund payment and death benefit?

A) 0 B) $\dfrac{1}{2}(1 - \bar{A}_{25})$ C) $50(1+i)^{1/2}$ D) $50v^{1/2}$ E) 50

5-14   Given:
$$Y = a_{\overline{K}|}, \quad K = 0, 1, 2, \ldots, 10$$
$$= 0, \quad K = 11, 12, \ldots$$

$$_{10}p_x = .60 \qquad A_{x:\overline{11}|} = .40$$
$$_{11}p_x = .50 \qquad d = .10$$

Find the net single premium $E(Y)$.

A) $5 - a_{\overline{10}|}$ B) $5 - \dfrac{3}{5}a_{\overline{10}|}$ C) $5 - \dfrac{1}{2}a_{\overline{10}|}$ D) $5 - \dfrac{2}{5}a_{\overline{10}|}$ E) 5

5-15   An apportionable life annuity due, purchased on June 1, makes payments each year according to the following schedule:

Date	Payment
June 1	100
Sept. 1	200
Nov. 1	100
April 1	200

If death occurs on May 1, find the amount of the refund.

A) $\dfrac{100}{1 + v^{1/12}}$ B) $\dfrac{200}{1 + v^{1/12}}$ C) $\dfrac{100}{1 + v^{1/2}}$ D) $\dfrac{200}{1 + v^{1/2}}$ E) 100

5–16   Continuous life annuities with \$10 payments per annum are sold to each of 100 lives. Find the minimum amount necessary in an initial fund so that the issuer of the annuities will be 95% confident that all annuity payments will be made on schedule.

Use a normal approximation; $\delta = .06$ and $\mu = .04$. (Answer to nearest \$100).

A) 10,700   B) 10,800   C) 11,200   D) 11,300   E) 11,400

5–17

$$\begin{aligned}
\text{Let } Y_1 &= a_{\overline{K}|}, & K &= 0, 1, 2, \ldots, n-1 \\
&= 0 & K &= n, n+1, \ldots \\
Y_2 &= \ddot{a}_{\overline{K+1}|}, & K &= 0, 1, 2, \ldots, n-1 \\
&= 0, & K &= n, n+1, \ldots
\end{aligned}$$

Find $E(Y_2) - E(Y_1)$.

A) $_n q_x$ B) $_n p_x$ C) $_{n-1|} q_x$ D) $_{n-1} p_x$ E) 1

5–18

Given: $\dfrac{\partial}{\partial i} a_x = -\dfrac{25}{3}$

          $\ddot{a}_x = \dfrac{17}{2}$

          $i = .02$

Find $(IA)_x$.

A) 8   B) $8\dfrac{1}{6}$ C) $8\dfrac{1}{3}$ D) $8\dfrac{1}{2}$ E) $8\dfrac{2}{3}$

5–19   The purchaser of a complete annuity with semiannual payments dies one month after issue. If $i = 0$, his death benefit would be \$70. If the interest rate is 1% per month, what would the death benefit be?

A) \$66   B) \$67   C) \$68   D) \$69   E) \$70

5–20   Given: De Moivre's Law is applicable

      $\overset{\circ}{e}_x = 10$

       $i = .05$

Find a_x.

A) $20 - a_{\overline{20}|}$ B) $20 - \ddot{a}_{\overline{20}|}$ C) $20 - v a_{\overline{20}|}$ D) $20 - (1 + i)\ddot{a}_{\overline{20}|}$ E) $20 v^{19}$

5-21

Let $Y = a_{\overline{K}|}$, $K = 0, 1, 2, \ldots$

$\text{VAR}(Y) = 20\frac{1}{2}$ for issue age x

$$^2\ddot{a}_x = 10$$

$$A_x = \frac{\sqrt{2}}{2}$$

Find d.

A) .020   B) .025   C) .030   D) .035   E) .040

5-22   Given $f_X(x) = \frac{1}{80}$, $0 \le x < 80$, and $i = 0$.

Find $a^{(4)}_{30:\overline{20}|}$.

A) 15.65   B) 15.80   C) 15.95   D) 16.15   E) None of these

5-23   Let $Y = \ddot{a}_{\overline{K+1}|}$, $K = 0, 1, 2$

$\qquad\quad = 0$, $K = 3, 4, \ldots$

$\qquad \delta = \ln\frac{3}{2}$; $\mu = \ln 2$ for all ages.

Find the standard deviation of Y.

A) .47   B) .52   C) .56   D) .60   E) .66

5-24   Assume that the forces of mortality and interest are constant. If $\overline{A}_x = \frac{3}{2}\overline{A}^{\,1}_{x:\overline{30}|}$, find $\bar{a}_x$.

A) 10   B) $\dfrac{15}{\ln 3}$ C) $\dfrac{30}{\ln 3}$ D) 20   E) Cannot be determined

5-25   The net single premium for an annuity to (33) is represented by the following quantity:

$$\frac{6\tilde{S}^{(6)}_{33} + 24S^{(6)}_{34} - 18\tilde{S}^{(6)}_{35} - KS^{(2)}_{36}}{D_{33}}$$

If the scheduled payment at exact age 37 is $10, find K.

A) 1   B) 2   C) 3   D) 4   E) 5

5-26

Let $Z = v^{K+1}$, $K = 0, 1, 2, \ldots$

$\qquad Y = \ddot{a}_{\overline{K+1}|}$, $K = 0, 1, 2, \ldots$

Find $\text{COV}(Y, Z)$, if $A_x = .6$, $^2A_x = .4$, and $i = .05$.

A) $-.84$ B) $-.80$ C) $-.40$ D) $-.04$ E) 0

5-27   Let $Y = \ddot{a}_{\overline{K+1}|}$, $K = 0, 1, 2, \dots$

Which of the following is/are equal to $E[Y^2]$?

    I. ${}^2\ddot{a}_x$
    II. $\frac{1}{d}[2\ddot{a}_x - (2 - d) \cdot {}^2\ddot{a}_x]$
    III. $\frac{2}{d}(\ddot{a}_x - {}^2\ddot{a}_x)$

A) I only   B) II only   C) III only   D) I and II   E) I and III

5-28   Let $Y = \bar{a}_{\overline{T}|}$, $T \geq 0$
    $\mu_x = .05$ for all x
    $\delta = .10$

Find the k th percentile of the distribution of Y.

A) $\dfrac{k}{10}$ B) $\dfrac{10000 - k^2}{125}$ C) $\dfrac{125k - k^2}{125}$ D) $\dfrac{200k - k^2}{1000}$ E) $\dfrac{200k - k^2}{500}$

5-29   Given: $A_x^{(4)} = .25$
           $v = (.98)^4$
          $\alpha(4) = 1.0005$
          $\beta(4) = .3879$

Find $\ddot{a}_x$, assuming UDD.

A) 9.375   B) 9.425   C) 9.750   D) 9.758   E) 9.903

5-30   Company XYZ charges $\bar{a}_x$ for a continuous whole life annuity to (x), based upon $\mu = .02$ and $\delta = .08$. What is the probability that as much as 25% of the net single premium will be available to cover XYZ's expenses?

A) .05   B) .10   C) .15   D) .20   E) .25

5-31   What is the net single premium for the death benefit under a complete annuity to (x) with \$1 annual payments? Assume UDD.
Given: $\bar{A}_x = .6$, $i = .05$, $\frac{i}{\delta} = 1.0248$.

A) \$0.30   B) \$0.50   C) \$1.00   D) \$1.20   E) \$1.50

5–32   Given: μ_x is constant for all x.

$$\delta = .2$$
$$(\bar{I}\bar{a})_x = 1 + 5\bar{A}_x.$$

Find $\overset{\circ}{e}_x$.

A) $3\frac{1}{3}$ B) $4\frac{1}{6}$ C) $5\frac{1}{9}$ D) $6\frac{2}{3}$ E) $7\frac{1}{2}$

5–33   One hundred people aged x each place $0.50 into a fund in anticipation of having $1 per survivor at age $x + 10$. If $i = .03$, what is the minimum number of deaths which must occur in order that this objective will be reached?

A) 31   B) 32   C) 33   D) 34   E) 35

5–34

Find $\ddot{a}^{(2)}_{\overline{1}|}$, given: $^{2}A_x = .03\dot{5}$

$A_x = .080$

$^{2}\ddot{a}_x = 2.679$

Assume UDD.

A) .89   B) .91   C) .93   D) .95   E) .97

5–35   A man aged x purchases a whole life annuity which pays $1000 at the beginning of each quarter; payments are made for an entire year, even in the year of death. At the end of the year of death, however, the estate must repay the insurer the value of all payments made subsequent to death, with accumulated interest at $i = (1.02)^4 - 1$. What is the expected amount of the interest component of this refunded lump-sum payment? Assume UDD.

A) $50.00   B) $50.50   C) $51.00   D) $51.50   E) $52.00

5–36   If $l_x = 10,000 - x^2$, $0 \le x \le 100$, and $i = .05$, evaluate $\dfrac{1 + v\ddot{a}_x - (1 + i)a_x}{A_x}$, for $x = 40$.

A) 1   B) 1.05   C) 1.95   D) 2   E) 2.05

5–37   If $i = .08$, and simple interest is assumed, find $\beta(4)$.

A) 0   B) .375   C) .3875   D) .425   E) Cannot be determined

5-38   Simplify: $\dfrac{\partial^2 (\overline{D}\overline{a})_{x:\overline{n}|}}{\partial n^2}$

A) $\overline{a}_{x:\overline{n}|}$ B) $\overline{a}_{x:\overline{n}|}(\mu_x + \delta) - (1 - {}_nE_x)$ C) $\overline{A}_{x:\overline{n}|}$ D) ${}_nE_x$

E) $-v(\overline{I}\overline{a})_{x:\overline{n}|}$

5-39   Under the uniform distribution of deaths assumption, simplify

$$1 + \frac{d^{(2)}(\ddot{a}_{\overline{1}|}^{(2)}\ddot{a}_{25} - \ddot{a}_{25}^{(2)})}{A_{25}}.$$

A) i B) $\ddot{a}_{\overline{1}|}^{(2)}$ C) $a_{\overline{1}|}^{(2)}$ D) $\ddot{s}_{\overline{1}|}^{(2)}$ E) $s_{\overline{1}|}^{(2)}$

5-40   A life aged 20 purchased an apportionable annuity-due with \$19 annual payments. His death occurred at age $20\frac{1}{2}$. What was the present value, at issue, of the income which he would receive and be allowed to keep?

Let $d = .19$.

A) \$9.00   B) \$9.25   C) \$9.50   D) \$9.75   E) \$10.00

5-41   Simplify

$$\frac{{}_{5|}\ddot{a}_{20}^{(4)} - \alpha(4)\ddot{a}_{20} + \alpha(4) + \alpha(4)a_{20:\overline{5}|}}{\alpha(4) - \beta(4)}$$

Assume UDD.

A) ${}_5E_{20}$ B) ${}_6E_{20}$ C) $\ddot{a}_{20:\overline{5}|}$ D) $\ddot{a}_{20:\overline{6}|}$ E) $\beta(6)$

5-42   Rank the following in increasing order of magnitude: $(i > 0)$

I. $\ddot{a}_x^{\{4\}}$ II. $\ddot{a}_x^{(3)}$ III. $\ddot{a}_x^{\{3\}}$ IV. $\ddot{a}_x^{(2)}$

A) I, II, III, IV   B) IV, III, II, I   C) I, III, II, IV   D) IV, II, III, I

E) I, III, IV, II

5-43   Given: $\dfrac{{}^2\overline{A}_x}{\overline{A}_x} = \dfrac{{}^2\overline{a}_x}{\overline{a}_x} = \dfrac{4}{5}$

Find δ.

A) .05   B) .08   C) .10   D) .20   E) Cannot be
                                                                    determined

5-44   Given: $i^{(2)} = \dfrac{2}{9}$

$\ddot{a}_x = 3.7000$

Assuming a uniform distribution of deaths over each year of age, find $\ddot{a}_x^{(2)}$ exactly.

A) 3.4150   B) 3.4325   C) 3.4500   D) 3.4675   E) 3.4850

5-45   A fully continuous whole life annuity of 1 is issued to (x). By what percentage should the net single premium be loaded in order that the insurer may be 75% confident that the premium is sufficient?

Given: $\mu = .2$; $\delta = .1$.

A) 25   B) 50   C) 75   D) 100   E) None of these

Answers to Chapter Five Exercises

5–1	D.	5–16	B.	5–31	A.
5–2	D.	5–17	A.	5–32	A.
5–3	A.	5–18	B.	5–33	C.
5–4	B.	5–19	C.	5–34	D.
5–5	E.	5–20	B.	5–35	B.
5–6	A.	5–21	B.	5–36	E.
5–7	A.	5–22	C.	5–37	C.
5–8	D.	5–23	D.	5–38	D.
5–9	C.	5–24	C.	5–39	E.
5–10	B.	5–25	D.	5–40	E.
5–11	D.	5–26	A.	5–41	A.
5–12	C.	5–27	B.	5–42	C.
5–13	A.	5–28	D.	5–43	E.
5–14	C.	5–29	D.	5–44	B.
5–15	B.	5–30	D.	5–45	B.

Solutions

5–1.

I.

Under the constant force assumption, deaths within a given year of age tend to occur more heavily in the first half of the year. Therefore, death claims must be paid sooner, on the average, than if the deaths were uniformly distributed.

Accordingly, $\bar{A}_x^{CF} > \bar{A}_x^{UDD} = \frac{i}{\delta}A_x$, and I is false.

II.

The constant force assumption implies that K follows a geometric distribution, as q_x is fixed for all x.

Accordingly, $A_x = \frac{q}{q+i}$, and II is true.

III.

Generally, $a_x = {}_1E_x \ddot{a}_{x+1}$. Under the constant force assumption, age is not a factor, and therefore $\ddot{a}_{x+1} = \ddot{a}_x$. Thus, III is true.

$\therefore$ <u>II and III only</u>

5-2.

Since the geometric distribution is implied for K,

$$A_x = \frac{q}{q+i} \text{ and } a_x = \frac{p}{q+i}$$
$$\therefore q = 2p$$
$$\therefore q = 2/3$$
$$\therefore p = 1/3$$
$$\therefore \mu = \underline{ln3}$$

5-3.

Notational Facts: $\dfrac{\tilde{N}_x^{(m)}}{D_x}$ represents the actuarial present value of payments of $\dfrac{1}{m}$, beginning at age $x + \dfrac{1}{m}$ and payable for life.

$\dfrac{\tilde{S}_x^{(m)}}{D_x}$ represents the actuarial present value of payments of $\dfrac{1}{m}$ at ages $x + \frac{1}{m}, x + \frac{2}{m}, \ldots, x + 1$, followed by payments of $\dfrac{2}{m}$ at ages $x + 1 + \frac{1}{m}, x + 1 + \frac{2}{m}, \ldots, x + 2$, and so on, continuing for life.

$\dfrac{S_x^{(m)}}{D_x}$ represents the same actuarial present value as $\dfrac{\tilde{S}_x^{(m)}}{D_x}$, except that payments are made at the beginning of each m th of a year of age.

The total payments may be represented diagrammatically as follows:

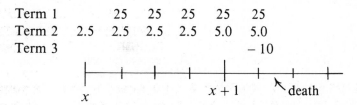

Term 1   25   25   25   25   25
Term 2   2.5   2.5   2.5   2.5   5.0   5.0
Term 3   − 10

Adding, we obtain \$135. Thus, $40(135) = \underline{5400}$.

5-4.

The following diagram depicts the year of death of Jones, i.e., the year of age between 56 and 57.

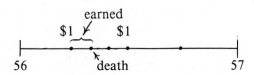

Actuarial Mathematics treats each \$1 payment of the complete annuity as a continuous payment of annualized amount $\dfrac{1}{\bar{s}_{\overline{1/4}|}}$. Accordingly, the portion of the scheduled payment at age $56\frac{1}{2}$ which was "earned" by the annuitant prior to his death was

$$\frac{1}{\bar{s}_{\overline{1/4}|}}\bar{s}_{\overline{1/12}|}.$$

Note that the approximate answer should logically be $\frac{1}{3}$ of a dollar, as $\frac{1}{3}$ of the second quarter of the year of age was lived by the annuitant. At an interest rate of zero, in fact, the *exact* answer is $\frac{1}{3}$.

5–5.

I.

The left-hand side of the equation is the UDD expression for $a^{(m)}_{x:\overline{n}|}$.

The right-hand side of the equation is the Woolhouse-based "traditional" approximation for $a^{(m)}_{x:\overline{n}|}$.

These are equal only if $m = 1$ or $i = 0$. Accordingly, I is false.

II.

$\ddot{a}^{(m)}_x = \ddot{a}^{(m)}_{\overline{1}|}\ddot{a}_x - \dfrac{A^{(m)}_x - A_x}{d^{(m)}}$ is exact. $\ddot{a}^{(m)}_x = \alpha(m)\ddot{a}_x - \beta(m)$ is a UDD approximation. Therefore II is false.

III.

$a^{(6)}_{30:\overline{4}|} = a_{30:\overline{4}|} + \frac{5}{12}(1 - {}_4E_{30})$ and $\ddot{a}^{(6)}_{30:\overline{4}|} = \ddot{a}_{30:\overline{4}|} - \frac{5}{12}(1 - {}_4E_{30})$ are exact if $i = 0$ and UDD is assumed.

Therefore $\ddot{a}^{(6)}_{30:\overline{4}|} - a^{(6)}_{30:\overline{4}|} = \ddot{a}_{30:\overline{4}|} - a_{30:\overline{4}|} - \frac{5}{6}(1 - {}_4E_{30})$

$$= \frac{1}{6}(1 - {}_4E_{30})$$

III is false.
∴ <u>None</u> are true.

5–6.

In the accompanying diagram, let h be that duration at which death of the annuitant would generate neither a gain nor a loss to the insurer.

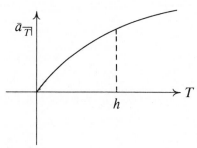

It is desired to find the probability that the insurer makes a "gain" on a random life, i.e., that the annuitant dies before the "break-even" duration h. Accordingly, we must find $_h q_{40}$.

The diagram tells us that $\bar{a}_{\overline{h|}} = \bar{a}_{40}$.

$$\therefore \frac{1 - v^h}{\delta} = \frac{1 - \bar{A}_{40}}{\delta} \; ; \; v^h = \bar{A}_{40} = \frac{\bar{a}_{\overline{40|}}}{40} = \frac{1 - e^{-40\delta}}{40\delta}$$

$$\therefore e^{-.1h} = \frac{1 - e^{-4}}{4} \; ; \; -.1h = ln\frac{1 - e^{-4}}{4}$$

$$\therefore h = -10 \, ln\frac{1 - e^{-4}}{4}$$

We need

$$_h q_{40} = \frac{h}{40} = -\frac{1}{4} ln\frac{1 - e^{-4}}{4}$$

$$= \frac{1}{4} ln\frac{4}{1 - e^{-4}}$$

5–7.

If $\mu = .03$ and $\delta = .09$, we have

$$\bar{a}_x = \frac{1}{.12} = 8\frac{1}{3} \qquad\qquad (CF)$$

$$VAR[\bar{a}_{\overline{T|}}] = \frac{^2\bar{A}_x - \bar{A}_x^2}{\delta^2} = \frac{\frac{.03}{.21} - \left(\frac{.03}{.12}\right)^2}{(.09)^2} = 9.92$$

Accordingly, I is true and II is false. The substantial part of this question, however, is III.

In the accompanying diagram, let h be that duration at which the death of the annuitant would result in a present value of total claim equal to $\frac{1}{2}$ of the net single premium.

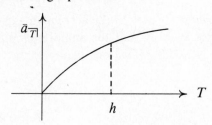

Thus $\bar{a}_{\overline{h}|} = \frac{1}{2}\bar{a}_x$. Since we want the probability that $\bar{a}_{\overline{T}|}$ is less than $\frac{1}{2}\bar{a}_x$, we need to determine $_h q_x$.

$$\therefore \frac{1 - e^{-.09h}}{.09} = \frac{1}{2} \cdot \frac{25}{3}; \; e^{-.09h} = .625$$

$$_h q_x = 1 - {}_h p_x = 1 - e^{-.03h} = 1 - (.625)^{1/3} = .145$$

Thus we see that III is false; it is the complement of the required probability.

$\therefore$ <u>I only</u>

5-8.

It should be recognized, without algebraic techniques, that

$$E[Y] = a_{25:\overline{5}|}.$$

Under de Moivre's Law,

$$a_{25:\overline{5}|} = \frac{1}{75}[74v + 73v^2 + 72v^3 + 71v^4 + 70v^5]$$

$$\doteq \underline{4.16}$$

Whereas this could be written as

$$a_{25:\overline{5}|} = \frac{1}{75}[70a_{\overline{5}|} + (Da)_{\overline{4}|}],$$

it is easier to evaluate from the first form given.

5-9.

Method One

Since the mean of Y has already been determined, only the second moment is now required.

$$E[Y^2] = \sum_{k=0}^{5} (a_{\overline{k}|})^2 {}_{k|}q_{25} + (a_{\overline{5}|})^2 {}_6 p_{25}$$

$$= \frac{1}{75}[(a_{\overline{1}|})^2 + (a_{\overline{2}|})^2 + (a_{\overline{3}|})^2 + (a_{\overline{4}|})^2 + 70(a_{\overline{5}|})^2]$$

$$= 17.82$$

Thus, $\text{VAR}[Y] = 17.82 - (4.16)^2 \doteq \underline{.51}$.

Method Two

$$\text{VAR}[Y] = \frac{{}^{2}A_{x:\overline{6}|} - (A_{x:\overline{6}|})^{2}}{d^{2}}$$

While this approach involves more time and arithmetic than the first, the student should be careful to understand why the formula involves $A_{x:\overline{6}|}$ rather than $A_{x:\overline{5}|}$.

5–10.

In the accompanying diagram, let h be the duration at death such that there is neither gain nor loss to the insurer.

$Y = 0,\ 0 \le T \le 10$
$\quad = \bar{a}_{\overline{T}|} - \bar{a}_{\overline{10}|},\ T > 10$

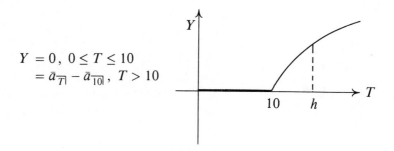

Since we desire the probability that the net single premium is insufficient, we need ${}_{h}p_{20}$.

From the diagram, we have

$$\bar{a}_{\overline{h}|} - \bar{a}_{\overline{10}|} = {}_{10|}\bar{a}_{20} = {}_{10}E_{20}\bar{a}_{30}$$

$$\therefore \frac{v^{10} - v^{h}}{.04} = e^{-.6}\frac{1}{.06}$$

$$\therefore v^{h} = e^{-.4} - \frac{2}{3}e^{-.6} = e^{-.04h}$$

$${}_{h}p_{20} = e^{-.02h}$$

$$= \left(e^{-.4} - \frac{2}{3}e^{-.6}\right)^{1/2}$$

$$\doteq \underline{\underline{.55}}$$

5–11.

In the accompanying diagram, let h be the duration at death such that there is neither gain nor loss to the insurer.

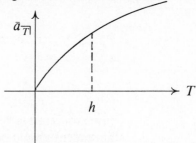

Given $\bar{a}_{\overline{h}|} = \bar{a}_x = \frac{1}{.12}$, we need ${}_hp_x$.

$$\therefore \frac{25}{3} = \frac{1 - v^h}{\delta} = \frac{1 - e^{-.1h}}{.1}$$

$$\therefore e^{-.1h} = \frac{1}{6}$$

$${}_hp_x = e^{-.02h} = \left(\frac{1}{6}\right)^{1/5}$$

5–12.

This annuity has scheduled payments of $600 at the beginning of each six months. The payment made on February 1 of the year of death is not entirely "earned" by the annuitant, as he died four months after that payment.

The $600 payment is treated in *Actuarial Mathematics* as being spread out over the ensuing six months with a continuous annualized payment of

$$\frac{600}{\bar{a}_{\overline{1/2}|}}.$$

From the diagram, it is seen that the appropriate refund at death is

$$\frac{600}{\bar{a}_{\overline{1/2}|}} \bar{a}_{\overline{1/6}|}.$$

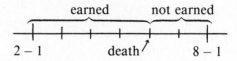

But

$$\frac{\bar{a}_{\overline{1/6}|}}{\bar{a}_{\overline{1/2}|}} = \frac{1 - v^{1/6}}{1 - v^{1/2}} = \frac{\dfrac{d^{(6)}}{6}}{\dfrac{d^{(2)}}{2}} = \frac{1}{3}\frac{d^{(6)}}{d^{(2)}}.$$

Finally,

$$600 \left(\frac{1}{3}\right) \frac{d^{(6)}}{d^{(2)}} = 200 \frac{d^{(6)}}{d^{(2)}}.$$

NOTE: In the absence of interest, the answer would be exactly $\frac{1}{3}(600) = 200$.

5–13.

The answer to this question is zero, based upon Observation #6 at the beginning of this section.

More formally, the sum paid under the complete annuity is

$$50(4) + \frac{50}{\bar{s}_{\overline{1/2}|}} \bar{s}_{\overline{1/3}|}.$$

The corresponding sum under the apportionable annuity is

$$50(5) - \frac{50}{\bar{a}_{\overline{1/2}|}} \bar{a}_{\overline{1/6}|}.$$

An appeal to compound interest relationships shows that these two expressions are equal.

5–14.

If $Y = a_{\overline{K}|}, \quad K = 0,1,2,\ldots,10$
$ = a_{\overline{10}|}, \quad K = 11,12,\ldots,$

then $E[Y] = a_{x:\overline{10}|}$.

Thus the expected value of the random variable here is

$$E[Y] = a_{x:\overline{10}|} - {}_{11}p_x a_{\overline{10}|}.$$

Since $\ddot{a}_{x:\overline{11}|} = \dfrac{1 - A_{x:\overline{11}|}}{d} = 6$, $a_{x:\overline{10}|} = 5$. Then $E[Y] = 5 - \frac{1}{2}a_{\overline{10}|}$.

5–15.

The $200 April 1 payment is only approximately half "earned" by the annuitant whose death falls in the middle of the period with which it is associated.

The refund is therefore

$$\frac{200}{\bar{a}_{\overline{1/6}|}} \bar{a}_{\overline{1/12}|}$$

Simplifying, we have

$$200 \frac{1 - v^{1/12}}{1 - v^{1/6}} = 200 \frac{1}{1 + v^{1/12}}$$

5–16.

$$\text{Let } Y = 10\bar{a}_{\overline{T}|}$$

$$\text{Let } S = Y_1 + Y_2 + \cdots + Y_{100}$$

$$E[Y] = 10\frac{1}{\mu + \delta} = 100 \qquad \text{(CF)}$$

$$\text{VAR}[Y] = 100\left[\frac{\frac{\mu}{\mu+2\delta} - \left(\frac{\mu}{\mu+\delta}\right)^2}{\delta^2}\right] \qquad \text{(CF)}$$

$$= 2500$$

$$\therefore E[S] = 10,000$$

$$\text{VAR}[S] = 250,000$$

$$\sigma[S] = 500$$

The amount necessary for 95% confidence is
$E[S] + 1.645\sigma[S] = \underline{\underline{10,822.50}}$.

5–17.

Key Approach: Rather than finding $E[Y_2]$ and $E[Y_1]$ independently, let us consider the random variable $Y_2 - Y_1$.

$$Y_2 - Y_1 = 1, \quad K = 0,1,2,\ldots,n-1$$
$$= 0, \quad K = n,n+1,\ldots$$
$$\therefore E[Y_2 - Y_1] = \underline{\underline{{}_nq_x}}$$

For additional practice, the student should verify that

$$E[Y_2] = \ddot{a}_{x:\overline{n}|} - {}_np_x\ddot{a}_{\overline{n}|}$$
$$\text{and}$$
$$E[Y_1] = a_{x:\overline{n-1}|} - {}_np_x a_{\overline{n-1}|}$$

5–18.

Key Formulas:

$$\frac{\partial}{\partial i} a_x = -v(Ia)_x$$

$$(IA)_x = \ddot{a}_x - d(I\ddot{a})_x$$

$$(I\ddot{a})_x = (Ia)_x + \ddot{a}_x$$

$$\therefore \frac{25}{3} = \frac{1}{1.02}(Ia)_x$$

$$\therefore (Ia)_x = 8.5$$

$$\therefore (I\ddot{a})_x = 17$$

$$\therefore (IA)_x = 8.5 - \frac{.02}{1.02}(17)$$

$$= 8\frac{1}{6}$$

5–19.

In a complete annuity with $i = 0$, the death benefit is simply the proportionate part of the next annuity payment which is "earned" prior to death. Accordingly, the semiannual payment in this annuity is $420.

The death benefit, where $i > 0$, is

$$\frac{420}{\bar{s}_{\overline{1/2}|}} \bar{s}_{\overline{1/12}|}$$

$$= 420 \frac{(1+i)^{1/12} - 1}{(1+i)^{1/2} - 1}$$

$$= 420 \frac{.01}{(1.01)^6 - 1}$$

$$= \underline{68.27}$$

5–20.

Since $\overset{\circ}{e}_x = 10$ and de Moivre's Law is assumed, $\omega = x + 20$.

Using the "estate tax" formula

$$1 = ia_x + (1+i)A_x,$$

we have

$$1 = .05a_x + (1.05)\frac{a_{\overline{20}|}}{20}$$

$$\therefore a_x = 20 - 1.05a_{\overline{20}|}$$

$$= \underline{20 - \ddot{a}_{\overline{20}|}}$$

5–21.

Key Formula: If $Y = a_{\overline{K}|}$, $K = 0, 1, 2, \ldots$, then

$$\text{VAR}[Y] = \frac{{}^2A_x - A_x^2}{d^2}$$

$$= \frac{1 - (2d - d^2) \cdot {}^2\ddot{a}_x - (A_x)^2}{d^2}$$

$$\therefore 20.5d^2 = 1 - 10(2d - d^2) - \frac{1}{2}$$

Solving the quadratic, the positive root of the equation is found to be $d = \underline{.0247}$.

5–22.

Key Facts: If we assume UDD and $i = 0$, the "traditional" approximations for annuities with m thly payments are exact.

De Moivre's Law, with $\omega = 80$, is assumed.

Then

$$a_{30:\overline{20}|}^{(4)} = a_{30:\overline{20}|} + \frac{3}{8}(1 - {}_{20}E_{30})$$

Letting $i = 0$,

$$a_{30:\overline{20}|}^{(4)} = e_{30:\overline{20}|} + \frac{3}{8}{}_{20}q_{30}$$

$$= \frac{49 + 48 + \cdots + 30}{50} + \frac{3}{8} \cdot \frac{20}{50}$$

$$= \underline{15.95}$$

5–23.

We should recognize that

$$E[Y] = \ddot{a}_{x:\overline{3}|} - {}_3p_x\ddot{a}_{\overline{3}|}.$$

Since, however, there is no simple formula for the second moment or the variance of Y, we should appeal to basic principles. The values of Y, and the associated probabilities, are given as follows: (Note $p = \frac{1}{2}$, $v = \frac{2}{3}$)

$$\begin{aligned}
Y &= 1, & K &= 0 \\
Y &= 1 + v, & K &= 1 \\
Y &= 1 + v + v^2, & K &= 2 \\
Y &= 0, & K &= 3, 4, 5, \ldots
\end{aligned}$$

Simplifying,

$$\Pr[Y = 1] = q_x = \frac{1}{2}$$

$$\Pr[Y = 5/3] = {}_{1|}q_x = \frac{1}{4}$$

$$\Pr[Y = 19/9] = {}_{2|}q_x = \frac{1}{8}$$

$$\Pr[Y = 0] = {}_3p_x = \frac{1}{8}$$

$$\therefore E[Y] = \frac{1}{2} + \frac{5}{12} + \frac{19}{72} = \frac{85}{72}$$

$$E[Y^2] = \frac{1}{2} + \frac{25}{36} + \frac{361}{648} = \frac{1135}{648}$$

$$\therefore \mathrm{VAR}[Y] = \frac{1855}{5184}$$

$$\therefore \sigma[Y] \doteq \underline{.598}$$

5–24.

Key Formula:
$$\bar{A}^{1}_{x:\overline{n|}} = \bar{A}_x(1 - {}_nE_x) \qquad \text{(CF)}$$

$$\therefore \bar{A}_x = \frac{3}{2}\bar{A}_x(1 - {}_{30}E_x)$$

$$\therefore {}_{30}E_x = \frac{1}{3}$$

$$\therefore \frac{1}{3} = e^{-30(\mu+\delta)}$$

$$\therefore 30(\mu + \delta) = ln3$$

$$\bar{a}_x = \frac{1}{\mu + \delta} = \frac{30}{\underline{ln3}} \qquad \text{(CF)}$$

5–25.

The four terms in the numerator generate, respectively, the following payment amounts at age 37:

$$4, 16, -6, -K$$

$$\therefore 4 + 16 - 6 - K = 10$$

$$\underline{K = 4}$$

5–26.

Key Formula: $$COV(Y,Z) = E[YZ] - E[Y]E[Z]$$

$$E[Y] = \ddot{a}_x = \frac{1 - A_x}{d} = 8.4$$

$$E[Z] = A_x = .6$$

$$YZ = \frac{1 - v^{K+1}}{d} v^{K+1} = \frac{v^{K+1} - v^{2(K+1)}}{d}$$

$$\therefore E[YZ] = \frac{1}{d}[A_x - {}^2A_x] = 4.2$$

$$\therefore COV[Y,Z] = 4.2 - 5.04 = \underline{\underline{-.84}}$$

5–27.

Key Formula: $$E[Y^2] = VAR[Y] + (E[Y])^2$$

We know

$$E[Y] = \ddot{a}_x$$

$$VAR[Y] = \frac{{}^2A_x - A_x^2}{d^2} = \frac{1 - (2d - d^2) \cdot {}^2\ddot{a}_x - (1 - d\ddot{a}_x)^2}{d^2}$$

$$= \frac{2d\ddot{a}_x - d^2 \cdot \ddot{a}_x^2 - (2d - d^2) \cdot {}^2\ddot{a}_x}{d^2}$$

$$= \frac{1}{d}[2\ddot{a}_x - (2 - d) \cdot {}^2\ddot{a}_x] - \ddot{a}_x^2$$

$$\therefore E[Y^2] = \frac{1}{d}[2\ddot{a}_x - (2 - d) \cdot {}^2\ddot{a}_x]$$

Thus II is correct. Since it is, III is not. Finally, I = II only if $\ddot{a}_x = {}^2\ddot{a}_x$. $\therefore$ I is false

NOTE: Many students labor under the misconception that if $E[Y] = \ddot{a}_x$, then $E[Y^2] = {}^2\ddot{a}_x$. This misconception probably arises through an improper extension of the fact that if $E[Z] = A_x$, then $E[Z^2] = {}^2A_x$.

5–28.

In the accompanying diagram, let h be the duration at death such that the value of $\bar{a}_{\overline{T}|}$ exceeds $\bar{a}_{\overline{h}|}$ exactly $(100 - k)\%$ of the time.

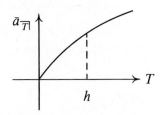

By definition, $_{h}p_{x} = \dfrac{100 - k}{100}$, and we wish to determine $\bar{a}_{\overline{h}|}$.

$$\therefore \frac{100 - k}{100} = e^{-.05h}$$

$$\bar{a}_{\overline{h}|} = 10(1 - e^{-.10h})$$

$$= 10\left(1 - \left(\frac{100 - k}{100}\right)^{2}\right)$$

$$= 10(1 - (1 - .01k)^{2})$$

$$= 10[-.0001k^{2} + .02k]$$

$$= \underline{\underline{\frac{200k - k^{2}}{1000}}}$$

5–29.

Key Formulas:

$$A_{x}^{(4)} = 1 - d^{(4)}\ddot{a}_{x}^{(4)}$$

$$\ddot{a}_{x}^{(4)} = \alpha(4)\ddot{a}_{x} - \beta(4)$$

Since

$$v^{1/4} = .98, \ d^{(4)} = .08$$

$$\ddot{a}_{x}^{(4)} = \frac{1 - A_{x}^{(4)}}{d^{(4)}} = \frac{.75}{.08}$$

$$\therefore \ddot{a}_{x} = \frac{\dfrac{.75}{.08} + \beta(4)}{\alpha(4)} = \underline{\underline{9.758}}$$

5–30.

Since the net single premium is $10 (per dollar of annuity payment), the question asks for the probability that the present value random variable $\bar{a}_{\overline{T}|}$ is less than 7.5.

Let h represent that duration at death such that the present value random variable equals 7.5.

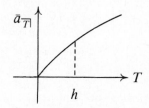

We wish to find $_hq_x$, given that $\bar{a}_{\overline{h}|} = 7.5$

$$\therefore \frac{1 - e^{-.08h}}{.08} = 7.5$$

$$\therefore e^{-.08h} = .4$$

$$_hp_x = e^{-.02h} = (.4)^{1/4}$$

$$\therefore {}_hq_x = 1 - (.4)^{1/4}$$

$$= \underline{.2047}$$

5–31.

Key Concept:

The net single premium for a complete annuity must purchase the immediate annuity payments as well as the death benefit. Thus, the net single premium for the death benefit is the excess of the entire net single premium over the premium for the annuity alone, i.e., $\overset{\circ}{a}_x - a_x$.

$$\overset{\circ}{a}_x - a_x = \overset{\circ}{a}_x - \ddot{a}_x + 1$$

$$= \frac{1 - \bar{A}_x}{i} - \frac{1 - A_x}{d} + 1$$

$$= \frac{A_x}{d} - \frac{\bar{A}_x}{i} \quad \left(\text{since } \frac{1}{d} - \frac{1}{i} = 1\right)$$

$$= 21A_x - 20\bar{A}_x$$

$$= \bar{A}_x\left(21\frac{\delta}{i} - 20\right) \quad \text{(UDD)}$$

$$= \underline{.295}$$

5–32.

Key Formula:
$$(\bar{I}\bar{a})_x = (\bar{a}_x)^2 \quad \text{(CF)}$$

$$\therefore (\bar{a}_x)^2 = 1 + 5(1 - .2\bar{a}_x) = 6 - \bar{a}_x$$

Solving the quadratic, $\bar{a}_x = 2$. Then

$$2 = \frac{1}{\mu + .2} \quad \text{(CF)}$$
$$\therefore \mu = .3$$
$$\therefore \overset{\circ}{e}_x = \underline{\underline{3\frac{1}{3}}}$$

5–33.

Letting $l_x = 100$, we have

$$\frac{100(.50)(1.03)^{10}}{l_{x+10}} \geq 1$$

$$\therefore 50(1.03)^{10} \geq l_x - {}_{10}d_x = 100 - {}_{10}d_x$$
$$\therefore {}_{10}d_x \geq 100 - 50(1.03)^{10} = 32.8$$
$$\therefore \text{ At least } \underline{\underline{33}} \text{ deaths are required.}$$

5–34.

Key Formula:
$${}^2A_x = 1 - (2d - d^2) \cdot {}^2\ddot{a}_x$$

$$\therefore (2d - d^2) = .36$$
$$\therefore d = .20$$
$$d^{(2)} = 2[1 - (.8)^{1/2}] \doteq .2111$$

Finally, $\ddot{a}_{\overline{1}|}^{(2)} = \frac{d}{d^{(2)}} = \underline{\underline{.947}}$

5–35.

Key Concept: This question is asking for the excess of $\beta(m)$ over $\dfrac{m-1}{2m}$.

Interest Values:
$$(1+i)^{1/4} = 1.02$$
$$\therefore i^{(4)} = .08$$
$$\therefore d^{(4)} = \frac{.08}{1.02}$$
$$i = (1.02)^4 - 1$$
$$\beta(4) = \frac{i - i^{(4)}}{i^{(4)}d^{(4)}} = .3876255$$
$$\therefore \beta(4) - \frac{3}{8} = .0126255$$

Multiplying by 4000, the result is $\underline{\$50.50}$.

Alternative for $\beta(4)$: $\beta(4) = \dfrac{1}{4} \cdot \dfrac{1}{4}[(1+i)^{3/4} + 2(1+i)^{1/2} + 3(1+i)^{1/4}]$

5–36.

Key Identities:
$$A_x = v\ddot{a}_x - a_x$$
$$1 = ia_x + (1+i)A_x$$

Then the fraction simplifies to

$$\frac{A_x(2+i)}{A_x} = 2 + i$$
$$= \underline{2.05}$$

NOTE: The given mortality law was irrelevant.

5-37.

Key Formula:
$$\beta(4) = \frac{1}{4} \cdot \frac{1}{4}[(1+i)^{3/4} + 2(1+i)^{1/2} + 3(1+i)^{1/4}]$$

Using simple interest,

$$\beta(4) = \frac{1}{16}\left(1 + \frac{3}{4}i + 2 + i + 3 + \frac{3}{4}i\right)$$

$$= \frac{1}{16}\left(6 + \frac{5}{2}i\right)$$

$$\therefore \beta(4) = \underline{\underline{.3875}}$$

5-38.

Key Formula:
$$(\overline{D}\bar{a})_{x:\overline{n}|} = \int_0^n (n-t)v^t\,{}_tp_x\,dt$$

Now,

$$\frac{\partial}{\partial n}(\overline{D}\bar{a})_{x:\overline{n}|} = \frac{\partial}{\partial n}\int_0^n nv^t\,{}_tp_x\,dt - \frac{\partial}{\partial n}\int_0^n tv^t\,{}_tp_x\,dt$$

$$= n \cdot {}_nE_x + \int_0^n v^t\,{}_tp_x\,dt - n \cdot {}_nE_x$$

$$= \bar{a}_{x:\overline{n}|}$$

Finally

$$\frac{\partial^2(\overline{D}\bar{a})_{x:\overline{n}|}}{\partial n^2} = \frac{\partial}{\partial n}\bar{a}_{x:\overline{n}|} = \underline{\underline{{}_nE_x}}.$$

5-39.

Key Formula:
$$\ddot{a}_{25}^{(2)} = \ddot{a}_{\overline{1}|}^{(2)}\ddot{a}_{25} - \beta(2)A_{25} \qquad \text{(UDD)}$$

The fraction then reduces to

$$\frac{\beta(2)A_{25}d^{(2)}}{A_{25}} = \frac{i - i^{(2)}}{i^{(2)}}$$

Adding 1, we have $\dfrac{i}{i^{(2)}}$, or $\underline{\underline{s_{\overline{1}|}^{(2)}}}$

5–40.

The annuitant received \$19 at age 20, but was required to return

$$\frac{19}{\bar{a}_{\overline{1}|}}\bar{a}_{\overline{1/2}|}$$

at age $20\frac{1}{2}$. The required present value, then, is

$$19 - \frac{19}{\bar{a}_{\overline{1}|}}\bar{a}_{\overline{1/2}|}v^{1/2}$$

$$= 19\left[1 - \frac{v^{1/2} - v}{1 - v}\right]$$

$$= 19\left(\frac{1 - v^{1/2}}{1 - v}\right)$$

$$= \frac{19}{1 + v^{1/2}}$$

$$= \frac{19}{1.9}$$

$$= \underline{\underline{10}}$$

5–41.

Key Formula:

$$_{5|}\ddot{a}_{20}^{(4)} = \alpha(4)_{5|}\ddot{a}_{20} - \beta(4)_5 E_{20}$$

Thus, the numerator is

$$\alpha(4)_{5|}\ddot{a}_{20} - \beta(4)_5 E_{20} - \alpha(4)a_{20} + \alpha(4)a_{20:\overline{5}|}$$

$$= \alpha(4)[_{5|}\ddot{a}_{20} - {}_{5|}a_{20}] - \beta(4)_5 E_{20}$$

$$= [\alpha(4) - \beta(4)]_5 E_{20}$$

$\therefore$ The fraction equals $\underline{\underline{_5 E_{20}}}$.

5–42.

Compare I and III:

$$\text{I}: \quad \frac{1 - \bar{A}_x}{d^{(4)}} \qquad\qquad \text{III.} \quad \frac{1 - \bar{A}_x}{d^{(3)}}$$

Since $d^{(4)} > d^{(3)}$, $\text{I} < \text{III}$

Compare II and III: II is greater than III; the payments are identical in amount and in timing, but the apportionable annuity (III) entails a refund of a portion of the final annuity payment at death.

$$\therefore \text{I} < \text{III} < \text{II}$$

Compare II and IV:

$$\ddot{a}_x^{(m)} < \ddot{a}_x^{(n)} \text{ if } n < m.$$

$$\therefore \text{ II} < \text{IV}$$

$$\therefore \underline{\text{I} < \text{III} < \text{II} < \text{IV}}$$

5–43.

Key Formula:

$$^2\overline{A}_x = 1 - 2\delta \cdot {}^2\overline{a}_x$$

$$\therefore \frac{1 - 2\delta \cdot {}^2\overline{a}_x}{1 - \delta \overline{a}_x} = \frac{1 - 2\delta(.8)\overline{a}_x}{1 - \delta \overline{a}_x} = \frac{4}{5}.$$

Solving,

$$\delta \overline{a}_x = \frac{1}{4}$$

$$\therefore \overline{A}_x = \frac{3}{4}$$

$$\therefore {}^2\overline{A}_x = \frac{3}{5}$$

$$\overline{a}_x = \frac{1}{4\delta}$$

$$\therefore {}^2\overline{a}_x = \frac{1}{5\delta}$$

Thus δ is not unique, and, accordingly, <u>cannot</u> <u>be</u> <u>determined</u>.

5–44.

Key Concept: To evaluate $\ddot{a}_x^{(2)}$, we need $\alpha(2)$ and $\beta(2)$.

Key Formula:

$$\ddot{a}_x^{(m)} = \alpha(m)\ddot{a}_x - \beta(m) \qquad \text{(UDD)}$$

Interest Values:

$$i^{(2)} = \frac{2}{9}$$

$$\therefore d^{(2)} = \frac{2}{10}$$

$$i = \left(\frac{10}{9}\right)^2 - 1 = \frac{19}{81}$$

$$\therefore d = \frac{19}{100}$$

$$\therefore \alpha(2) = \frac{\frac{19}{81} \cdot \frac{19}{100}}{\frac{2}{9} \cdot \frac{2}{10}} = \frac{361}{360}$$

$$\beta(2) = \frac{\frac{19}{81} - \frac{2}{9}}{\frac{2}{9} \cdot \frac{2}{10}} = \frac{5}{18}$$

$$\therefore \ddot{a}_x^{(2)} = \frac{361}{360}(3.7) - \frac{5}{18} = \frac{1235.7}{360}$$

$$= \underline{3.4325}$$

5–45.

Key Concept:

Since the insurer requires 75% confidence that the net single premium is sufficient, he is willing for the present value random variable to exceed the single premium 25% of the time.

Accordingly, in the accompanying diagram, let h be that duration at death which is exceeded by 25% of the annuitants.

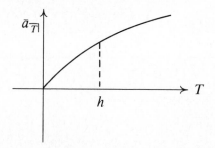

We know that $_h p_x = .25$ and that $\bar{a}_{\overline{h}|} =$ the single premium π.

$$\therefore e^{-.2h} = \frac{1}{4}$$

$$1 - e^{-.1h} = .1\pi$$

$$\therefore \pi = 5$$

Since the net single premium is $\dfrac{1}{\mu + \delta} = \dfrac{10}{3}$, and the loaded premium is $\pi = 5$, the loading is $\underline{50\%}$ of the net premium.

Chapter Six

Supplementary Concepts

1. The variances of prospective loss random variables L are closely related to those of insurance-related present value random variables. The variance formulas are very compact where the equivalence principle is assumed, but are not as simple or as easy to remember in the absence of the equivalence principle.

    Example 1

    If $L = v^T - \overline{P}\overline{a}_{\overline{T}|}$, $T \geq 0$, then $\text{VAR}[L] = \dfrac{{}^2\overline{A}_x - \overline{A}_x^2}{(1 - \overline{A}_x)^2}$ if the equivalence principle is assumed, i.e., if $\overline{P} = \overline{P}(\overline{A}_x)$. Otherwise,

    $$\text{VAR}[L] = ({}^2\overline{A}_x - \overline{A}_x^2)\left(1 + \frac{\overline{P}}{\delta}\right)^2.$$

    Example 2

    If

    $$L = v^T - \overline{P}\overline{a}_{\overline{T}|}, \ 0 \leq T \leq n$$
    $$= v^n - \overline{P}\overline{a}_{\overline{n}|}, \ T > n,$$

    then

    $$\text{VAR}[L] = \frac{{}^2\overline{A}_{x\,:\,\overline{n}|} - (\overline{A}_{x\,:\,\overline{n}|})^2}{(1 - \overline{A}_{x\,:\,\overline{n}|})^2}$$

    if the equivalence principle is assumed, i.e., if $\overline{P} = \overline{P}(\overline{A}_{x\,:\,\overline{n}|})$. Otherwise,

    $$\text{VAR}[L] = [{}^2\overline{A}_{x\,:\,\overline{n}|} - (\overline{A}_{x\,:\,\overline{n}|})^2]\left(1 + \frac{\overline{P}}{\delta}\right)^2.$$

    Analogous formulas exist for fully discrete whole life and endowment loss random variables.

2. Unfortunately, simple variance formulas similar to those just stated do not exist for loss random variables associated with products other than whole life or endowment insurance. When variances of such random variables are required, they are best obtained through an appeal to basic principles or through a technique to be introduced in Chapter Seven.

3.   The pure endowment annual premium $P_{x:\overline{n}|}^{\,1}$ equals the reciprocal of the foreborne annuity $\ddot{s}_{x:\overline{n}|}$. This is because the share of the survivor who has deposited $P_{x:\overline{n}|}^{\,1}$ at the beginning of each year for n years is the contractual \$1 pure endowment, i.e.,

$$P_{x:\overline{n}|}^{\,1}\ddot{s}_{x:\overline{n}|} = 1.$$

4.   Net level premiums such as $_nP_x$, $P_{x:\overline{n}|}^{\,1}$, and $P_{x:\overline{n}|}$ purchase identical insurance between ages x and $x+n$, i.e., the difference in the magnitude of the premiums is solely attributable to the investment feature of the contract.

Accordingly, comparisons of the policy values of survivors at age $x+n$ may be effected by analyzing future benefits; past benefits may be ignored because they are equivalent.

Examples

$$(_nP_x - P_{x:\overline{n}|}^{\,1})\ddot{s}_{x:\overline{n}|} = A_{x+n}$$
$$(P_{x:\overline{n}|} - _nP_x)\ddot{s}_{x:\overline{n}|} = 1 - A_{x+n}$$
$$(P_{x:\overline{n}|} - P_{x:\overline{n}|}^{\,1})\ddot{s}_{x:\overline{n}|} = 1$$

These concepts will be extended after the introduction of the notion of reserves in Chapter Seven.

5.   We have seen that we may treat apportionable annuities by crediting the annuitant with the discounted value (at interest only) of each year's payments at the beginning of the year. Should death occur before yearend, an appropriate refund is made from the annuitant's estate.

A common application of this concept is used with apportionable premiums for insurance products. The discounted value (at interest only) of the fully continuous premium for the entire year (or m th of a year, as the case may be) is paid by the policyholder in advance. Should death intervene before the next periodic premium is due, the estate would receive an appropriate refund.

The total apportionable premium, then, really purchases two benefits—the pure insurance and the value of the premium refund. Specifically, for annual premium whole life with apportionable premiums,

$$P^{\{1\}}(\bar{A}_x) = P(\bar{A}_x) + P(\bar{A}_x^{PR}).$$

The actual amount of the premium refund clearly depends upon the point within the year that the insured dies. The net single premium for the premium refund is

$$\bar{A}_x^{PR} = \frac{\overline{P}(\bar{A}_x)}{\delta}[\bar{A}_x - A_x]$$

and the corresponding annual premium is

$$P(\bar{A}_x^{PR}) = \frac{\overline{P}(\bar{A}_x)}{\delta}[P(\bar{A}_x) - P_x].$$

Analysis of a diagram should help with the understanding of these formulas.

6. An insurance policy with an ancillary benefit of the return of net level premiums with accrued interest at the valuation rate has often presented difficulties to students of life contingencies. Problems of this type should not be approached with a specific formula, but with the following thought process.

If a policyholder is entitled to a return of his net premiums with interest for a fixed term beginning at the inception of the policy, the mathematical interpretation is that of a "waiver" of net premiums for that limited period of time. Upon termination of that period, the insured, if living, would be expected to repay the insurer all delinquent premiums accumulated with interest. According to this rationale, both the insured and the insurer are treated appropriately from a financial point of view, whether or not the insured survives the prescribed period.

For example, consider a fully discrete whole life policy with ten annual premiums, issued to (x), with a $1000 face amount. In addition, net premiums paid are to be returned with interest if the insured dies before age $x + 15$. The equivalence principle equation is given by

$$\pi \ddot{a}_{x\,:\,\overline{10|}} = 1000 A_x + \pi \ddot{a}_{x\,:\,\overline{10|}} - {}_{15}E_x \pi \ddot{s}_{\overline{10|}}(1 + i)^5.$$

The second term on the right effectively waives the ten premiums. The last term requires that the insured, upon attainment of age $x + 15$, must return the insurer to its rightful economic position by paying all delinquent premiums with accumulated interest.

Special Mortality Laws

I. Constant Force of Mortality

$$P_x = v q_x$$
$$\overline{P}(\overline{A}_x) = \mu$$

For fully discrete whole life,
$$\mathrm{VAR}[L] = p \cdot {}^2A_x$$
if the equivalence principle is assumed.

For fully continuous whole life,
$$\mathrm{VAR}[L] = {}^2\overline{A}_x$$
if the equivalence principle is assumed.

II. Uniform Distribution of Deaths

$$P(\bar{A}_x) = \frac{i}{\delta} P_x$$

$$P(\bar{A}^1_{x\,:\,\overline{n}|}) = \frac{i}{\delta} P^1_{x\,:\,\overline{n}|}$$

$$P(\bar{A}_{x\,:\,\overline{n}|}) = \frac{i}{\delta} P^1_{x\,:\,\overline{n}|} + P_{x\,:\,\overline{n}|}^{1}$$

$$P^{(m)}_x = \frac{P_x}{\alpha(m) - \beta(m)(P_x + d)}$$

$$P^{(m)}_{x\,:\,\overline{n}|} = \frac{P_{x\,:\,\overline{n}|}}{\alpha(m) - \beta(m)(P^1_{x\,:\,\overline{n}|} + d)}$$

$$_nP^{(m)}_x = \frac{_nP_x}{\alpha(m) - \beta(m)(P^1_{x\,:\,\overline{n}|} + d)}$$

$$_hP^{(m)}(\bar{A}^1_{x\,:\,\overline{n}|}) = \frac{i}{\delta} \cdot {_hP^{1(m)}_{x\,:\,\overline{n}|}}$$

Exercises

6-1   Given that $-\phi \frac{\partial}{\partial x} \overline{P}(\bar{A}_x) = \frac{\partial}{\partial x} \bar{a}_x$, $\delta = .1$, and $\bar{A}_x = .60$, find ϕ.

   A) 16   B) 20   C) 24   D) 32   E) 64

6-2   Given constant force of mortality with $q = 0.01$, and $i = 0.10$, what is the variance of the loss random variable for a \$1 fully discrete whole life policy?

   A) .030   B) .035   C) .040   D) .045   E) .050

6-3   Simplify $\dfrac{_mP_{x\,:\,\overline{m+n}|} - {_mP_x}}{P_{x\,:\,\overline{m}|}^{1}}$.

   A) $A_{x+m} - A_{x+m\,:\,\overline{n}|}$ B) $A_{x+n\,:\,\overline{m}|} - A_{x+n}$

   C) $A_{x+m\,:\,\overline{n}|} - A_{x+m}$ D) $A_{x+m\,:\,\overline{n}|} - A_{x+n}$ E) None of these

6-4 A \$500 whole life policy is issued to (20) and calls for 30 level annual premiums. In addition, should death occur before age 60, all premiums paid are to be returned with interest at the valuation rate.

Find the net annual premium, given $i = .05$ and $q_x = .01$ for all integral x. (Answer to nearest .10)

A) \$6.70   B) \$7.70   C) \$8.70   D) \$9.70   E) \$10.70

6-5 Given: $_{k|}q_x = .79(.21)^k, \ k = 0, 1, 2, \cdots$

         $i = 10\%$

What is the ratio of the standard deviation of the loss random variable associated with the annual premium for a fully discrete whole life policy of 1 to (35), to that of its single premium counterpart?

A) 8.6   B) 8.9   C) 9.4   D) 9.7   E) 10.0

6-6 If $i = .25$ and $_{k|}q_x = .2(.8)^k, \ k = 0, 1, 2, \cdots$, find $\overline{A}_x$.

A) .4444   B) .4676   C) .5000   D) .5074   E) Cannot be determined

6-7 Find P_0 by the equivalence principle if $_{k|}q_0 = \frac{k}{10}, \ k = 0, 1, 2, 3, 4$, and $i = .05$.

A) .09   B) .17   C) .19   D) .22   E) .25

6-8 Given: $\ddot{a}_x^{(4)} = \frac{10}{9}\ddot{a}_x^{(12)}$

         $P_x^{(4)} = .027$

Find $P_x^{(12)}$.

A) .025   B) .030   C) .033   D) .035   E) .042

6-9 Given: $A_x = .4$ for all integral x

         $i = .06$

Find, to the nearest \$1000, the variance of the loss random variable on a \$1000 fully discrete whole life policy to (30), if the net annual premium is determined by the equivalence principle.

A) \$205,000   B) \$210,000   C) \$230,000   D) \$235,000   E) \$250,000

6-10

Let $\alpha = P^{(m)}(\overline{A}_{x\,:\,\overline{m}|})$

$\beta = P^{\{m\}}(\overline{A}_{x\,:\,\overline{m}|})$

$\gamma = P^{\{m+1\}}(\overline{A}_{x\,:\,\overline{m}|})$

Which is true?

A) $\alpha < \beta < \gamma$ B) $\gamma < \beta < \alpha$ C) $\alpha < \gamma < \beta$ D) $\beta < \gamma < \alpha$ E) $\gamma < \alpha < \beta$

6-11

Assuming $\mu_x = \mu$ and $i = 100\%$, and given that the variance of the loss random variable L associated with a \$1 fully discrete whole life policy is $\frac{1}{14}$, find the sum of all possible values that q_x can assume.

A) $\frac{3}{14}$ B) $\frac{3}{7}$ C) $\frac{1}{2}$ D) $\frac{13}{14}$ E) $\frac{15}{14}$

6-12

A 5-year deferred, 10-year temporary life annuity due with annual payments of 1 calls for annual premiums at the beginning of each year for five years. If there is a death benefit during the premium payment period of return of premiums with interest at the valuation rate, which of the following represents the net annual premium to (x)?

A) $\dfrac{\ddot{a}_{x+5\,:\,\overline{10}|}}{\ddot{s}_{\overline{5}|}}$ B) $\dfrac{\ddot{a}_{x+5\,:\,\overline{10}|}}{_5E_x\ddot{s}_{\overline{5}|}}$ C) $\ddot{a}_{x+5\,:\,\overline{10}|} - _{10}E_x\ddot{s}_{\overline{10}|}$

D) $_5E_x\ddot{a}_{x+5\,:\,\overline{10}|}$ E) $\ddot{a}_{x+5\,:\,\overline{10}|}$

6-13

If $\delta = .05 = \mu_x$ for all x, find $P^{\{2\}}(\overline{A}_x)$.

A) $d^{(2)}$ B) $i^{(2)}$ C) δ D) $v^{1/2}$ E) $1 - v^{1/2}$

6-14

Assuming de Moivre's Law with $\omega = 100$, calculate $1000\check{P}^1_{50\,:\,\overline{15}|}$, if $i = 0$.

A) 9   B) 10   C) 11   D) 12   E) 13

6-15

Given the random variable

$$Y = 0, \qquad\qquad 0 \le T < 10$$
$$= \bar{a}_{\overline{T}|} - \bar{a}_{\overline{10}|}, \quad 10 \le T < 30$$
$$= \bar{a}_{\overline{30}|} - \bar{a}_{\overline{10}|}, \quad 30 \le T,$$

it is determined that $E[Y] = 2.8$. If it is further known that $\delta = .10$ and $\bar{a}_{30\,:\,\overline{30}|} = 6.8$, find the annual premium, payable continuously, for a \$1,000 10-year endowment insurance to (30) payable at the instant of death.

A) \$140   B) \$150   C) \$160   D) \$170   E) \$180

6-16   True quarterly premiums of $20 are paid for a $1,000 whole life policy to (x). Claims are paid at the end of the quarter-year in which death occurs.

If $\ddot{a}_x^{(4)} = 10$, and $i = \left(\frac{200}{199}\right)^4 - 1$, find the expected value of the loss random variable L. Assume a uniform distribution of deaths over each year of age.

A) $-.10$ B) $-.05$ C) 0 D) $.05$ E) $.10$

6-17   A fully continuous whole life policy is issued to (30) with premiums determined by the equivalence princple.

If $\mu = .05$ and $\delta = .03$, find the probability that the insurer will not sustain a loss.

A) $\frac{1}{2}$ B) $\left(\frac{3}{8}\right)^{5/3}$ C) $\left(\frac{3}{5}\right)^{3/5}$ D) $\left(\frac{5}{8}\right)^{5/3}$ E) $\left(\frac{8}{5}\right)^{3/5}$

6-18   Which of the following equals $P(\overline{A}\,^{PR}_{\genfrac{}{}{0pt}{}{1}{x\,:\,\overline{n}|}})$?

A) $\dfrac{d\overline{A}^1_{x\,:\,\overline{n}|}}{1 - A_{x\,:\,\overline{n}|}} \cdot \dfrac{\overline{A}^1_{x\,:\,\overline{n}|} - A^1_{x\,:\,\overline{n}|}}{1 - \overline{A}_{x\,:\,\overline{n}|}}$ B) $\dfrac{\delta\overline{A}^1_{x\,:\,\overline{n}|}}{1 - A_{x\,:\,\overline{n}|}} \cdot \dfrac{\overline{A}^1_{x\,:\,\overline{n}|} - A^1_{x\,:\,\overline{n}|}}{1 - \overline{A}_{x\,:\,\overline{n}|}}$

C) $\dfrac{\delta\overline{A}^1_{x\,:\,\overline{n}|}}{1 - A_{x\,:\,\overline{n}|}} \cdot \dfrac{\overline{A}_{x\,:\,\overline{n}|} - A_{x\,:\,\overline{n}|}}{1 - \overline{A}_{x\,:\,\overline{n}|}}$ D) $\dfrac{dA^1_{x\,:\,\overline{n}|}}{1 - A_{x\,:\,\overline{n}|}} \cdot \dfrac{\overline{A}^1_{x\,:\,\overline{n}|} - A^1_{x\,:\,\overline{n}|}}{1 - \overline{A}^1_{x\,:\,\overline{n}|}}$ E) None of these

6-19   Find the minimum annual premium which can be charged for a fully discrete $1,000 whole life policy to (30) if the insurer insists on making a profit on at least 90% of its policies.

Given:

x	l_x
30	800
31	720
32	580
33	320
34	200
$\vdots$	$\vdots$

A) $\dfrac{1000}{\ddot{s}_{\overline{1}|}}$ B) $\dfrac{1000}{\ddot{s}_{\overline{1}|}} + \varepsilon$ C) $\dfrac{1000}{\ddot{s}_{\overline{2}|}}$ D) $\dfrac{1000}{\ddot{s}_{\overline{2}|}} + \varepsilon$ E) $\dfrac{1000}{\ddot{s}_{\overline{3}|}}$

6-20   The net single premium for the premium refund feature for a $1 whole life policy to (x), with apportionable premiums payable annually, is $0.40. If $A_x = \frac{7}{8}\overline{A}_x$, find $\overline{A}_x$.

A) .2   B) .4   C) .5   D) .6   E) .8

6-21   Find the quarterly apportionable premium to (x) for a unit death benefit payable if death occurs prior to age $x + 10$. Assume that $\mu_x = 2\delta$ for all x.

A) $\frac{1}{2}d^{(4)}$ B) $d^{(4)}$ C) $\frac{1}{2}\delta$ D) δ E) $2d^{(4)}$

6-22
Given: $Z = v^T,\qquad T \geq 0$
$\qquad\qquad Y = \bar{a}_{\overline{T}|},\qquad T \geq 0$
$\qquad\qquad L = Z - \overline{P} \cdot Y,\quad T \geq 0$

Assuming the equivalence principle, which of the following is/are necessarily true?

$\quad$ I. $\sigma[L] = \dfrac{\sigma[Y]}{E[Y]} = \dfrac{\sigma[Z]}{1 - E[Z]}$

$\quad$ II. $\sigma[Z] \leq \sigma[L] \leq \sigma[Y]$

$\quad$ III. $E[L] \leq E[Z] \leq E[Y]$

A) I only   B) II only   C) III only   D) I and II   E) Some other
$\qquad\qquad\qquad\qquad\qquad\qquad\qquad\qquad\qquad\qquad\qquad\qquad\qquad\qquad$ combination

6-23   An insurer issues 1800 fully continuous $1000 whole life policies with annualized premiums of $200. If $\mu = 2\delta = .10$, find the probability that the insurer will incur a loss on the block of business. Use the normal approximation.

A) 0   B) .01   C) .03   D) .05   E) .10

6-24   A $1000 fully continuous 10-year term insurance policy is issued to (40). If the annualized premium is $100, find the probability that the insurer will not sustain a loss.

Given: $\mu_x = .084$ for all x; $\delta = .021$.

A) $\frac{1}{4}$ B) $(\frac{10}{11})^8$ C) $\frac{3}{4}$ D) $(\frac{10}{11})^4$ E) None of these

6-25
Given: $f_K(k) = \dfrac{1}{10}$, $k = 0, 1, 2, \ldots, 9$, for (80)

$\qquad\qquad\quad i = \dfrac{1}{10}$

Find P_{80}.

A) $\dfrac{(1.1)^{10} - 1}{10}$ B) $\dfrac{(1.1)^{11} - 1}{11}$ C) $\dfrac{(1.1)^{10} - 1}{11}$ D) $\dfrac{(1.1)^{11} - 1}{10}$ E) $\dfrac{1}{10}$

6-26

Given: $P(\overline{A}_{x:\overline{n}|}) = .200$

$P(\overline{A}^1_{x:\overline{n}|}) = .150$

$_nP_x = .150$

$\overline{s}_{\overline{1}|} = 1.25$

Find A_{x+n}, assuming UDD.

A) .500 B) .56$\dot{6}$ C) .600 D) .63$\dot{3}$ E) .66$\dot{6}$

6-27

A \$10,000 fully discrete 30 year term policy to (20) also provides for a return of all net premiums, at the end of the year of death, with interest at the valuation rate, if the insured does not survive the term period. The net level annual premium is \$317.46.

Assuming de Moivre's Law with $\omega = 80$, find the valuation rate of interest.

A) 1% B) 2% C) 3% D) 4% E) 5%

6-28

Which of the following is/are true, assuming a uniform distribution of deaths over each year of age?

I. $\dfrac{P^{(m)}_{x:\overline{n}|}}{P_{x:\overline{n}|}} = \dfrac{P^{1(m)}_{x:\overline{n}|}}{P^1_{x:\overline{n}|}}$

II. $\dfrac{P^{(m)}_{x:\overline{n}|} - {_nP^{(m)}_x}}{P^{(m)}_{x:\overline{n}|}} = 1 - A^{(m)}_{x+n}$

III. $\dfrac{\ddot{a}^{(m)}_{x:\overline{n}|}}{\ddot{a}_{x:\overline{n}|}} = \alpha(m) - \beta(m)[P_{x:\overline{n}|} + d]$

IV. $\dfrac{P^{(m)}(\overline{A}_x)}{P^{(m)}(A_x)} = \dfrac{\alpha(m) - \beta(m)[P(\overline{A}_x) + d]}{\alpha(m) - \beta(m)[P_x + d]} \cdot \dfrac{i}{\delta}$

A) None B) I only C) II only D) III only E) IV only

6-29

If deaths are uniformly distributed over each year of age, and $i = 0$, simplify

$$4\left[1 - \frac{\ddot{a}^{(2)}_{50:\overline{20}|}}{\ddot{a}_{50:\overline{20}|}}\right].$$

A) $_{20}P_{50}$ B) $_{20}P^{(2)}_{50}$ C) $P_{50:\overline{20}|}$ D) $P^1_{50:\overline{20}|}$ E) $P_{50:\overline{20}|}^{1}$

6-30   Given: $\tilde{A}^1_{x:\overline{m}|} = .11$
$A_{x:\overline{m}|} = .36$
$\ddot{s}_{\overline{m}|} = 40$

Find $\tilde{P}^1_{x:\overline{m}|}$.

A) .008   B) .010   C) .011   D) .012   E) .014

6-31   A single premium $1 continuous life annuity to (x), deferred for ten years, has a loss random variable L whose expected value is $-.32$. Find the probability that the issuer of the contract sustains a loss.

Given: $\mu = .08$
$\delta = .02$
$e^{-1} = .368$
$e^{-.2} = .819$

A) .22   B) .25   C) .28   D) .30   E) .33

6-32   An eight-year deferred annuity-due, with $1 annual payments, is purchased by (50). Annual premiums are paid for eight years; all premiums paid are to be returned at the end of the year of death with interest at the valuation rate, if death occurs prior to the first annuity payment.

If $i = 10\%$ and $q_x = .01$ for all x, find the death benefit if death occurs during the fourth year.

A) $4.06   B) $4.12   C) $4.90   D) $5.17   E) $6.03

6-33   A $50,000 whole life policy is purchased on 12/1/85 by (50) with apportionable premiums payable twice a year. Upon death on 9/1/87, find the amount of premium to be returned along with the $50,000 benefit.

Given: $\mu = .08$
$\delta = .04$

A) 1000   B) 2000   C) 4000   D) $25,000\,d^{(4)}$ E) $50,000\,d^{(4)}$

6-34   Find the smallest net annual premium for a $1000 fully discrete whole life policy to (16) such that the probability of a loss to the insurer is less than 30%. Use $i = 10\%$.

Given: $_{k|}q_0 = .01, \ k = 0, 1, 2, \ldots, 99$

$s_{\overline{25}|.10} = 98.35$

(Answer to nearest .05).

A) $8.35   B) $9.15   C) $9.25   D) $10.15   E) $10.25

6-35   A 15-pay, 5-year deferred $1000 fully discrete insurance policy to (15) has an additional benefit of the return of all net premiums paid upon death prior to age 35. Find the net level annual premium based upon the equivalence principle.

A) $\dfrac{1000M_{20}}{15M_{35} + d(S_{15} - S_{35})}$ B) $\dfrac{1000M_{20}}{15M_{30} + d(S_{15} - S_{30})}$

C) $\dfrac{1000M_{20}}{15M_{35} + d(S_{15} - S_{30})}$ D) $\dfrac{1000M_{20}}{15M_{30} + d(S_{15} - S_{30})}$ E) None of these

6-36   Given: $P_{45 : \overline{15}|} = .060$

$P^1_{45 : \overline{15}|} = .035$

$A_{60} = .700$

$d = .050$

D_{x+t} is linear, $0 \le t \le 1$, for integral x.

Find $10,000 \, _{15}P^{(4)}_{45}$.

A) 136   B) 137   C) 138   D) 542   E) 546

6-37   A $10,000 fully discrete whole life policy to (25) has the smallest possible net annual premium such that the insurer is expected to sustain a positive loss less than 33% of the time. Based upon de Moivre's Law with $\omega = 100$, find the amount of loss incurred by the insurer if the insured dies at age 48.6.

A) 0   B) $\dfrac{10,000}{\ddot{s}_{\overline{24}|}}$ C) $\dfrac{10,000}{s_{\overline{25}|}}$ D) $\dfrac{10,000}{\ddot{s}_{\overline{25}|}}$ E) $\dfrac{10,000}{s_{\overline{26}|}}$

6-38   A \$1 fully continuous whole life policy is issued to a newborn. The equivalence principle is assumed, with the forces of mortality and interest both being constant and equal to .02.

Find the expected value of the insurer's positive loss, i.e., the expected loss prior to the point at which the policy becomes profitable.

A) 1   B) $\frac{1}{2}$ C) $\frac{1}{3}$ D) $\frac{1}{4}$ E) $\frac{1}{5}$

6-39   The net annual premium paid for a decreasing term insurance policy is represented by $1000\tilde{P}^1_{x:\overline{10|}} = 30$. If $i = .04$, determine the amount of insurance produced by this policy in its 5th policy year.

A) 354   B) 451   C) 500   D) 549   E) 646

6-40   A fully discrete \$1 four-year term policy is issued to (20), with an annual premium of \$0.15. Letting $v = .9$, and using the accompanying table, find the probability that the insurer will make a profit.

x	l_x
20	20
21	18
22	12
23	9
24	6
25	3
26	0

A) .30   B) .40   C) .45   D) .55   E) .70

6-41   A \$10,000 fully discrete whole life policy is issued to (97). Find the annual premium that an insurer should charge if it desires an expected profit of \$75 per policy.

Given: $l_x = (100 - x)^2$, $0 \le x \le 100$; $i = .05$.

(Answer to nearest \$5).

A) \$6035   B) \$6085   C) \$6135   D) \$6185   E) \$6235

6-42

Let $L = v^{K+1} - \pi_x \ddot{a}_{\overline{K+1}|}$, $K = 0, 1$

$q_x = \dfrac{1}{2}$; $q_{x+1} = 1$

The absolute difference between the values of π_x obtained a) by the equivalence principle and b) by setting $E[L] = \frac{1}{2}$ is .35. Find i.

A) $\frac{1}{6}$ B) $\frac{1}{7}$ C) $\frac{1}{8}$ D) $\frac{1}{9}$ E) $\frac{1}{10}$

6-43

If $q_{30} = i = .1$, evaluate $1000\tilde{P}^1_{30\,:\,\overline{2}|}$.

A) 24.01 B) 25.62 C) 26.19 D) 27.26 E) Cannot be determined

6-44

Which of the following is/are true?

I. $\tilde{P}^1_{x\,:\,\overline{n}|} = \dfrac{1}{\ddot{a}_{x\,:\,\overline{n}|}} - \dfrac{1}{\ddot{a}_{\overline{n}|}}$

II. $P^{\{1\}}(\overline{A}_x) = \dfrac{d\,\overline{A}^{PR}_x}{\overline{A}_x - A_x}$

III. $P_x = \dfrac{P^{(4)}_x \ddot{a}^{(4)}_{\overline{1}|}}{1 + \beta(4)P^{(4)}_x}$ $\quad (UDD)$

IV. $d = \dfrac{P^{\{1\}}(\overline{A}_x)[P(\overline{A}_x) - P_x]}{P(\overline{A}^{PR}_x)}$

A) All but I B) All but II C) All but III D) All but IV E) All

6-45

A \$10,000 fully discrete whole life policy to (50) has premiums based upon the equivalence principle. Assuming $i = .05$ and de Moivre's Law with $\omega = 100$, find the probability that the insurer will sustain a loss.

A) $\frac{19}{50}$ B) $\frac{2}{5}$ C) $\frac{21}{50}$ D) $\frac{11}{25}$ E) $\frac{23}{50}$

6-46

A fully discrete \$1 whole life policy with quarterly apportionable premiums is issued to (x). Find an expression for the annualized premium for the premium refund.

A) $\dfrac{d^{(4)}\overline{A}_x(\overline{A}_x - A_x)}{(1 - \overline{A}_x)(1 - A_x)}$

B) $\dfrac{d^{(4)}\overline{A}_x(\overline{A}_x - A^{(4)}_x)}{(1 - \overline{A}_x)(1 - A^{(4)}_x)}$

C) $\dfrac{d^{(4)}\overline{A}_x(A^{(4)}_x - A_x)}{(1 - \overline{A}_x)(1 - A^{(4)}_x)}$

D) $\dfrac{d^{(4)}\overline{A}_x(A^{(4)}_x - A_x)}{(1 - \overline{A}_x)(1 - A_x)}$

E) None of these

Answers to Chapter Six Exercises

6–1	A.	6–17	D.	6–32	A.
6–2	D.	6–18	A.	6–33	D.
6–3	C.	6–19	D.	6–34	A.
6–4	B.	6–20	E.	6–35	C.
6–5	B.	6–21	A.	6–36	D.
6–6	E.	6–22	A.	6–37	C.
6–7	D.	6–23	A.	6–38	D.
6–8	B.	6–24	B.	6–39	D.
6–9	D.	6–25	C.	6–40	A.
6–10	A.	6–26	E.	6–41	C.
6–11	D.	6–27	E.	6–42	A.
6–12	A.	6–28	B.	6–43	C.
6–13	A.	6–29	D.	6–44	E.
6–14	C.	6–30	C.	6–45	B.
6–15	B.	6–31	D.	6–46	B.
6–16	C.				

Solutions

6–1.

Key Fact:

$$\frac{\partial}{\partial x}\overline{P}(\overline{A}_x) = \frac{\partial}{\partial x}\left(\frac{1}{\bar{a}_x} - \delta\right) = \frac{\partial}{\partial x}(\bar{a}_x)^{-1}$$

$$\therefore -\phi\frac{\partial}{\partial x}(\bar{a}_x)^{-1} = \frac{\partial}{\partial x}\bar{a}_x$$

$$\therefore \phi(\bar{a}_x)^{-2}\frac{\partial}{\partial x}\bar{a}_x = \frac{\partial}{\partial x}\bar{a}_x$$

$$\therefore \phi = (\bar{a}_x)^2 = \frac{(1 - \overline{A}_x)^2}{\delta^2} = \underline{\underline{16}}$$

6-2.

Key Formula: $\text{VAR}[L] = p \cdot {}^2 A_x$ where L is the fully discrete whole life loss random variable and the force of mortality is constant.

$$^2 A_x = \frac{q}{(1+i)^2 - p} = \frac{.01}{1.21 - .99} = \frac{1}{22}$$

$$\therefore p \cdot {}^2 A_x = \frac{.99}{22} = \underline{\underline{.045}}$$

6-3.

Key Concept: Since both premiums in the numerator are payable for only m years, the quantity

$$\left({}_m P_{x\,:\,\overline{m+n|}} - {}_m P_x \right) \ddot{s}_{x\,:\,\overline{m|}}$$

represents the difference in the value of the future benefits available to the survivors at age $x + m$.

Accordingly, the result is

$$\underline{\underline{A_{x+m\,:\,\overline{n|}} - A_{x+m}}}.$$

6-4.

Key Concept: The present value of the return of premiums with interest is found by "waiving" the premiums for the duration of that benefit, and then requiring repayment with interest of all delinquent premiums upon the expiry of that benefit.

Therefore, the net premium equation is

$$\pi \ddot{a}_{20\,:\,\overline{30|}} = 500 A_{20} + \pi \ddot{a}_{20\,:\,\overline{30|}} - {}_{40}E_{20}\pi \ddot{s}_{\overline{30|}}(1 + i)^{10}$$

Solving,

$$\pi = \frac{500 A_{20}}{{}_{40}p_{20}\ddot{a}_{\overline{30|}}}$$

Using $A_{20} = \frac{q}{q + i} = \frac{1}{6}$ and ${}_{40}p_{20} = (.99)^{40}$, we have $\pi = \underline{\underline{7.72}}$.

NOTE: The student should attempt to justify the equation

$$\pi \ddot{a}_{\overline{30|}}\,{}_{40}p_{20} = 500 A_{20},$$

thus eliminating the first step above.

6-5.

The question requires the square root of the ratio of

$$\frac{{}^{2}A_x - A_x^2}{(1 - A_x)^2}$$

to

$${}^{2}A_x - A_x^2.$$

Thus the result is

$$\frac{1}{1 - A_x}.$$

Since we are given the geometric distribution for K, with $q = .79$,

$$A_x = \frac{q}{q + i} = \frac{79}{89}.$$

$$\therefore \frac{1}{1 - A_x} = \underline{\underline{8.9}}$$

6-6.

Key Concept:

This question requires the exact value of $\overline{A}_x$, for which some assumption is necessary regarding the distribution of T. Since our only assumption involves the distribution of K, the determination of $\overline{A}_x$ is impossible.

NOTE: Since the geometric distribution is given for K, with $q = .2$, it might be tempting to assume that

$$\mu = -ln(.8) = ln\frac{5}{4}.$$

Since $\delta = ln\frac{5}{4}$ also,

$$\frac{\mu}{\mu + \delta} = \frac{1}{2}.$$

As indicated above, however, this assumption and this solution are incorrect.

6-7.

Key Formula:

$$P_0 = \frac{1}{\ddot{a}_0} - d$$

As $\ddot{a}_0$ is required, the tabular depiction of the mortality model is helpful.

x	l_x
0	10
1	10
2	9
3	7
4	4
5	0

Then, $\ddot{a}_0 = 1 + v(1) + v^2(.9) + v^3(.7) + v^4(.4) = 3.7025$.

Finally, $P_0 = \frac{1}{3.7025} - \frac{.05}{1.05} = \underline{\underline{.22}}$.

6–8.

Key Formula: $P_x^{(m)} = P_x^{(n)} \dfrac{\ddot{a}_x^{(n)}}{\ddot{a}_x^{(m)}}$

Accordingly, $P_x^{(12)} = P_x^{(4)} \dfrac{\ddot{a}_x^{(4)}}{\ddot{a}_x^{(12)}}$

$= \underline{\underline{.03}}$.

6–9.

Key Concept: Since the equivalence principle is assumed, and K follows a geometric distribution, we have

$$\text{VAR}[L] = p \cdot {}^2A_x$$

for a fully discrete whole life policy of face amount 1.

$$A_x = \frac{q}{q+i} = \frac{q}{q+.06} = .4 \Rightarrow q = .04$$

$${}^2A_x = \frac{q}{(1+i)^2 - p} = \frac{.04}{(1.06)^2 - .96}$$

Therefore, the variance of the loss random variable for a $1000 policy is

$$\frac{(1000)^2(.96)(.04)}{(1.06)^2 - .96} = \underline{\underline{234,719}}.$$

6-10.

First, compare α with β:

β exceeds α because it is sufficient to provide the same pure insurance as α, but it provides the additional benefit of a partial premium refund at death.

Then, compare β with γ:

$$\beta = \overline{P}(\overline{A}_{x\,:\,\overline{m}|})\frac{d^{(m)}}{\delta}$$

$$\gamma = \overline{P}(\overline{A}_{x\,:\,\overline{m}|})\frac{d^{(m+1)}}{\delta}$$

If $d^{(m)}$ and $d^{(m+1)}$ are equivalent rates, as is implicit here, then $d^{(m+1)}$ is numerically greater.

$$\therefore \underline{\underline{\alpha < \beta < \gamma}}$$

6-11.

Key Formula: $\mathrm{VAR}[L] = p \cdot {}^{2}A_{x}$ (CF)

$$\therefore \frac{1}{14} = \frac{pq}{q + 2i + i^2} = \frac{q - q^2}{q + 2 + 1}$$

This produces the quadratic

$$14q^2 - 13q + 3 = 0.$$

Elementary theory of equations leads to the conclusion that the sum of the roots is $\frac{13}{14}$.

Alternatively, solution of the quadratic produces the roots $\frac{1}{2}$ and $\frac{3}{7}$, the sum of which is $\underline{\underline{\frac{13}{14}}}$.

6-12.

Method One

The standard approach for problems involving return of premiums with interest is applicable here.

$$\pi\ddot{a}_{x\,:\,\overline{5}|} = {}_{5}E_{x}\ddot{a}_{x+5\,:\,\overline{10}|} + \pi\ddot{a}_{x\,:\,\overline{5}|} - {}_{5}E_{x}\pi\ddot{s}_{\overline{5}|}$$

$$\therefore \pi = \frac{\ddot{a}_{x+5\,:\,\overline{10}|}}{\underline{\underline{\ddot{s}_{\overline{5}|}}}}$$

Method Two

Should death occur between ages x and $x+5$, both the insurer and the purchaser are restored to their initial financial condition due to the return of premiums with interest at the valuation rate. Accordingly, mortality is irrelevant, i.e., a person who dies within this period has neither positive nor negative financial impact upon the insurer. In situations such as this, it is appropriate for all accumulations and discountings to be effected at interest *only*.

Therefore, at duration five, we have

$$\pi \ddot{s}_{\overline{5|}} = \ddot{a}_{x+5\,:\,\overline{10|}}.$$

6–13.

Key Formula:

$$P^{\{2\}}(\overline{A}_x) = \frac{d^{(2)}}{\delta}\overline{P}(\overline{A}_x)$$

Since the constant force assumption implies that $\overline{P}(\overline{A}_x) = \mu$, we have
$$P^{\{2\}}(\overline{A}_x) = \frac{\mu}{\delta}d^{(2)} = \underline{\underline{d^{(2)}}}.$$

6–14.

Key Formula:

$$\tilde{P}^{1}_{x\,:\,\overline{n|}} = P_{x\,:\,\overline{n|}} - \frac{1}{\ddot{s}_{\overline{n|}}}$$

Since $i = 0$,
$$\tilde{P}^{1}_{50\,:\,\overline{15|}} = \frac{1}{\ddot{a}_{50\,:\,\overline{15|}}} - \frac{1}{15}$$

and
$$\ddot{a}_{50\,:\,\overline{15|}} = 1 + e_{50\,:\,\overline{14|}}$$
$$= \frac{50 + 49 + \cdots + 36}{50} = 12.9.$$
$$\therefore \tilde{P}^{1}_{50\,:\,\overline{15|}} = \frac{1}{12.9} - \frac{1}{15} = .01085$$
$$\therefore 1000\tilde{P}^{1}_{50\,:\,\overline{15|}} \doteq \underline{\underline{11}}$$

6–15.

The expected value of Y, most easily determined directly rather than mathematically, is

$$E[Y] = {}_{10|20}\bar{a}_{30} = \bar{a}_{30\,:\,\overline{30|}} - \bar{a}_{30\,:\,\overline{10|}}.$$

$$\therefore \bar{a}_{30\,:\,\overline{10|}} = 6.8 - 2.8 = 4.0$$

$$\therefore \overline{P}(\overline{A}_{30\,:\,\overline{10|}}) = \frac{1}{\bar{a}_{30\,:\,\overline{10|}}} - \delta = .15$$

Thus, $1000\overline{P}(\overline{A}_{30\,:\,\overline{10|}}) = \underline{\underline{150}}$

6–16.

Key Concept: Since the equivalence principle is not necessarily being assumed, we cannot assume that $E[L] = 0$.

$$E[L] = 1000A_x^{(4)} - 80\ddot{a}_x^{(4)}$$
$$= 1000(1 - d^{(4)}\ddot{a}_x^{(4)} - .08\ddot{a}_x^{(4)})$$
$$= 1000(.2 - 10d^{(4)})$$

But $d^{(4)} = 4(1 - v^{1/4}) = 4(1 - \frac{199}{200}) = .02$ $\therefore E[L] = \underline{\underline{0}}$

NOTE: Since $E[L]$ is in fact zero, the $20 true quarterly premium must in fact have been the equivalence principle premium.

This is verified by realizing that the equivalence principle premium for this product is

$$\frac{A_x^{(4)}}{\ddot{a}_x^{(4)}} = \frac{1}{\ddot{a}_x^{(4)}} - d^{(4)} = .08$$

6–17.

In the accompanying diagram, let h be that duration at death such that the present value of the claim equals the present value of the premiums paid, i.e., such that there is neither gain nor loss to the insurer.

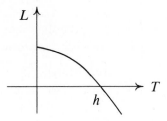

We know that $v^h - \overline{P}(\overline{A}_x)\bar{a}_{\overline{h}|} = 0$; we desire the probability ${}_hp_x$.

$$\therefore e^{-.03h} = \frac{.05}{.03}(1 - e^{-.03h})$$

$$\therefore e^{-.03h} = 5/8$$

$${}_hp_x = e^{-.05h} = (e^{-.03h})^{5/3} = \underline{\left(\frac{5}{8}\right)^{5/3}}$$

6–18.

Analogous to the formula

$$P(\overline{A}_x^{PR}) = \frac{\overline{P}(\overline{A}_x)}{\delta}[P(\overline{A}_x) - P_x],$$

we have

$$P(\overline{A}_{x\,:\,\overline{n}|}^{1\,PR}) = \frac{\overline{P}(\overline{A}_{x\,:\,\overline{n}|}^{1})}{\delta}[P(\overline{A}_{x\,:\,\overline{n}|}^{1}) - P_{x\,:\,\overline{n}|}^{1}].$$

$$\therefore P(\overline{A}_{x\,:\,\overline{n}|}^{1\,PR}) = \frac{\overline{A}_{x\,:\,\overline{n}|}^{1}}{1 - \overline{A}_{x\,:\,\overline{n}|}} \cdot \frac{\overline{A}_{x\,:\,\overline{n}|}^{1} - A_{x\,:\,\overline{n}|}^{1}}{\ddot{a}_{x\,:\,\overline{n}|}}$$

$$= \underline{\underline{\frac{\overline{A}_{x\,:\,\overline{n}|}^{1}}{1 - \overline{A}_{x\,:\,\overline{n}|}} \cdot \frac{d(\overline{A}_{x\,:\,\overline{n}|}^{1} - A_{x\,:\,\overline{n}|}^{1})}{1 - A_{x\,:\,\overline{n}|}}}}.$$

6-19.

Key Concept: This question does not presume the equivalence principle; in fact, an entirely different principle is adopted.

In this case, the insurer is willing to incur a loss for those deaths which occur in the first policy year, or exactly 10% of the policyholders. Further, the insurer cannot accept a loss on deaths of the second policy year, but it requires a gain on such policies. This gain, however, according to the wording of the question, may be miniscule.

Accordingly, it may be seen that if the insurer had been willing to break even on deaths of the second policy year, the net premium π would be determined from the equation

$$\pi \ddot{s}_{\overline{2}|} = 1000.$$

Therefore, since a gain is demanded for deaths during the second year, the required premium exceeds $\frac{1000}{\ddot{s}_{\overline{2}|}}$ by any small amount, and may be represented by

$$\underline{\underline{\frac{1000}{\ddot{s}_{\overline{2}|}} + \varepsilon.}}$$

6-20.

Key Formula:

$$\overline{A}_x^{PR} = \frac{\overline{P}(\overline{A}_x)}{\delta}(\overline{A}_x - A_x)$$

$$\therefore \overline{A}_x^{PR} = \frac{\overline{A}_x}{1 - \overline{A}_x}(\overline{A}_x - A_x)$$

$$\therefore .4 = \frac{\overline{A}_x}{1 - \overline{A}_x} \cdot \frac{1}{8}\overline{A}_x$$

Solving the quadratic which results, we obtain $\overline{A}_x = \underline{\underline{.8}}$.

6–21.

Key Formulas:

$$P^{\{4\}}(\bar{A}_{x\,:\,\overline{10|}}^{\,1}) = \frac{d^{(4)}}{\delta}\overline{P}(\bar{A}_{x\,:\,\overline{10|}}^{\,1})$$

$$\overline{P}(\bar{A}_{x\,:\,\overline{10|}}^{\,1}) = \mu \qquad\qquad \text{(CF)}$$

$$\therefore P^{\{4\}}(\bar{A}_{x\,:\,\overline{10|}}^{\,1}) = \frac{d^{(4)}}{\delta}2\delta = 2d^{(4)}$$

Therefore, the *quarterly* premium is $\dfrac{d^{(4)}}{2}$.

6–22.

Relevant Formulas:

$$E[Z] = \bar{A}_x$$

$$\text{VAR}[Z] = {}^{2}\bar{A}_x - \bar{A}_x^{\,2}$$

$$E[Y] = \bar{a}_x$$

$$\text{VAR}[Y] = \frac{{}^{2}\bar{A}_x - \bar{A}_x^{\,2}}{\delta^2}$$

$$E[L] = 0$$

$$\text{VAR}[L] = \frac{{}^{2}\bar{A}_x - \bar{A}_x^{\,2}}{(1 - \bar{A}_x)^2}$$

I. Using the relationships above, it is easily seen that I is true.

II. We are testing the following inequality:

$$ {}^{2}\bar{A}_x - \bar{A}_x^{\,2} \le \frac{{}^{2}\bar{A}_x - \bar{A}_x^{\,2}}{(1 - \bar{A}_x)^2} \le \frac{{}^{2}\bar{A}_x - \bar{A}_x^{\,2}}{\delta^2}$$

The first component of the inequality is true; the second half is tempting, since normally $1 - \bar{A}_x > \delta$. However, should δ be greater than 1, the inequality fails.

III. We are testing the following inequality:

$$0 \le \bar{A}_x \le \bar{a}_x$$

Again, this is normally true, but at very old ages, say age $\omega - .1$, the value of $\bar{A}_x$ would exceed the value of $\bar{a}_x$.

Only I is true.

6–23.

$$\text{Let} \quad L = 1000(v^T - .2\bar{a}_{\overline{T|}}),\ T \ge 0$$

$$= 1000(5v^T - 4)$$

Let $S = L_1 + L_2 + \cdots + L_{1800}.$

$$\therefore E[L] = 1000(5\bar{A}_x - 4) = \frac{-2000}{3}$$

$$\text{VAR}[L] = (1000)^2(5)^2({}^2\bar{A}_x - \bar{A}_x^2) = \frac{(5000)^2}{18}$$

$$\therefore E[S] = -2000(600) = -1,200,000$$

$$\text{VAR}[L] = (5000)^2(100)$$

$$\therefore \sigma[L] = 50,000$$

In order for the insurer to incur a loss, the value of the random variable must exceed its mean by at least $\dfrac{1,200,000}{50,000}$ standard deviations.

The probability that a normal random variable will exceed its mean by as much as 24 standard deviations is essentially <u>zero</u>.

NOTE: The equivalence principle premium for this product would be \$100. Therefore, it is not surprising that an annual premium of twice this amount for a large number of policies would almost surely insulate the insurer from loss.

6–24.

In the accompanying diagram, let h represent that duration at death at which the insurer would neither make a gain nor incur a loss.

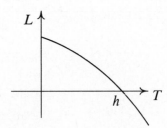

We know that $1000v^h - 100\bar{a}_{\overline{h}|} = 0$; we wish to determine ${}_hp_x$.

$$\therefore 10v^h = \frac{1 - v^h}{\delta}$$

$$.21v^h = 1 - v^h$$

$$e^{-.021h} = \frac{1}{1.21}$$

$${}_hp_x = e^{-.084h} = \left(\frac{1}{1.21}\right)^4 = \left(\frac{1}{1.1}\right)^8 = \underline{\underline{\left(\frac{10}{11}\right)^8}}$$

6–25.

Key Observations: De Moivre's Law is assumed with $\omega = 90$.

$$\text{Thus, } P_x = \frac{dA_x}{1 - A_x} = \frac{d a_{\overline{\omega - x|}}}{(\omega - x) - a_{\overline{\omega - x|}}}$$

$$\begin{aligned}
\therefore P_{80} &= \frac{\frac{1}{11} a_{\overline{10|}}}{10 - a_{\overline{10|}}} \\
&= \frac{\frac{10}{11}(1 - v^{10})}{10 - 10(1 - v^{10})} \\
&= \frac{1 - v^{10}}{11 - v^{10}} \\
&= \frac{1}{11}[(1.1)^{10} - 1]
\end{aligned}$$

6–26.

Key Formulas:

$$\frac{P_{x:\overline{n|}} - {}_nP_x}{P_{x:\overline{n|}}^{\;\;1}} = 1 - A_{x+n}$$

$$P^1_{x:\overline{n|}} \bar{s}_{\overline{1|}} = P(\bar{A}^1_{x:\overline{n|}})$$

$$P_{x:\overline{n|}}^{\;\;1} = P(\bar{A}_{x:\overline{n|}}) - P(\bar{A}^{\;\;1}_{x:\overline{n|}})$$

$$\begin{aligned}
\therefore P^1_{x:\overline{n|}} &= .100 \\
P_{x:\overline{n|}}^{\;\;1} &= .075 \\
P_{x:\overline{n|}} &= .175 \\
\therefore \frac{.175 - .150}{.075} &= 1 - A_{x+n} \\
\therefore A_{x+n} &= \frac{2}{3}
\end{aligned}$$

NOTE: An alternative formula is

$$\frac{{}_nP_x - P^1_{x:\overline{n|}}}{P_{x:\overline{n|}}^{\;\;1}} = A_{x+n}.$$

6–27.

Using the standard approach for questions involving the return of premiums with interest, the following equation results:

$$\pi \ddot{a}_{20:\overline{30}|} = 10,000 A^1_{20:\overline{30}|} + \pi \ddot{a}_{20:\overline{30}|} - {}_{30}E_{20} \pi \ddot{s}_{\overline{30}|}$$

$$\therefore \pi = \frac{10,000 A^1_{20:\overline{30}|}}{{}_{30}p_{20} \ddot{a}_{\overline{30}|}}$$

Applying de Moivre's Law,

$$\pi = \frac{10,000 \dfrac{a_{\overline{30}|}}{60}}{\frac{1}{2} \ddot{a}_{\overline{30}|}}$$

$$= \frac{333\frac{1}{3}}{1+i}.$$

Setting $\pi = 317.46$, we have

$$\underline{i = .05}.$$

6–28.

I. Each side of the equation equals

$$\frac{\ddot{a}_{x:\overline{n}|}}{\ddot{a}^{(m)}_{x:\overline{n}|}}.$$

Thus, I is correct.

II. The left-hand side, upon multiplying numerator and denominator by $\ddot{a}^{(m)}_{x:\overline{n}|}$, becomes

$$\frac{A_{x:\overline{n}|} - A_x}{{}_nE_x}.$$

Since this is not a function of m, II is clearly false.

Note, however, that this fraction equals $1 - A_{x+n}$; accordingly, the equation is only valid if $m = 1$.

III. The left-hand side equals $\dfrac{P_{x:\overline{n}|}}{P^{(m)}_{x:\overline{n}|}}$. Since $P^{(m)}_{x:\overline{n}|} =$

$$\frac{P_{x:\overline{n}|}}{\alpha(m) - \beta(m)(P^1_{x:\overline{n}|} + d)}, \text{ the equation is false.}$$

IV. The left-hand side equals $\dfrac{i}{\delta}$; accordingly, IV is false.

$$\therefore \underline{\text{I only}}$$

6–29.

Key Formulas: If $i = 0$, $\ddot{a}^{(2)}_{50\,:\,\overline{20}|} = \ddot{a}_{50\,:\,\overline{20}|} - \frac{1}{4}(1 - {}_{20}E_{50})$

$$\frac{1 - {}_{20}E_{50}}{\ddot{a}_{50\,:\,\overline{20}|}} = P_{50\,:\,\overline{20}|} + d - P_{50\,:\,\overline{20}|}^{\,1}$$

$$= P_{50\,:\,\overline{20}|}^{\,1} + d$$

Thus the bracketed quantity reduces to

$$\frac{1}{4}(P_{50\,:\,\overline{20}|}^{\,1} + d).$$

Since $i = 0$, the result is $\underline{\underline{P_{50\,:\,\overline{20}|}^{\,1}}}$.

6–30.

Key Formula: $P_{x\,:\,\overline{n}|} = \tilde{P}^{\,1}_{x\,:\,\overline{n}|} + \dfrac{1}{\ddot{s}_{\,\overline{n}|}}$

Therefore, $A_{x\,:\,\overline{n}|} = \tilde{A}^{\,1}_{x\,:\,\overline{n}|} + \dfrac{\ddot{a}_{x\,:\,\overline{n}|}}{\ddot{s}_{\,\overline{n}|}}.$

$$\therefore \ddot{a}_{x\,:\,\overline{n}|} = 10$$

$$\therefore \tilde{P}^{\,1}_{x\,:\,\overline{n}|} = .036 - .025 = \underline{\underline{.011}}$$

6–31.

In the accompanying diagram, let h be that duration at death such that the insurer neither makes a gain nor sustains a loss.

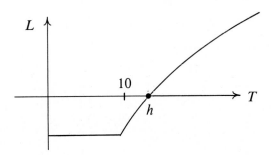

NOTE: L is defined by

$$L = -\pi, \ 0 \le T \le 10$$

$$= \bar{a}_{\,\overline{T}|} - \bar{a}_{\,\overline{10}|} - \pi, \ T > 10.$$

Thus, $E[L] = {}_{10|}\bar{a}_x - \pi = -.32$. Since ${}_{10|}\bar{a}_x = {}_{10}E_x\bar{a}_x = e^{-1}(10)$, we have $\pi = 3.68 + .32 = 4.00$.

We know that $\bar{a}_{\overline{h|}} - \bar{a}_{\overline{10|}} - \pi = 0$; we need the probability ${}_hp_x$.

$$\bar{a}_{\overline{h|}} = 4 + \bar{a}_{\overline{10|}} = 4 + \frac{.181}{.02} = 13.05$$

$$\therefore e^{-.02h} = .739$$

$$\therefore {}_hp_x = e^{-.08h} = (.739)^4 \doteq \underline{\underline{.30}}$$

6–32.

Key Concept: Since mortality is of no relevance during the first eight contract years, premiums are accumulated with interest only.

Accordingly, incorporating the geometric distribution we have

$$\pi\ddot{s}_{\overline{8|}} = \ddot{a}_{58} = \frac{1.1}{.11} = 10.$$

The question requires $\pi\ddot{s}_{\overline{4|}}$.

Since $\ddot{s}_{\overline{8|}} = \ddot{s}_{\overline{4|}}[(1.1)^4 + 1]$,

$$\pi\ddot{s}_{\overline{4|}} = \frac{\pi\ddot{s}_{\overline{8|}}}{(1.1)^4 + 1} = \underline{\underline{4.06}}.$$

6–33.

Since the semiannual apportionable premium is

$$\frac{50{,}000}{2}P^{\{2\}}(\bar{A}_{50}),$$

the premium refund upon death halfway between two premium payments is

$$25{,}000\frac{P^{\{2\}}(\bar{A}_{50})}{\bar{a}_{\overline{\frac{1}{2}|}}}\bar{a}_{\overline{\frac{1}{4}|}}.$$

This equals $25{,}000\dfrac{d^{(2)}}{\delta}\mu\dfrac{1 - v^{1/4}}{1 - v^{1/2}}$ (CF)

$$= 25{,}000(2)d^{(2)}\frac{\dfrac{d^{(4)}}{4}}{\dfrac{d^{(2)}}{2}}$$

$$\underline{\underline{25{,}000d^{(4)}}}.$$

6–34.

Key Concept: De Moivre's Law is assumed with $\omega = 100$. Therefore, of lives aged 16, 30% of the deaths are expected to occur prior to age 41.2. Accordingly, the insurer is willing to accept losses on policies terminating by death before age 41, or $\frac{25}{84}$ of the cases. The wording of the question indicates that the insurer is willing to break even on deaths between ages 41 and 42.

$$\therefore \pi \ddot{s}_{\overline{26|}} = 1000$$

Since $\ddot{s}_{\overline{26|}} = s_{\overline{25|}}(1+i)^2 + (1+i) = 120.1035$,

$$\pi = \underline{8.33}.$$

6–35.

Key Concept: Insurances with benefits including return of premiums without interest are handled with increasing insurance symbols.

Key Formula: $N_x - R_x = dS_x$

The net premium equation is
$$\pi(N_{15} - N_{30}) = 1000M_{20} + \pi(R_{15} - R_{30} - 15M_{35}).$$
$$\therefore \pi = \frac{1000M_{20}}{N_{15} - N_{30} - R_{15} + R_{30} + 15M_{35}}$$
$$= \underline{\frac{1000M_{20}}{d(S_{15} - S_{30}) + 15M_{35}}}.$$

6–36.

Key Concept: The assumption of linearity of D_{x+t}, $0 \le t \le 1$, produces the "traditional" formulas for mth-ly annuities and true annual premiums.

Key Formula: $\dfrac{P_{45\,:\,\overline{15|}} - {}_{15}P_{45}}{P_{45\,:\,\overline{15|}}} = 1 - A_{60}$

Thus, $\dfrac{.06 - {}_{15}P_{45}}{.025} = .3 \Rightarrow {}_{15}P_{45} = .0525$

$${}_{15}P_{45}^{(4)} = \dfrac{{}_{15}P_{45}}{1 - \frac{3}{8}(P_{45\,:\,\overline{15|}}^{1} + d)}$$

$$= .0542$$

Finally, $10,000(.0542) = \underline{542}$.

6–37.

Key Concept: Of 75 lives aged 25, expected to die uniformly over the next 75 years, the insurer is willing to accept a loss upon the death of the first 24. It is willing to break even on deaths between ages 49 and 50.

Therefore, the net premium π is determined from the equation

$$\pi \ddot{s}_{\overline{25|}} = 10,000.$$

For deaths between ages 48 and 49, the loss random variable L assumes the value

$$10000v^{24} - \dfrac{10000}{\ddot{s}_{\overline{25|}}} \ddot{a}_{\overline{24|}}$$

$$= 10,000v^{24}\left[1 - \dfrac{\ddot{s}_{\overline{24|}}}{\ddot{s}_{\overline{25|}}}\right]$$

$$= 10,000v^{24}\dfrac{(1+i)^{25}}{\ddot{s}_{\overline{25|}}}$$

$$= \underline{\underline{\dfrac{10,000}{s_{\overline{25|}}}}}.$$

6–38.

Key Concept: We must determine the "break-even" duration h, and then calculate the expected value of the loss incurred prior to that point.

Let $L = v^{T} - .02\bar{a}_{\overline{T|}} = 2v^{T} - 1$, $T \geq 0$.
Solving for h,

$$v^{h} = \dfrac{1}{2}$$

$$\therefore h = 50\,ln2$$

The required expected value is

$$\int_0^{50\,ln2} (2v^t - 1)\,{}_tp_x u_{x+t}\, dt$$

$$= 2\bar{A}^1_{x\,:\,\overline{50\,ln2}|} - {}_{50\,ln2}q_x$$

$$= 2(\bar{A}_x)(1 - {}_{50\,ln2}E_x) - (1 - e^{-50(.02)/ln2})$$

$$= \left(1 - \frac{1}{4}\right) - \left(1 - \frac{1}{2}\right) = \underline{\underline{\frac{1}{4}}}.$$

6–39.

Key Formula: The death protection provided in the 5th policy year is

$$1000 \left(1 - \frac{\ddot{s}_{\overline{5}|}}{\ddot{s}_{\overline{10}|}}\right).$$

Interest tables generate an answer of $\underline{549}$.

6–40.

Key Concept: A question such as this is best approached by specifying the loss random variable and the associated probabilities.

Specifically,

Value of L		Probability
$v - \pi$	$= .75$	.10
$v^2 - \pi\ddot{a}_{\overline{2}|}$	$= .525$	.30
$v^3 - \pi\ddot{a}_{\overline{3}|}$	$= .3225$	.15
$v^4 - \pi\ddot{a}_{\overline{4}|}$	$= .14025$	.15
$-\pi\ddot{a}_{\overline{4}|}$	$= -.51585$	.30

Accordingly, $\Pr[L < 0] = \underline{.30}$.

6–41.

Key Concept: The wording of the question indicates that $E[L] = -75$.

Accordingly, we must specify L:

Value of L	Probability
$10000v - \pi$	5/9
$10000v^2 - \pi\ddot{a}_{\overline{2|}}$	3/9
$10000v^3 - \pi\ddot{a}_{\overline{3|}}$	1/9

$$\therefore E[L] = \frac{1}{9}(50000v + 30000v^2 + 10000v^3)$$
$$- \frac{\pi}{9}(5 + 3 + 3v + 1 + v + v^2) = -75$$

Solving, $\pi = \underline{6134.28}$.

6–42.

Key Concept: L assumes either the value $v - \pi$ or $v^2 - \pi(1 + v)$; the probability of each is $\frac{1}{2}$. We need $E[L]$ under each of the stated premium principles.

In general, $$E[L] = \frac{1}{2}(v + v^2) - \frac{\pi}{2}(2 + v)$$

Principle (a):

$$E[L] = 0$$
$$\therefore \pi_a = \frac{v + v^2}{2 + v}$$

Principle (b):

$$E[L] = \frac{1}{2}$$
$$\therefore \pi_b = \frac{v + v^2 - 1}{2 + v}$$
$$\therefore \frac{1}{2 + v} = .35$$
$$\therefore v = \frac{6}{7}$$
$$\therefore i = \underline{\underline{\frac{1}{6}}}$$

6-43.

Key Concept: Since $\tilde{P}^1_{x:\overline{n}|}$ provides no death protection in the nth policy year, $\tilde{P}^1_{30:\overline{2}|}$ provides a benefit only in the first year.

$$\therefore \tilde{P}^1_{30:\overline{2}|} \ddot{a}_{30:\overline{2}|} = vq_{30}\left(1 - \frac{\ddot{s}_{\overline{1}|}}{\ddot{s}_{\overline{2}|}}\right)$$

$$\therefore \tilde{P}^1_{30:\overline{2}|}\left(1 + \frac{10}{11}\cdot\frac{9}{10}\right) = \frac{10}{11}\cdot\frac{1}{10}\left(1 - \frac{1}{2.1}\right)$$

$$\therefore \tilde{P}^1_{30:\overline{2}|} = .02619$$

Finally, $1000(.02619) = \underline{26.19}$

Alternative first step:

$$\tilde{P}^1_{30:\overline{2}|} = P_{30:\overline{2}|} - \frac{1}{\ddot{s}_{\overline{2}|}}$$

$$= \frac{1}{\ddot{a}_{30:\overline{2}|}} - d - \frac{1}{\ddot{s}_{\overline{2}|}}$$

6-44.

I. Key Formulas:

$$\frac{1}{\ddot{a}_{x:\overline{n}|}} = P_{x:\overline{n}|} + d$$

$$\frac{1}{\ddot{a}_{\overline{n}|}} = \frac{1}{\ddot{s}_{\overline{n}|}} + d$$

$$\tilde{P}^1_{x:\overline{n}|} = P_{x:\overline{n}|} - \frac{1}{\ddot{s}_{\overline{n}|}}$$

The result follows directly.

II. Key Formulas:

$$\bar{A}^{PR}_x = \frac{\overline{P}(\bar{A}_x)}{\delta}(\bar{A}_x - A_x)$$

$$P^{\{1\}}(\bar{A}_x) = \frac{d}{\delta}\overline{P}(\bar{A}_x)$$

The result follows directly.

III. Key Formula:

$$P^{(4)}_x = \frac{A_x}{\ddot{a}^{(4)}_{\overline{1}|}\ddot{a}_x - \beta(4)A_x} = \frac{P_x}{\ddot{a}^{(4)}_{\overline{1}|} - \beta(4)P_x}$$

Solving for P_x, the result follows.

IV. Key Formula:
$$P(\bar{A}_x^{PR}) = \frac{\bar{P}(\bar{A}_x)}{\delta}\left(P(\bar{A}_x) - P_x\right) = \frac{P^{\{1\}}(\bar{A}_x)}{d}(P(\bar{A}_x) - P_x)$$

The result follows directly.

∴ <u>All are true.</u>

6-45.

Key Concept:

We need the probability that $L = v^{K+1} - P_x\ddot{a}_{\overline{K+1}|}$ will assume a positive value.

Under de Moivre's Law,
$$P_{50} = \frac{dA_{50}}{1 - A_{50}} = \frac{d\frac{a_{\overline{50}|}}{50}}{1 - \frac{a_{\overline{50}|}}{50}} = \frac{da_{\overline{50}|}}{50 - a_{\overline{50}|}}$$
$$= .5751d, \text{ from interest tables.}$$

Then
$$L = v^{K+1} - .5751d\ddot{a}_{\overline{K+1}|}$$
$$= 1.5751v^{K+1} - .5751$$

∴ $L > 0$ when $v^{K+1} > \frac{.5751}{1.5751} = .365$

From interest tables, $K + 1 < 21$.
$$\therefore K < 20$$
$$\Pr[K < 20] = {}_{20}q_{50} = \underline{.40}$$

6-46.

The question here is to find a simplified expression for $P^{\{4\}}(\bar{A}_x) - P^{(4)}(\bar{A}_x)$.

$$P^{\{4\}}(\bar{A}_x) - P^{(4)}(\bar{A}_x) = \frac{d^{(4)}}{\delta}\bar{P}(\bar{A}_x) - \frac{\bar{A}_x}{\ddot{a}_x^{(4)}}$$
$$= \frac{d^{(4)}\bar{A}_x}{1 - \bar{A}_x} - \frac{\bar{A}_x d^{(4)}}{1 - A_x^{(4)}}$$

Combining the fractions with a lowest common demoninator, the result follows.

Accordingly, the required premium is
$$\frac{d^{(4)}\bar{A}_x(\bar{A}_x - A_x^{(4)})}{(1 - \bar{A}_x)(1 - A_x^{(4)})}.$$

Chapter Seven

Supplementary Concepts

1. The variance of loss random variables at policy duration t (or k) are closely related to those at policy duration zero and, in turn, to those of insurance-related present value random variables.

   Example 1

   If $_tL = v^U - \overline{P}\,\overline{a}_{\overline{U}|}$, $U \geq 0$, then $\text{VAR}[_tL] = \left(1 + \dfrac{\overline{P}}{\delta}\right)^2 ({}^2\overline{A}_{x+t} - \overline{A}_{x+t}^2)$.

   If the equivalence principle is assumed, then $\text{VAR}[_tL] = \dfrac{{}^2\overline{A}_{x+t} - \overline{A}_{x+t}^2}{(1 - \overline{A}_x)^2}$.

   Clearly, if $t = 0$, this formula reduces to the key variance formula from Chapter Six.

   Example 2

   If $_tL = v^U - \overline{P}\,\overline{a}_{\overline{U}|}$, $0 \leq U \leq n - t$,
   $\qquad = v^{n-t} - \overline{P}\,\overline{a}_{\overline{n-t}|}$, $U > n - t$, then

   $$\text{VAR}[_tL] = \left(1 + \dfrac{\overline{P}}{\delta}\right)^2 ({}^2\overline{A}_{x+t:\overline{n-t}|} - \overline{A}_{x+t:\overline{n-t}|}^2).$$

   If the equivalence principle is assumed, then

   $$\text{VAR}[_tL] = \dfrac{{}^2\overline{A}_{x+t:\overline{n-t}|} - \overline{A}_{x+t:\overline{n-t}|}^2}{(1 - \overline{A}_{x:\overline{n}|})^2}.$$

   Analogous formulas exist for fully discrete whole life and endowment loss random variables.

2. As discussed in Chapter Six, we know

   $$P^{\{1\}}(\overline{A}_x) = P(\overline{A}_x) + P(\overline{A}_x^{PR}).$$

It is logical, then, that the products purchased by these premiums would have identical terminal reserves, i.e.,

$$_k V^{\{1\}}(\overline{A}_x) = {}_k V(\overline{A}_x) + {}_k V(\overline{A}_x^{PR}).$$

It is also very helpful to realize that apportionable reserves equal fully continuous reserves at the end of any policy year. This equality, however, does not hold at fractional durations, as the apportionable reserve has an unearned premium component while the fully continuous reserve does not.

3.   Perhaps the most useful reserve relationships are the recursion formulas connecting successive terminal reserves, i.e.,

$$({}_k V + P)(1 + i) = {}_{k+1}V + q_{x+k}(1 - {}_{k+1}V)$$
$$= p_{x+k} \cdot {}_{k+1}V + q_{x+k}$$

The concept here is elementary. The funds available at the end of policy year $k + 1$ must be sufficient to cover the insurer's obligation both for those policyholders who died and those who did not. The quantity $(1 - {}_{k+1}V)$ may be easily adjusted if the face amount for policy year $k + 1$ does not equal 1. In fact, if the death benefit is the terminal reserve, the resulting "interest-only" formula

$$({}_k V + P)(1 + i) = {}_{k+1}V$$

reflects the fact that mortality is irrelevant.

4.   The recursion formulas may be used in the determination of reserves at fractional durations as well, obviating the necessity to memorize complex formulas for this purpose.

   Example
$$({}_k V_x + P_x)(1 + i)^{1/3} = {}_{1/3}p_{x+k} \cdot {}_{k+1/3}V_x + {}_{1/3}q_{x+k} \cdot v^{2/3}$$

5.   An extension of the recursion formulas may be used to relate terminal reserves at durations which are two or more years apart by logically providing the appropriate benefits to all who died and to all who did not.

   Example
$$({}_k V_x + P_x)(1 + i)^2 + p_{x+k} \cdot P_x(1 + i)$$
$$= q_{x+k}(1 + i) + {}_{1|}q_{x+k} + {}_2 p_{x+k} \cdot {}_{k+2}V_x$$

6.   When a constant force of mortality is assumed for types of insurance which provide level death protection, terminating at the end of the premium-paying period, net level reserves are zero at all durations. This results from the fact that mortality rates are neither increasing nor decreasing with age; accordingly, the product is on a "pay-as-you-go" basis. Reserves would not be zero where an investment element is involved, such as in an endowment policy or in the case of limited-pay whole life plans.

Similar comments are applicable for *terminal* reserves on fully discrete policies where the geometric distribution is assumed for K.

7. Extending a concept introduced in Observation 4 of Chapter 6, accumulated differences of certain level premiums may be logically expressed in terms of attained-age differences in net level reserves.

Examples

$$(_nP_x - P^1_{x:\overline{n}|})\ddot{s}_{x:\overline{n}|} = {}^n_nV_x - {}_nV^1_{x:\overline{n}|} = A_{x+n} - 0$$

$$(_nP_x - P_x)\ddot{s}_{x:\overline{n}|} = {}^n_nV_x - {}_nV_x = P_x\ddot{a}_{x+n}$$

$$(P_{x:\overline{n}|} - P_x)\ddot{s}_{x:\overline{n}|} = {}_nV_{x:\overline{n}|} - {}_nV_x = 1 - {}_nV_x$$

$$(_mP_{x:\overline{n}|} - {}_mP_x)\ddot{s}_{x:\overline{n}|} = {}^m_mV_{x:\overline{n}|} - {}^m_mV_x = A_{x+m:\overline{n-m}|} - A_{x+m}$$

8. The traditional retrospective reserve formula involves the accumulation of past premiums (with interest and survivorship) and the accumulated cost of insurance. Another formula, involving the accumulation of past premiums with interest only, is especially useful when the death benefit in any given year is a function of the policy's reserve.

This formula is best remembered from an inspection of the following diagram; the death benefit in policy year h is b_h.

$$_nV = \pi\ddot{s}_{\overline{n}|} - \sum_{h=1}^{n} q_{x+h-1}(b_h - {}_hV)(1+i)^{n-h}$$

Should the death benefit b_h equal the net level reserve $_hV$, the n th reserve is the accumulation of premiums with interest only, a logical result because the element of risk does not exist. More commonly, this formula is useful when the death benefit is a unit face amount *plus* the reserve, or some variation thereof.

9. With the exceptions of fully discrete and fully continuous whole life and endowment insurance policies, variances for prospective loss random variables involve rather complex formulas. In order to facilitate the determination of such variances, Hattendorf's Theorem and its applications are quite helpful.

The working formula for this process is (7.10.7) of *Actuarial Mathematics*. This formula appears quite tedious, largely because of the net amount at risk expression and the apparently infinite number of terms. However, in many applications, the net amount at risk is constant. In addition, there are often only a small number of terms because, upon the expiration of insurance protection or the attainment of the limiting age of mortality table, all subsequent terms are zero.

10. A quite useful formula relating various terminal reserves for whole life insurance are as follows:

$$_{m+n+p}V_x = 1 - (1 - {}_mV_x)(1 - {}_nV_{x+m})(1 - {}_pV_{x+m+n})$$

This form may be extended to a larger (or smaller) number of factors, as may be seen from the following example:

$$_{13}V_{33} = 1 - (1 - {}_2V_{33})(1 - {}_4V_{35})(1 - {}_1V_{39})(1 - {}_6V_{40}).$$

Fully continuous whole life reserves may also be expressed in this manner, e.g.,

$$_{10}\overline{V}(\overline{A}_{30}) = 1 - (1 - {}_3\overline{V}(\overline{A}_{30}))(1 - {}_7\overline{V}(\overline{A}_{33})).$$

The general form of this identity may be extended to fully discrete or fully continuous endowment reserves as well, as illustrated by the following:

$$_{10}\overline{V}(\overline{A}_{25:\overline{40|}}) = 1 - (1 - {}_6\overline{V}(\overline{A}_{25:\overline{40|}}))(1 - {}_4\overline{V}(\overline{A}_{31:\overline{34|}})).$$

Special Mortality Laws

I. Constant Force of Mortality

$$_t\overline{V}(\overline{A}_x) = 0, \quad t \geq 0$$
$$_kV_x = 0, \quad k = 1, 2, 3, \ldots$$

For fully discrete whole life,

$$\text{VAR}[{}_kL] = p \cdot {}^2A_x, \quad \text{if the equivalence principle is assumed.}$$

For fully continuous whole life,

$$\text{VAR}[{}_tL] = {}^2\overline{A}_x, \quad \text{if the equivalence principle is assumed.}$$

II. Uniform Distribution of Deaths

$$_k^h V_{x:\overline{n|}}^{(m)} = {}_k^h V_{x:\overline{n|}} + \beta(m)\,{}_hP_{x:\overline{n|}}^{(m)} \cdot {}_kV_{x:\overline{h|}}^1$$

$$_k^h V^{(m)}(\overline{A}_{x:\overline{n|}}) = {}_k^h V(\overline{A}_{x:\overline{n|}}) + \beta(m)\,{}_hP^{(m)}(\overline{A}_{x:\overline{n|}})\,{}_kV_{x:\overline{h|}}^1$$

$$_k^h V(\overline{A}_{x:\overline{n|}}) = \frac{i}{\delta} \cdot {}_k^h V_{x:\overline{n|}}^1 + {}_k^h V_{x:\overline{n|}}^{1}$$

Derivatives

$$\frac{\partial}{\partial t}\,{}_t\overline{V}(\overline{A}_x) = \overline{P}(\overline{A}_x) + \delta\,{}_t\overline{V}(\overline{A}_x) - \mu_{x+t}(1 - {}_t\overline{V}(\overline{A}_x))$$

Exercises

7–1   The annual premium for a fully discrete whole life policy of 1 to (45) is .30. If de Moivre's Law applies with $\omega = 50$ and $i = .10$, find $E[_2L]$.

A) .1488   B) .2645   C) .3107   D) .6842   E) .7935

7–2   Which of the following is/are true?

    I. $E[U] = \overset{\circ}{e}_{x+t}$

    II. $E[U] = \overset{\circ}{e}_x - t$

    III. $E[X] = \overset{\circ}{e}_x + x$

    IV. $VAR(U) = VAR(T)$

A) I only   B) I, II only   C) I, II, III only
D) II, III, IV only   E) All

7–3   Find $E(_tL)$ and $Var(_tL)$ for a fully continuous whole life policy of 1 to (x), given $\mu = .06 = \delta$. Assume the equivalence principle.

	$E(_tL)$	$Var(_tL)$
A)	1/6	1/6
B)	1/6	7/6
C)	0	1/3
D)	0	1/6
E)	0	7/6

7–4   Assuming UDD, simplify $_kV^{\{m\}}(\overline{A}_x) - _kV(\overline{A}_x)$.

A) $\beta(m)P^{\{m\}}(\overline{A}_x)_kV_x$ B) $\beta(m)\overline{P}(\overline{A}_x)_kV_x$
C) $\beta(\infty)P^{\{m\}}(\overline{A}_x)_kV_x$ D) $\beta(\infty)P^{(m)}(\overline{A}_x)_kV_x$
E) $\beta(\infty)\overline{P}(\overline{A}_x)_kV_x$

7–5   Assuming UDD, simplify $_kV^{\{5\}}(\overline{A}_x) - _kV^{(5)}(\overline{A}_x) + \beta(5) \cdot P^{(5)}(\overline{A}_x)_kV_x$.

A) $\overline{A}_x^{PR}$ B) $\overline{P}(\overline{A}_x^{PR})$ C) $_kV(\overline{A}_x^{PR})$ D) $_kV(\overline{A}_x)$ E) $_kV_x$

7–6   Which of the following is an expression for the random variable measuring, at duration t, the prospective loss for whole life insurance issued on a fully continuous basis to (x)? Assume the equivalence principle.

I. $v^U \left(\dfrac{1}{\delta \bar{a}_x} \right) - \dfrac{\overline{P}(\overline{A}_x)}{\delta}$

II. $\dfrac{v^U}{1 - \overline{A}_x} - \dfrac{\overline{A}_x}{1 - \overline{A}_x}$

III. $v^U \left(1 + \dfrac{\overline{P}(\overline{A}_x)}{\delta} \right) - \dfrac{\overline{P}(\overline{A}_x)}{\delta}$

IV. $\overline{A}_{x+t} - \overline{P}(\overline{A}_x)\bar{a}_{x+t}$

A) All   B) All but I   C) All but II   D) All but III   E) All but IV

7–7   Given: $P_{40:\overline{10|}} = .038$; $P_{40} = .024$; $\ddot{s}_{40:\overline{10|}} = 30$; $_4V_{40} = .2$. Find $_6V_{44}$.

A) .22   B) .36   C) .42   D) .48   E) .56

7–8   Which of the following is/are correct, assuming UDD?

I. $_{10}V(\overline{A}_x^{PR}) = {}_{10}V^{\{1\}}(\overline{A}_x) - {}_{10}\overline{V}(\overline{A}_x)$

II. $_{10}V(\overline{A}_x^{PR}) = {}_{10}V^{\{4\}}(\overline{A}_x) - {}_{10}V^{(4)}(\overline{A}_x) + \beta(4) \cdot P^{(4)}(\overline{A}_x){}_{10}V_x$

III. $_{10}V(\overline{A}_x^{PR}) = {}_{10}\overline{V}(\overline{A}_x) - {}_{10}V(\overline{A}_x)$

A) III only   B) I, II   C) II, III   D) I, III   E) All

7–9   If $VAR(T) = \dfrac{(70 - x)^2}{12}$ for all x, and $i = .04$, evaluate $_3k_{40}$.

A) .084   B) .096   C) .116   D) .118   E) .124

7–10   Assuming $\mu_{x+t} = \mu$, $t \geq 0$, and given that $\int_0^\beta (1 - {}_t\overline{V}(\overline{A}_x)) \, {}_tp_x \, dt + \int_\beta^\infty {}_tp_x \, dt = 10$, find μ.

A) .10   B) .20   C) .50   D) .75   E) .80

7–11   Given: $_{10}\overline{V}(\overline{A}_{30}) = .40$

$_5\overline{V}(\overline{A}_{35}) = .30$

$_{15}\overline{V}(\overline{A}_{25}) = .45$

Find $_{10}\overline{V}(\overline{A}_{25}) - {}_5\overline{V}(\overline{A}_{30})$.

A) $-\frac{1}{7}$ B) $-\frac{1}{14}$ C) 0   D) $\frac{1}{14}$ E) $\frac{1}{7}$

7-12   If, for a fully continuous whole life contract of 1 to (x), $\mathrm{VAR}[{}_t L]$ is 10% larger than $E[{}_t L]$, ${}^2\bar{A}_{x+t} = .60$, and $\bar{A}_{x+t} = .70$, find $\bar{A}_x$. Assume the equivalence principle.

A) .50   B) .52   C) .54   D) .56   E) .58

7-13   Given that ${}_{k|}q_{90} = \dfrac{k+1}{6}$, $k = 0, 1, 2$, and $i = 0$, find $\mathrm{VAR}[{}_1 L]$ for a fully discrete increasing insurance to (90) with death protection following the pattern $1, 2, 3, \ldots$. The net level annual premium π is determined by the equivalence principle.

A) 0.0   B) 0.2   C) 0.4   D) 0.8   E) 1.0

7-14   Which of the following is/are true?

I. $\dfrac{{}_{10}P_{30} - P_{30:\overline{10|}}^{1}}{P_{30:\overline{10|}}^{1}} = A_{40} + {}_{10}k_{30}$

II. $P_{20} - P_{20:\overline{15|}}^{1}\, {}_{15}k_{20} = ({}_{12}V_{20} - {}_{12}V_{20:\overline{15|}}^{1})P_{20:\overline{12|}}^{1}$

III. ${}_{10}V_{30:\overline{40|}}^{1} = \dfrac{{}_{30}^{20}V^{(4)}(\bar{A}_{30:\overline{40|}}) - {}_{30}^{20}V(\bar{A}_{30:\overline{40|}})}{\beta(4)\,{}_{20}P^{(4)}(\bar{A}_{30:\overline{40|}})}$

A) I only   B) II only   C) III only   D) Exactly two   E) All

7-15   Given: ${}_3V_{20:\overline{10|}} = .25$
                     ${}_3V_{20:\overline{15|}} = .15$
                     ${}_{10}V_{20:\overline{15|}} = .50$

Find: ${}_3V_{20:\overline{10|}}^{1}$.

A) .02   B) .03   C) .05   D) .07   E) .10

7-16   Given: ${}_{11}V_{30} = .8 \cdot {}_{12}V_{30}$
                     $v = .9$
                     $l_x = 50 - x,\ 0 \le x \le 50$

Find P_{30} .

A) .02   B) .05   C) .10   D) .20   E) .25

7-17   A fully discrete insurance policy to (x) has a death benefit equal to the reserve for the first 10 policy years, at which time the face amount becomes $10,000 plus 100 times the insured's age at death.

The policy reserve increases by $389.74 during the a th policy year. If $i = .10$ and $\ddot{s}_{\overline{a}|} = 10.436$, find the annual premium.

A) $150   B) $200   C) $250   D) $300   E) $350

7-18   Given: $_5V_x^{(4)} = \frac{1}{5}$

$_6V_x^{(4)} = \frac{3}{10}$

$_{5\frac{5}{9}}V_x^{(4)} = \frac{41}{144}$

Using standard approximations, find $P_x^{(4)}$.

A) .10   B) .11   C) .12   D) .14   E) .15

7-19   Which of the following is/are true under the assumption of a constant force of mortality?

I. $k_x = \dfrac{1}{e_x}$

II. $\bar{k}_x = \dfrac{1}{\overset{\circ}{e}_x}$

III. $_tV^{\{m\}}(\bar{A}_{x:\overline{n}|}) = 0,\ 0 \le t \le n$.

A) I only   B) II only   C) III only   D) I and II only   E) All

7-20   A four year, fully discrete, term policy to (50) has death protection of $1000, $2000, $3000, and $4000 in addition to the net level terminal reserve.

Assume that $v^2 = .875$ and that $q_{52} = q_{53} = \frac{1}{2}$.
Find $\text{VAR}[_2L]$.

A) 3,000,000   B) 3,500,000   C) 4,000,000   D) 4,500,000   E) 5,000,000

7-21   Which of the following is/are equal to $_tV(\bar{A}_x)$?

I. $\dfrac{\overline{M}_{x+t} - P(\bar{A}_x)N_{x+t} + P(\bar{A}_x)N_x - \overline{M}_x}{D_{x+t}}$

II. $[P(\bar{A}_{x+t}) - P(\bar{A}_x)]a_{x+t} + \dfrac{\ddot{a}_x A_{x+t} - \ddot{a}_{x+t}\bar{A}_x}{\ddot{a}_x \ddot{a}_{x+t}}$

III. $[1 - \dfrac{P(\bar{A}_x)}{P(\bar{A}_{x+t})}]\bar{A}_{x+t}$

A) I only   B) II only   C) III only   D) I and III   E) All

7-22   Simplify: $\dfrac{{}^{10}_{5}V_{x:\overline{20|}} - {}_{5}V_{x:\overline{20|}}}{{}_{5}V_{x:\overline{20|}} - {}_{5}V_{x:\overline{10|}}}$

A) $A_{x:\overline{20|}}$ B) $-A_{x:\overline{20|}}$ C) $P_{x:\overline{20|}}$ D) $P_{x:\overline{20|}} - P_{x:\overline{10|}}$

E) $_{10}P_{x:\overline{20|}} - P_{x:\overline{10|}}$

7-23   Given: $A_{x:\overline{n|}} = .40$

$A_x = .20$

$A_{x:\frac{1}{n|}} = .36$

$i = .20$

Find $_nV_x$.

A) $\frac{5}{18}$ B) $\frac{11}{36}$ C) $\frac{1}{3}$ D) $\frac{13}{36}$ E) $\frac{7}{18}$

7-24   Given: $_5V_{25:\overline{15|}} = .25$

$_5V_{20:\overline{20|}} = .20$

$_{15}V_{20:\overline{20|}} = .64$

Find $_5V_{30:\overline{10|}}$.

A) .25   B) .30   C) .35   D) .40   E) .45

7-25   A fully discrete whole life policy of 1 is issued to (20). Find $\text{VAR}[_{15}L]$ if $i = \frac{1}{6}$ and $q_{20+k} = \frac{2}{3}$, $k = 0, 1, 2, \ldots$. Assume the equivalence principle.

A) $\frac{2}{9}$ B) $\frac{8}{37}$ C) $\frac{4}{19}$ D) $\frac{8}{39}$ E) $\frac{1}{5}$

7-26   Why did the hypothesis of Question 7-25 include the equivalence principle?

A)   Because the variance of a loss random variable is undefined in the absense of the equivalence principle.

B)   Because the assumption of any other premium principle would invalidate the formula

$$\text{VAR}[_kL] = \left(1 + \frac{P}{d}\right)^2 ({}^2A_{x+k} - A_{x+k}^2)$$

C)   Because the assumption of any other premium principle would invalidate the formula

$$\text{VAR}[_kL] = \frac{{}^2A_{x+k} - A_{x+k}^2}{(1 - A_x)^2}$$

D)   Because non-equivalence principle problems are beyond the scope of this course.

E)   To confuse the student unnecessarily.

7-27   Assuming de Moivre's Law, simplify $\dfrac{_{10}\overline{V}(\overline{A}_{20})}{_{10}V(\overline{A}_{20})}$.

A) $\dfrac{i}{\delta}$ B) $\dfrac{\delta}{i}$ C) $\dfrac{\overline{A}_{20}}{A_{20}}$ D) $\dfrac{A_{20}}{\overline{A}_{20}}$ E) $\dfrac{\ddot{a}_{20}}{\overline{a}_{20}}\overline{a}_{\overline{1}|}$

7-28   Given: $i = .06$

$\beta(12) = .468$

$\ddot{a}_{65} = 9.900$

$\ddot{a}_{70} = 8.800$

$\ddot{a}_{65}^{(12)} = 9.435$

Assuming UDD, calculate $1000\,_5V_{65}^{(12)}$.

A) 110   B) 112   C) 114   D) 116   E) 118

7-29   A fully continuous whole life policy with a varying face amount was issued to (90) t years ago, where t is a positive integer; $l_x = 100 - x$, $0 \leq x \leq 100$.

Given: The death benefit upon death at duration $t+u$ is $2u(1+i)^u$; the annualized rate of premium payment at duration $t + u$ is $\frac{1}{2}(10 - t)(1 + i)^u$.

At which of the following durations from issue is the reserve equal to .91 ?

A) 8.0   B) 8.2   C) 8.4   D) 8.6   E) 8.8

7-30   Given: $_{k+1/3}V_x^{(4)} = \dfrac{1}{4}$

$_kV_x = \dfrac{1}{8}$

$_{k+1}V_x = \dfrac{3}{8}$

$i = 0$

Using standard approximations, including but not limited to UDD, find the true quarterly premium.

A) $\frac{2}{47}$ B) $\frac{4}{47}$ C) $\frac{8}{47}$ D) $\frac{16}{47}$ E) $\frac{32}{47}$

7-31   A five year fully discrete term policy with face amount F was issued to (x). If $v^2 = .8$, $\mu = ln5$ for all ages, and $VAR[\,_2L] = 2371.2$, find F.

A) 100   B) 125   C) 150   D) 175   E) 200

7-32   Simplify: $\ddot{a}_x \sum\limits_{t=1}^{10} \left(\dfrac{1}{\ddot{a}_{x+t}} - \dfrac{1}{\ddot{a}_{x+t-1}} \right)$

A) $_{10}V_x$ B) $\dfrac{1}{_{10}V_x}$ C) $\dfrac{_{10}V_x}{1 - _{10}V_x}$ D) $\dfrac{1 - _{10}V_x}{_{10}V_x}$

E) $_{10}V_x(1 - _{10}V_x)$

7-33   A three-year fully discrete term policy whose face amount doubles each year is issued to (85). The net level annual premium, based on the equivalence principle, is $8. From the following facts, determine the face amount for the first year.

$$q_{86} = .4$$
$$q_{87} = .5$$
$$i = 0$$
$$\text{VAR}[_1L] = 255.36$$

A) $5   B) $10   C) $20   D) $40   E) $100

7-34   A five-year, fully discrete, $1 term policy is issued to (30). Premiums are determined by the equivalence principle and are based on the accompanying table with $i = 0$.

Find $\text{VAR}[_2L]$ to the nearest .01.

x	l_x
30	100
31	95
32	85
33	75
34	65
35	60

A) .26   B) .28   C) .30   D) .32   E) .34

7-35 A \$5000, fully discrete, seven year term policy was issued to each of ten persons aged 40. Four years later, seven persons have died and the size of the aggregate reserve fund is \$500. What is the probability that the fund will be sufficient to pay all future claims when due?

Given: $\pi = 450$

$i = .10$

$p_{x+1} = 2(p_x)^2, \ x = 44, 45, 46$

$_3p_{44} = \frac{1}{8}$

A) 0   B) $\frac{1}{8}$ C) $\frac{1}{64}$ D) $\frac{1}{128}$ E) $\frac{1}{256}$

7-36 Given: $_{k+1/3}V_x - {}_{k+2/3}V_x = .00165$

$_{k+1}V_x = .3$

$v = .95$

Using standard approximations, find q_{x+k}.

A) .01   B) .02   C) .03   D) .04   E) .05

7-37 A \$1 fully continuous whole life plan has net annual premiums of .03 and .04 for issue ages 30 and 40, respectively.

If $\delta = .06$, and the variance of the 10th prospective loss random variable for such a policy to (30) is .2025, find $^2\overline{A}_{40}$.

A) .15   B) .20   C) .25   D) .30   E) .35

7-38 Simplify:

$$\int_0^n [\mu_{x+t} \cdot {}_t\overline{V}(\overline{A}_x) + \overline{P}(\overline{A}_x)\overline{A}_{x+t} + \delta \overline{A}_{x+t} - \mu_{x+t}] \, dt$$

A) $1 - {}_n\overline{V}(\overline{A}_x)$ B) $_n\overline{V}(\overline{A}_x)$ C) $\overline{P}(\overline{A}_x)$ D) $\overline{A}_x$ E) $\bar{a}_x$

7-39 Using standard approximations, simplify

$$_{5\frac{1}{4}}V^{\{3\}}(\overline{A}_x) - \frac{3}{4} \cdot {}_5\overline{V}(\overline{A}_x) - \frac{1}{4} \cdot {}_6\overline{V}(\overline{A}_x)$$

A) 0   B) $\frac{1}{12}\overline{P}(\overline{A}_x)$ C) $\frac{1}{4}\overline{P}(\overline{A}_x)$ D) $\frac{1}{12}\overline{P}(\overline{A}_x)\bar{a}_{\overline{\frac{1}{3}}|}$ E) $\frac{1}{4}\overline{P}(\overline{A}_x)\bar{a}_{\overline{\frac{1}{3}}|}$

7-40   A fully discrete three-year term policy is issued to (90) with respective face amounts of 1, 6, and 9 dollars. The equivalence principle level premium was based on $d = .1$ and $_{k|}q_{90} = \frac{k+1}{6}$, $k = 0, 1, 2$.

Find $VAR(\Lambda_1)$.

A) .0060   B) .0080   C) .0096   D) .0100   E) .0108

7-41   Given: $_tV_{x:\overline{n}|} = .7$

$_tV^1_{x:\overline{n}|} = .1$

$\overline{A}_{x:\overline{n}|} = .4$

$\delta = .0800$

$i = .0833$

Evaluate $1{,}000{,}000 \cdot {}_tV(\overline{A}_{x:\overline{n}|})$, assuming UDD.

A) 706,875   B) 713,125   C) 728,875   D) 731,625   E) 756,375

7-42   If $\dfrac{{}_5V(\overline{A}^{PR}_{30})}{{}_5\overline{V}(\overline{A}_{30}) - {}_5V_{30}} = .4$, and $\delta = .05$, evaluate $\overline{a}_{30}$.

A) 8   B) 10   C) 12   D) 14   E) Cannot be determined

Answers to Chapter Seven Exercises

7–1	B.	7–15	C.	7–29	D.
7–2	A.	7–16	C.	7–30	A.
7–3	C.	7–17	B.	7–31	B.
7–4	E.	7–18	E.	7–32	C.
7–5	C.	7–19	A.	7–33	B.
7–6	E.	7–20	B.	7–34	A.
7–7	D.	7–21	E.	7–35	D.
7–8	C.	7–22	B.	7–36	C.
7–9	D.	7–23	B.	7–37	C.
7–10	A.	7–24	D.	7–38	B.
7–11	D.	7–25	B.	7–39	E.
7–12	A.	7–26	C.	7–40	C.
7–13	A.	7–27	E.	7–41	A.
7–14	B.	7–28	C.	7–42	C.

Solutions

7–1.

Key Fact: The value of $E[_2L]$ is not the second net level reserve unless the equivalence principle is assumed. Here, the value of P_{45} is approximately .285 (smaller than the actual premium given), so the value of $E[_2L]$ should be logically seen to be smaller than the reserve.

Since $E[_2L] = A_{47} - .3\ddot{a}_{47} = 1 - (.3 + d)\ddot{a}_{47}$, we need only $\ddot{a}_{47}$.

Thus $\ddot{a}_{47} = 1 + vp_{47} + v^2 {}_2p_{47} = 1.8815427$, and we have

$$E[_2L] = \underline{.2645}.$$

NOTE: As anticipated, it is easy to show that $E[L] = -.0399$, a negative number, since the insurer "expects" to do better than break even.

7-2.

Key Concept: Definitional-type "statements" such as $T = X - x$ and $U = T - t$ are fallacious. If, for example, T were really equal to $X - x$, we would have

$$E[T] = E[X - x]$$
$$= E[X] - E[x], \text{ or}$$
$$\overset{\circ}{e}_x = \overset{\circ}{e}_0 - x, \text{ an absurdity.}$$

I. $E[U] = \overset{\circ}{e}_{x+t}$, by definition.

II. This purports to say $\overset{\circ}{e}_{x+t} = \overset{\circ}{e}_x - t$, which is clearly not true.

III. Similarly, this purports to say $\overset{\circ}{e}_x = \overset{\circ}{e}_0 - x$, and is thus false.

IV. Perhaps the simplest way to show that this is false is with a special case. For example, let $x = 10$, $t = 89$, and $\omega = 100$. Since U is the future lifetime random variable for a life aged 99 and T is the future lifetime random variable for a life aged 10 (thus involving much more uncertainty), their variances are not equal.

$\therefore$ I only

NOTE: IV would be correct under an assumption of a constant force of mortality.

7-3.

Key Concept: Under constant force and the equivalence principle, $E[{}_tL] = \underline{\underline{0}}$.

Key Formula: $\text{VAR}[{}_tL] = {}^2\overline{A}_x = \dfrac{\mu}{\mu + 2\delta}$.

Thus, $\dfrac{\mu}{\mu + 2\delta} = \underline{\underline{\dfrac{1}{3}}}$.

7–4.

Key Concept: $_kV^{\{m\}}(\overline{A}_x) = {}_k\overline{V}(\overline{A}_x)$

Key Formula: $_k\overline{V}(\overline{A}_x) = {}_kV(\overline{A}_x) + \beta(\infty)\overline{P}(\overline{A}_x)\,{}_kV_x$

Thus, the given quantity simplifies to $\underline{\underline{\beta(\infty)\overline{P}(\overline{A}_x)\,{}_kV_x}}$.

7–5.

Key Formula: $_kV^{(5)}(\overline{A}_x) - {}_kV(\overline{A}_x) = \beta(5)P^{(5)}(\overline{A}_x)\,{}_kV_x$

Rearranging the question, and applying the above formula, we have
the quantity $_k\overline{V}(\overline{A}_x) - {}_kV(\overline{A}_x),$

which equals $\underline{\underline{{}_kV(\overline{A}_x^{PR})}}$.

7–6.

The most straightforward form of the question is
$$v^U - \overline{P}(\overline{A}_x)\ddot{a}_{\overline{U|}}.$$

Elementary operations with identities generate I, II, and III. However,
IV is not correct, as it represents the *expected value* of the random
variable rather than the random variable itself.

$\therefore$ $\underline{\text{All but IV}}$

7–7.

Key Formulas: $(P_{40:\overline{10|}} - P_{40})\ddot{s}_{40:\overline{10|}} = 1 - {}_{10}V_{40}$

$_{10}V_{40} = 1 - (1 - {}_4V_{40})(1 - {}_6V_{44})$

Therefore, $_{10}V_{40} = 1 - (.014)(30) = .58$, and

$$1 - {}_6V_{44} = \frac{1 - .58}{1 - .2} = .525$$

$$_6V_{44} = \underline{\underline{.475}}$$

7–8.

I.   This relationship is incorrect, as the right hand side equals
     zero.

II. Simplifying the right hand side, we have

$$_{10}\overline{V}(\overline{A}_x) - [\,_{10}V^{(4)}(\overline{A}_x) - \beta(4)P^{(4)}(\overline{A}_x)\,_{10}V_x]$$
$$= \,_{10}\overline{V}(\overline{A}_x) - \,_{10}V(\overline{A}_x)$$
$$= \,_{10}V(\overline{A}_x^{PR})$$

III.   True, as in II.

$\therefore$ <u>II and III</u>

7–9.

Key Fact: $\mathrm{VAR}[T] = \dfrac{(70-x)^2}{12}$ implies de Moivre's Law with $\omega = 70$.

Key Formulas:

$$_3k_{40} = \frac{d_{40}(1+i)^2 + d_{41}(1+i) + d_{42}}{l_{43}}$$

$$_3\bar{k}_{40} = \frac{i}{\delta}\,_3k_{40}$$

Therefore,

$$_3k_{40} = \tfrac{1}{27}s_{\overline{3}|}$$

and

$$_3\bar{k}_{40} = \tfrac{1}{27}\bar{s}_{\overline{3}|}$$

From interest tables,

$$_3\bar{k}_{40} = \underline{.1179}$$

7–10.

Key Facts: Under constant force, $_t\overline{V}(\overline{A}_x) = 0$, and $\overset{\circ}{e}_x = \frac{1}{\mu}$.

Therefore, we have

$$\int_0^\beta {}_tp_x\,dt + \int_\beta^\infty {}_tp_x\,dt = \overset{\circ}{e}_x = 10 = \frac{1}{\mu}$$

$$\therefore \mu = \underline{\tfrac{1}{10}}$$

7–11.

Key Formulas:

$$_{15}\overline{V}(\overline{A}_{25}) = 1 - (1 - {}_{10}\overline{V}(\overline{A}_{25}))(1 - {}_5\overline{V}(\overline{A}_{35}))$$
$$_{10}\overline{V}(\overline{A}_{30}) = 1 - (1 - {}_5\overline{V}(\overline{A}_{30}))(1 - {}_5\overline{V}(\overline{A}_{35}))$$

From the first equation,

$$_{10}\overline{V}(\overline{A}_{25}) = \frac{3}{14} \, ;$$

from the second equation,

$$_{5}\overline{V}(\overline{A}_{30}) = \frac{1}{7}.$$

Thus, we have

$$\frac{3}{14} - \frac{1}{7} = \underline{\underline{\frac{1}{14}}}.$$

7–12.

Key Formulas:

$$E[\,_{t}L] = \frac{\overline{A}_{x+t} - \overline{A}_{x}}{1 - \overline{A}_{x}}$$

$$\text{VAR}[\,_{t}L] = \frac{{}^{2}\overline{A}_{x+t} - \overline{A}_{x+t}^{2}}{(1 - \overline{A}_{x})^{2}}$$

Thus, we have

$$\frac{{}^{2}\overline{A}_{x+t} - \overline{A}_{x+t}^{2}}{(1 - \overline{A}_{x})^{2}} = 1.1 \frac{\overline{A}_{x+t} - \overline{A}_{x}}{1 - \overline{A}_{x}} \, , \text{ and}$$

$$\frac{.11}{(1 - \overline{A}_{x})^{2}} = \frac{1.1(.7 - \overline{A}_{x})}{1 - \overline{A}_{x}}$$

Solving, $\overline{A}_{x} = \underline{\underline{.5}}$.

Note that the extraneous root $\overline{A}_{x} = 1.2$ must be discarded.

7–13.

Method One

First, we need the premium π. Taking advantage of the fact that $i = 0$, and using the accompanying mortality model, we have

x	l_x
90	6
91	5
92	3
93	0

$$\pi \ddot{a}_{90} = (IA)_{90}$$

$$\pi \left(1 + \frac{5}{6} + \frac{3}{6} \right) = \left(\frac{1}{6} + 2 \cdot \frac{2}{6} + 3 \cdot \frac{3}{6} \right)$$

$$\therefore \pi = 1$$

The loss random variable may then be expressed in tabular form as follows:

$_1L$	Probability
$2 - \pi = 1$	$2/5$
$3 - 2\pi = 1$	$3/5$

Since $_1L$ always equals the same value, $\mathrm{VAR}[_1L] = \underline{\underline{0}}$.

Method Two

To employ Hattendorf's Theorem, we need $_2V$.

$$_2V = 3vq_{92} - \pi = 2$$

Then,

$$\mathrm{VAR}[_1L] = v^2(2 - {_2V})^2 p_{91}q_{91} + v^4(3 - {_3V})^2 p_{92}q_{92}p_{91}$$
$$= \underline{\underline{0}}, \text{ since } p_{92} = 0.$$

7–14.

I. Key Formula:

$$_{10}P_{30}\ddot{s}_{30:\overline{10|}} = A_{40} + {_{10}k_{30}}$$

Thus, I is incorrect.

II. Key Formula:

$$P_{x:\overline{n|}}\,{_nk_x} = P^1_{x:\overline{n|}}$$

Thus, this question is a rearrangement of the identity

$$(P_{20} - P^1_{20:\overline{15|}})\ddot{s}_{20:\overline{12|}} = {_{12}V_{20}} - {_{12}V^1_{20:\overline{15|}}}.$$

III.

Since the premium-payment period is complete, the right-hand side of this relationship is zero.

$\therefore$ $\underline{\underline{\text{II only}}}$

7–15.

Key Formula:

$$_3V_{20:\overline{15|}} = {_3V^1_{20:\overline{10|}}} + {_3V_{20:\overline{10|}}} \cdot {_{10}V_{20:\overline{15|}}}$$

Substituting the given values, and realizing that
$_3V_{20:\overline{10|}}^{\frac{1}{}} = {_3V_{20:\overline{10|}}} - {_3V_{20:\overline{10|}}^1}$, we have

$$_3V_{20:\overline{10|}}^1 = \underline{.05}$$

7-16.

Key Formula:
$$(_{11}V_{30} + P_{30})(1 + i) = {_{12}V_{30}} + q_{41}(1 - {_{12}V_{30}})$$

Using $q_{41} = \frac{1}{9}$, we have

$$(.8 \,_{12}V_{30} + P_{30})\frac{10}{9} = {_{12}V_{30}} + \frac{1}{9}(1 - {_{12}V_{30}})$$
$$\therefore \frac{8}{9} \,_{12}V_{30} + \frac{10}{9}P_{30} = \frac{8}{9} \,_{12}V_{30} + \frac{1}{9}$$
$$P_{30} = \underline{\frac{1}{10}}$$

7-17.

Key Concept: For the first ten policy years, the reserve is simply the accumulation of the annual premiums with interest only. Here, it should be clear that $a < 10$.

Thus, the increase in reserves in the a th policy year is
$$_aV - {_{a-1}V} = \pi(\ddot{s}_{\overline{a|}} - \ddot{s}_{\overline{a-1|}}) = \pi(1 + i)^a.$$
Also, since $(1 + i)^a = 1 + d\ddot{s}_{\overline{a|}}$, we have
$$\pi(1 + d\ddot{s}_{\overline{a|}}) = 389.74$$
$$\therefore \pi = \underline{200}$$

7-18.

Key Concept: The proportion of the *annualized* premium that is unearned as of duration $5\frac{5}{9}$ on a quarterly premium plan is $\frac{3}{4} - \frac{5}{9}$, or $\frac{7}{36}$.

Key Formula:
$$_{5\frac{5}{9}}V_x^{(4)} \doteq \frac{5}{9} \cdot {_6V_x^{(4)}} + \frac{4}{9} \cdot {_5V_x^{(4)}} + \frac{7}{36}P_x^{(4)}$$

Evaluating, $P_x^{(4)} = \underline{.15}$

7–19.

I. Under constant force,

$$k_x = q/p \quad \text{and} \quad e_x = p/q.$$

Thus I is true.

II. Since I is true, i.e.,

$$k_x e_x = 1,$$

and since $\bar{k}_x > k_x$ and $\overset{\circ}{e}_x > e_x$, then II cannot be true.

III. Since there is a pure endowment build-up with this policy, reserves are not zero even though the force of mortality is constant.

$$\therefore \underline{\text{I only}}$$

7–20.

Using the Hattendorf result, we obtain

$$\mathrm{VAR}[\,_2L] = v^2(3000)^2 p_{52}q_{52} + v^4(4000)^2 p_{53}q_{53}p_{52}$$
$$= \underline{\underline{3,500,000}}$$

7–21.

I. Since the sum of the last two terms in the numerator is zero, we have

$$\bar{A}_{x+t} - P(\bar{A}_x)\ddot{a}_{x+t},$$

and thus I is true.

II. Since the fraction equals

$$P(\bar{A}_{x+t}) - P(\bar{A}_x),$$

we have, upon combination with the rest of the expression,

$$[P(\bar{A}_{x+t}) - P(\bar{A}_x)]\ddot{a}_{x+t}$$

and thus II is true.

III. Since $\dfrac{\bar{A}_{x+t}}{P(\bar{A}_{x+t})} = \ddot{a}_{x+t}$, we have $\bar{A}_{x+t} - P(\bar{A}_x)\ddot{a}_{x+t}$, and thus III is true.

$$\therefore \underline{\text{All are true}}.$$

7–22.

Key Formulas:

$$(\,_{10}P_{x:\overline{20|}} - P_{x:\overline{20|}})\ddot{s}_{x:\overline{5|}} = \,^{10}V_{x:\overline{20|}} - \,_5V_{x:\overline{20|}}$$
$$(P_{x:\overline{20|}} - P_{x:\overline{10|}})\ddot{s}_{x:\overline{5|}} = \,_5V_{x:\overline{20|}} - \,_5V_{x:\overline{10|}}$$

Thus the given fraction equals

$$-\frac{_{10}P_{x:\overline{20|}} - P_{x:\overline{20|}}}{P_{x:\overline{10|}} - P_{x:\overline{20|}}}.$$

Then, multiplying numerator and denominator by $\ddot{s}_{x:\overline{10|}}$, the fraction becomes

$$-\frac{A_{x+10:\overline{20|}} - {_{10}V_{x:\overline{20|}}}}{1 - {_{10}V_{x:\overline{20|}}}}$$

$$= -\frac{P_{x:\overline{20|}} \ddot{a}_{x+10:\overline{10|}}}{\dfrac{\ddot{a}_{x+10:\overline{10|}}}{\ddot{a}_{x:\overline{20|}}}}$$

$$= \underline{\underline{-A_{x:\overline{20|}}}}$$

7–23.

Key Formulas:

$$A_x = A_{x:\overline{n|}}^1 + A_{x:\overline{n|}}^{\;\;1} A_{x+n}$$

$$_nV_x = \frac{A_{x+n} - A_x}{1 - A_x}$$

Thus $A_{x+n} = 4/9$ and

$$_nV_x = \underline{\underline{11/36}}$$

7–24.

Key Formula:

$$_{15}V_{20:\overline{20|}} = 1 - (1 - {_5V_{20:\overline{20|}}})(1 - {_5V_{25:\overline{15|}}})(1 - {_5V_{30:\overline{10|}}})$$

Substituting,

$$_5V_{20:\overline{10|}} = \underline{\underline{.4}}$$

7–25.

Key Formula:

$$\text{VAR}[{_{15}L}] = p \cdot {^2A_x} = p\frac{q}{(1+i)^2 - p}$$

Thus, we have

$$\frac{\frac{1}{3} \cdot \frac{2}{3}}{(\frac{7}{6})^2 - \frac{1}{3}} = \underline{\underline{\frac{8}{37}}}$$

7-26.

Key Concept: The formula

$$\text{VAR}[\,_kL] = \frac{{}^2A_{x+k} - A^2_{x+k}}{(1 - A_x)^2}\,,$$

from which the formula

$$\text{VAR}[\,_kL] = p \cdot {}^2\overline{A}_x$$

is derived, is only valid when the equivalence principle is assumed.

$$\therefore \underline{\underline{C}}$$

7-27.

Key Formula: $$_{10}V(\overline{A}_{20}) = \frac{i}{\delta}\,_{10}V_{20} = \frac{\overline{A}_{30} - \overline{A}_{20}}{1 - A_{20}}$$

Thus, we have

$$\frac{_{10}\overline{V}(\overline{A}_{20})}{_{10}V(\overline{A}_{20})} = \frac{\dfrac{\overline{A}_{30} - \overline{A}_{20}}{1 - \overline{A}_{20}}}{\dfrac{\overline{A}_{30} - \overline{A}_{20}}{1 - A_{20}}}$$

$$= \frac{1 - A_{20}}{1 - \overline{A}_{20}}$$

$$= \frac{d\,\ddot{a}_{20}}{\delta\,\bar{a}_{20}}$$

$$= \bar{a}_{\overline{1}|}\frac{\ddot{a}_{20}}{\bar{a}_{20}}$$

7-28.

Key Formulas: $$_5V^{(12)}_{65} = \,_5V_{65}[1 + \beta(12)P^{(12)}_{65}] \qquad \text{(UDD)}$$

$$P^{(12)}_{65} = \frac{1 - d\ddot{a}_{65}}{\ddot{a}^{(12)}_{65}}$$

$$_5V_{65} = 1 - \frac{\ddot{a}_{70}}{\ddot{a}_{65}}$$

Therefore,

$$P_{65}^{(12)} = .046595,$$

$$_5V_{65} = \frac{1}{9}, \text{ and}$$

$$_5V_{65}^{(12)} = .11353$$

$$\therefore 1000\ _5V_{65}^{(12)} = \underline{114}.$$

7-29.

Key Concept: Since both premiums and benefits vary with duration, the reserve at duration t is found by the generalized prospective formula.

$$_tV = \int_0^{10-t} 2u(1+i)^u v^u\ _up_{90+t}\mu_{90+t+u}\,du$$

$$- \int_0^{10-t} \frac{1}{2}(10-t)(1+i)^u v^u\ _up_{90+t}\,du$$

$$= \int_0^{10-t} 2u\left(\frac{1}{10-t}\right)\,du - \frac{1}{2}\int_0^{10-t}(10-t)\frac{10-t-u}{10-t}\,du$$

$$= \frac{1}{10-t}(10-t)^2 - \frac{1}{4}(10-t)^2$$

Thus $(10-t) - \frac{1}{4}(10-t)^2 = .91$.

Solving, $t = 7.4$ or $\underline{8.6}$.

7-30.

Key Formulas:

$$_{k+\frac{1}{3}}V_x^{(4)} \doteq \frac{2}{3}\ _kV_x^{(4)} + \frac{1}{3}\ _{k+1}V_x^{(4)} + \frac{1}{6}P_x^{(4)}$$

$$_kV_x^{(4)} \doteq\ _kV_x\left(1 + \frac{3}{8}P_x^{(4)}\right) \quad (\text{since } i = 0)$$

Substituting,

$$\frac{1}{4} = \frac{2}{3}\ _kV_x\left(1 + \frac{3}{8}P_x^{(4)}\right) + \frac{1}{3}\ _{k+1}V_x\left(1 + \frac{3}{8}P_x^{(4)}\right) + \frac{1}{6}P_x^{(4)}$$

$$= \left[\frac{2}{3}\left(\frac{1}{8}\right) + \frac{1}{3}\left(\frac{3}{8}\right)\right]\left(1 + \frac{3}{8}P_x^{(4)}\right) + \frac{1}{6}P_x^{(4)}$$

Solving

$$P_x^{(4)} = \frac{8}{47}$$

Thus, the true quarterly premium is $\dfrac{2}{\underline{47}}$.

7–31.

Key Concept: Under constant force, terminal reserves are all equal to zero, and Hattendorf's approach is facilitated.

$$\text{VAR}[{}_2L] = v^2 F^2 pq + v^4 F^2 pqp + v^6 F^2 pqp^2$$

Using $p = \frac{1}{5}$, we have

$$237\dot{1}.2 = F^2 \left[(.8)(\tfrac{1}{5})(\tfrac{4}{5}) + (.8)^2(\tfrac{1}{5})^2(\tfrac{4}{5}) + (.8)^3(\tfrac{1}{5})^3(\tfrac{4}{5}) \right]$$

Solving, $F = \underline{125}$.

7–32.

Key Algebraic Result: $\displaystyle\sum_{1}^{10} \left(\frac{1}{\ddot{a}_{x+t}} - \frac{1}{\ddot{a}_{x+t-1}} \right) = \frac{1}{\ddot{a}_{x+10}} - \frac{1}{\ddot{a}_x}$

Thus, we have
$$\frac{\ddot{a}_x}{\ddot{a}_{x+10}} - 1$$

$$= \frac{1}{1 - {}_{10}V_x} - 1$$

$$= \frac{{}_{10}V_x}{1 - {}_{10}V_x}$$

7–33.

Key Concept: Use of the Hattendorf approach requires the value of ${}_2V$.

Letting the face amounts equal F , $2F$, and $4F$,

$$\begin{aligned} {}_2V &= 4Fvq_{87} - 8 \\ &= 2F - 8 \end{aligned}$$

Then,

$$\text{VAR}[{}_1L] = (2F - (2F - 8))^2 p_{86}q_{86} + (4F)^2 p_{87}q_{87}p_{86}$$
$$255.36 = 64(.4)(.6) + 16F^2(.5)(.5)(.6)$$

Solving, $F^2 = 100$. $\therefore F = \underline{10}$.

7-34.

Key Concept: In order to find $_2L$, we need the premium $P^1_{30:\overline{5}|}$.

$$P^1_{30:\overline{5}|}\ddot{a}_{30:\overline{5}|} = A^1_{30:\overline{5}|}$$

$$P^1_{30:\overline{5}|}(1 + e_{30:\overline{4}|}) = {}_5q_{30}$$

$$\therefore P^1_{30:\overline{5}|} = \frac{.4}{4.2} = \frac{2}{21}$$

Specifying the values of the random variable $_2L$:

$_2L$	Probability
$1 - P^1_{30:\overline{5}|} = \frac{19}{21}$	10/85
$1 - P^1_{30:\overline{5}|}(2) = \frac{17}{21}$	10/85
$1 - P^1_{30:\overline{5}|}(3) = \frac{15}{21}$	5/85
$-P^1_{30:\overline{5}|}(3) = \frac{-6}{21}$	60/85

Thus,

$$E[_2L] = \frac{5}{119} \text{ and}$$

$$E[(_2L)^2] = \frac{1957}{7497}.$$

Finally, $\text{VAR}[_2L] = \underline{.25927}$.

NOTE: The Hattendorf approach may be used here, but it involves somewhat more tedious arithmetic.

7-35.

Key Concept: In order to analyze the sufficiency of the fund, we must first determine probabilities of death at ages 44, 45, and 46.

We are told that

$$p_{46} = (p_{45})^2 \cdot 2 = (p_{44})^4(.8)$$

and that

$$p_{44}p_{45}p_{46} = \frac{1}{8}.$$

Thus

$$(p_{44})2(p_{44})^2 8(p_{44})^4 = 16(p_{44})^7 = \frac{1}{8}$$

and $p_{44} = \frac{1}{2} = p_{45} = p_{46}$.

The fund at $t = 4$ is $500.

The fund at $t = 5$, if there are no claims, is
$[500 + 3(450)](1.1) = 2035$, and a claim payment would cause ruin.

The fund at $t = 6$, if there are no claims, is
$[2035 + 3(450)](1.1) = 3723.50$, and a claim payment would cause ruin.

The fund at $t = 7$, if there are no claims, is
$[3723.50 + 3(450)](1.1) = 5580.85$, and funds are available to pay one claim.

The desired probability, therefore, is that no deaths will occur between ages 44 and 46 and that at most one death will occur between ages 46 and 47, i.e.,

$$(p_{44})^3(p_{45})^3[(p_{46}) + 3(p_{46})^2 q_{46}] = \underline{\underline{\frac{1}{128}}}$$

7–36.

Key Formulas:

$$_{k+\frac{1}{3}}V_x \doteq \frac{1}{3}\,_{k+1}V_x + \frac{2}{3}\,_kV_x + \frac{2}{3}P_x$$

$$_{k+\frac{2}{3}}V_x \doteq \frac{2}{3}\,_{k+1}V_x + \frac{1}{3}\,_kV_x + \frac{1}{3}P_x$$

Subtracting,

$$.00165 = -\frac{1}{3}(.3) + \frac{1}{3}(_kV_x + P_x)$$

Then,

$$_kV_x + P_x = .30495$$

But

$$_kV_x + P_x = v[_{k+1}V_x + q_{x+k}(1 - _{k+1}V_x)]$$

Therefore,

$$.30495 = .95[.3 + (.7)q_{x+k}], \text{ and}$$

$$q_{x+k} = \underline{\underline{.03}}.$$

7–37.

Key Formulas:

$$\text{VAR}[_{10}L] = \frac{{}^2\overline{A}_{40} - \overline{A}_{40}^2}{(1 - \overline{A}_{30})^2}$$

$$\overline{A}_x = \frac{\overline{P}(\overline{A}_x)}{\overline{P}(\overline{A}_x) + \delta}$$

Thus $\bar{A}_{30} = \dfrac{.03}{.09} = \dfrac{1}{3}$ and

$$\bar{A}_{40} = \frac{.04}{.10} = \frac{2}{5}$$

Finally, $\text{VAR}[_{10}L] = \dfrac{{}^{2}\bar{A}_{40} - .16}{\frac{4}{9}} = .2025$.

Solving, ${}^{2}\bar{A}_{40} = \underline{.25}$.

Note that the equivalence principle is implied by the term "net annual premium."

7–38.

Key Formula:

$$\frac{\partial}{\partial t}{}_{t}\bar{V}(\bar{A}_{x}) = \bar{P}(\bar{A}_{x}) + \delta\,{}_{t}\bar{V}(\bar{A}_{x}) + \mu_{x+t}\cdot{}_{t}\bar{V}(\bar{A}_{x}) - \mu_{x+t}$$

Thus, the integrand is

$$\frac{\partial}{\partial t}{}_{t}\bar{V}(\bar{A}_{x}) - \bar{P}(\bar{A}_{x}) - \delta\,{}_{t}\bar{V}(\bar{A}_{x}) + \bar{P}(\bar{A}_{x})\bar{A}_{x+t} + \delta\bar{A}_{x+t},$$

$$= \frac{\partial}{\partial t}{}_{t}\bar{V}(\bar{A}_{x}) - \bar{P}(\bar{A}_{x})\delta\bar{a}_{x+t} + \delta\bar{A}_{x+t} - \delta\,{}_{t}\bar{V}(\bar{A}_{x})$$

$$= \frac{\partial}{\partial t}{}_{t}\bar{V}(\bar{A}_{x}) + \delta(\bar{A}_{x+t} - \bar{P}(\bar{A}_{x})\bar{a}_{x+t} - {}_{t}\bar{V}(\bar{A}_{x}))$$

$$= \frac{\partial}{\partial t}{}_{t}\bar{V}(\bar{A}_{x})$$

Then, $\displaystyle\int_{0}^{n}\frac{\partial}{\partial t}{}_{t}\bar{V}(\bar{A}_{x})\,dt = \underline{{}_{n}\bar{V}(\bar{A}_{x})}$.

7–39.

Key Concept: Apportionable reserves do not equal fully continuous reserves at durations at which there are unearned premiums.

Key Formula:

$$_{5\frac{1}{4}}V^{\{3\}}(\bar{A}_{x}) = \frac{3}{4}\,{}_{5}\bar{V}(\bar{A}_{x}) + \frac{1}{4}\,{}_{6}\bar{V}(\bar{A}_{x}) + \frac{1}{12}P^{\{3\}}(\bar{A}_{x})$$

Thus the result is

$$\frac{1}{12}P^{\{3\}}(\bar{A}_{x}), \text{ or } \frac{1}{12}\bar{P}(\bar{A}_{x})\cdot\frac{d^{(3)}}{\delta}.$$

This, in turn, may be expressed as

$$\frac{1}{12}\bar{P}(\bar{A}_{x})\cdot 3\bar{a}_{\overline{\frac{1}{3}}|}$$

$$= \underline{\frac{1}{4}\bar{P}(\bar{A}_{x})\bar{a}_{\overline{\frac{1}{3}}|}}$$

7–40.

Key Formula: $\text{VAR}[\Lambda_1] = v^2(6 - {}_2V)^2 p_{91}q_{91}p_{90}$

Thus, we need to calculate the net premium π and, in turn, ${}_2V$.

$$\pi\ddot{a}_{90:\overline{3}|} = vq_{90} + 6v^2\,{}_{1|}q_{90} + 9v^3\,{}_{2|}q_{90}$$

$$\pi(1 + \tfrac{5}{6}v + \tfrac{3}{6}v^2) = v(\tfrac{1}{6}) + 6v^2(\tfrac{2}{6}) + 9v^3(\tfrac{3}{6})$$

$$\therefore \pi = 2.34362$$

and

$${}_2V = 9v - \pi = 5.75638$$

Finally,

$$\text{VAR}[\Lambda_1] = \underline{.009615}$$

7–41.

Key Formula: $${}_t\overline{V}(\overline{A}_{x:\overline{n}|}) = {}_tV(\overline{A}_{x:\overline{n}|}) + \beta(\infty)\overline{P}(\overline{A}_{x:\overline{n}|})\,{}_tV^{\,1}_{x:\overline{n}|}$$

$$= \frac{i}{\delta}\,{}_tV^{\,1}_{x:\overline{n}|} + {}_tV_{x:\overline{n}|}^{\,1} + \frac{i-\delta}{\delta^2}\cdot\frac{\delta\overline{A}_{x:\overline{n}|}}{1 - \overline{A}_{x:\overline{n}|}}\,{}_tV^{\,1}_{x:\overline{n}|}$$

Substituting the given values, we have

$${}_t\overline{V}(\overline{A}_{x:\overline{n}|}) = \frac{.0833}{.08}(.1) + (.7 - .1) + \frac{.0033}{.08}\cdot\frac{.4}{.6}(.1)$$

$$= \underline{.706875}$$

7–42.

Key Formula: $${}_5V(\overline{A}^{PR}_{30}) = {}_5\overline{V}(\overline{A}_{30}) - {}_5V(\overline{A}_{30})$$

$$= P(\overline{A}_{30})\,\ddot{a}_{35} - \overline{P}(\overline{A}_{30})\bar{a}_{35}$$

$$= \overline{A}_{30}\frac{\ddot{a}_{35}}{\ddot{a}_{30}} - \overline{A}_{30}\frac{\bar{a}_{35}}{\bar{a}_{30}}$$

Also,

$${}_5\overline{V}(\overline{A}_{30}) - {}_5V_{30} = \frac{\ddot{a}_{35}}{\ddot{a}_{30}} - \frac{\bar{a}_{35}}{\bar{a}_{30}}$$

Thus, the fraction clearly equals $\overline{A}_{30}$.

Thus

$$\overline{A}_{30} = .4$$

$$\therefore \bar{a}_{30} = \frac{1 - \overline{A}_{30}}{\delta} = \underline{\underline{12}}$$

Chapter Eight

Supplementary Concepts

1. The variances of present value random variables for multiple life insurances and annuities, as well as basic multiple life identities themselves, are closely related to those for single life functions.

   Examples

$$A_x = 1 - d\ddot{a}_x$$
$$A_{xy} = 1 - d\ddot{a}_{xy}$$
$$A_{\overline{xy}} = 1 - d\ddot{a}_{\overline{xy}}$$

$$\overline{A}_x = 1 - \delta\bar{a}_x$$
$$\overline{A}_{xy} = 1 - \delta\bar{a}_{xy}$$
$$\overline{A}_{\overline{xy}} = 1 - \delta\bar{a}_{\overline{xy}}$$

$$A_x = v\ddot{a}_x - a_x$$
$$A_{xy} = v\ddot{a}_{xy} - a_{xy}$$
$$A_{\overline{xy}} = v\ddot{a}_{\overline{xy}} - a_{\overline{xy}}$$

If $Z = \bar{a}_{\overline{T(x)}|}$, $T(x) \geq 0$, then

$$E[Z] = \bar{a}_x$$

$$\text{VAR}[Z] = \frac{{}^2\overline{A}_x - \overline{A}_x^2}{\delta^2}$$

If $Z = \bar{a}_{\overline{T(xy)}|}$, $T(xy) \geq 0$, then

$$E[Z] = \bar{a}_{xy}$$

$$\text{VAR}[Z] = \frac{{}^2\overline{A}_{xy} - \overline{A}_{xy}^2}{\delta^2}$$

If $Z = \bar{a}_{\overline{T(\overline{xy})}|}$, $T(\overline{xy}) \geq 0$, then

$$E[Z] = \bar{a}_{\overline{xy}}$$

$$\text{VAR}[Z] = \frac{{}^2\overline{A}_{\overline{xy}} - \overline{A}_{\overline{xy}}^2}{\delta^2}$$

2. Under Gompertz' Law, if $xy \equiv w$, then

$$\mu_x + \mu_y = \mu_w \text{ and}$$
$$c^x + c^y = c^w.$$

   Under Makeham's Law, if $xy \equiv ww$, then

$$\mu_x + \mu_y = 2\mu_w \text{ and}$$
$$c^x + c^y = 2c^w.$$

3. If it is assumed that deaths of *individuals* are uniformly distributed over each year of age, then

$$q^1_{xy} = q_x \cdot {}_{1/2}p_y$$
$$= q_x(1 - \tfrac{1}{2}q_y)$$
$$= q_x - \tfrac{1}{2}q_x q_y$$

and

$$q^2_{xy} = q_x q_y \cdot \tfrac{1}{2}.$$

The latter identity, clearly true for $x = y$ under *any* assumption, is true for *any* x and y under the stated UDD assumption.

4. If it is assumed that failures of joint-life statuses (xy) are uniformly distributed over each year of age, i.e., ${}_t q_{xy} = t \cdot q_{xy}$, $0 \le t \le 1$, then

$$\overline{A}_{xy} = \frac{i}{\delta} A_{xy}$$

and

$$\bar{a}_{xy} = \alpha(\infty)\ddot{a}_{xy} - \beta(\infty).$$

If, however, it is the individual lives whose failures are assumed to be uniformly distributed, much more complex formulas arise for $\overline{A}_{xy}$ and $\bar{a}_{xy}$.

5. Consider the quantity

$${}_n q^1_{xy} - {}_n q^2_{xy}.$$

The first term contains two separate probabilities, i.e., that *only* (x) dies within n years and that *both* die within n years, with (x) dying first. The second term represents only the probability that both die within n years, with (x) dying first. The difference, then, is the probability that (x) dies within n years and that (y) does not. Thus,

$${}_n q^1_{xy} - {}_n q^2_{xy} = {}_n q_x \, {}_n p_y$$

is an especially valuable relationship, as it replaces two contingent probabilities with the product of two single life probabilities.

A similar thought process produces

$$A^1_{xy} - A^2_{xy} = A_{xy} - A_y$$
$$= d(\ddot{a}_y - \ddot{a}_{xy}).$$

6. The Makeham formula

$$\overline{A}{}^1_{xy:\overline{n}|} = \frac{c^x}{c^x + c^y} \overline{A}_{\frac{1}{xy}:\overline{n}|} + A\left(1 - \frac{2c^x}{c^x + c^y}\right)\bar{a}_{xy:\overline{n}|}$$

is of primary importance because of the substantial number of special cases which result. For example, if a Gompertz result is needed, A is set equal to zero. If probabilities are required instead of insurances, the interest rate i is set equal to zero. If whole life insurances and annuities are involved, n is replaced by ∞. Combinations of these special cases generate important results as well.

Examples (Makeham)

$$\bar{A}^{\,1}_{xy} = \frac{c^x}{c^x + c^y}\,\bar{A}_{xy} + A\left(1 - \frac{2c^x}{c^x + c^y}\right)\bar{a}_{xy}$$

$$_\infty q^{\,1}_{xy} = \frac{c^x}{c^x + c^y} + A\left(1 - \frac{2c^x}{c^x + c^y}\right)\overset{\circ}{e}_{xy}$$

$$\bar{A}^{\,1}_{xx:\overline{n}|} = \frac{1}{2}\bar{A}^{\,1}_{xx\,:\,\overline{n}|}$$

Examples (Gompertz)

$$\bar{A}^{\,1}_{xy} = \frac{c^x}{c^x + c^y}\,\bar{A}_{xy}$$

$$_\infty q^{\,1}_{xy} = \frac{c^x}{c^x + c^y}$$

$$_n q^{\,1}_{xy} = \frac{c^x}{c^x + c^y}\, _n q_{xy} = \,_\infty q^{\,1}_{xy}\, _n q_{xy}$$

7.   The contingent probability $_\infty q^{\,1}_{xy}$, when de Moivre's Law is assumed, may be quickly determined by a logical consideration of the consequences of de Moivre's Law. This is accomplished by looking at the *older* of the two lives and realizing that his *expected* duration until death is one-half the length of time until attainment of age ω. The younger life is then analyzed in light of the expected time of death of the older; accordingly, contingent probabilities are replaced by single life probabilities.

Examples (All assuming $\omega = 100$)

$$_\infty q^{\,1}_{30:50} = \,_{25}q_{30} = \frac{25}{75}$$

$$_\infty q^{\,2}_{20:70} = \,_{15}p_{20} = \frac{65}{80}$$

$$_\infty q^{\,1}_{40:60} = \,_{20}p_{40} = \frac{40}{60}$$

$$_\infty q^{\,2}_{50:80} = \,_{10}q_{50} = \frac{10}{50}$$

8.   The probability that (x) will die more than n years after the death of (y) is given by

$$\int_0^\infty \,_t p_y \mu_{y+t}\, _{n+t}p_x\, dt$$

$$= \,_n p_x\, _\infty q^{\,2}_{\overline{x+n}:y}$$

The following table is then easily constructed. Note that the sum of the probabilities is one.

Time of Death of (x)	Probability
i) Before the death of (y)	$_\infty q^1_{xy}$
ii) Within n years after the death of (y)	$_\infty q^2_{xy} - {}_nP_x \, _\infty q^2_{\overline{x+n}:y}$
iii) More than n years after the death of (y)	$_nP_x \, _\infty q^2_{\overline{x+n}:y}$

Combinations of these, such as the probability that the deaths of (x) and (y) are separated by at least n years, can now easily be determined.

9. The present value of an insurance of 1, payable at the death of (x) if he dies more than n years after the death of (y), is given by

$$\int_0^\infty v^{n+t} \, {}_{n+t}p_x \mu_{x+n+t} \cdot {}_tq_y \, dt$$

$$= {}_nE_x \bar{A}^2_{\overline{x+n}:y}.$$

The following table is then easily constructed for policies payable at the instant of death of (x).

Note that the sum of the net single premiums is $\bar{A}_x$.

Time of Death of (x)	Net Single Premium
i) Before the death of (y)	$\bar{A}^1_{xy}$
ii) Within n years after the death of (y)	$\bar{A}^2_{xy} - {}_nE_x \bar{A}^2_{\overline{x+n}:y}$
iii) More than n years after the death of (y)	$_nE_x \bar{A}^2_{\overline{x+n}:y}$

10. From Chapter Three, we recall the following:

$$\text{If } \mu_x = \frac{k}{\omega - x}, \ 0 \le x < \omega, \text{ then}$$

$$\overset{\circ}{e}_x = \frac{\omega - x}{k + 1}.$$

Similarly, if $\mu_x = \frac{k}{\omega - x}$, $0 \le x < \omega$, then

$$\overset{\circ}{e}_{xx} = \int_0^{\omega - x} {}_tp_{xx} \, dt$$

$$= \frac{\omega - x}{2k + 1}.$$

Finally, suppose that (x_1) is subject to

$$\mu_x = \frac{k}{\omega - x}, \quad 0 \le x < \omega,$$

and (x_2) is subject to

$$\mu_x = \frac{m}{\omega - x}, \quad 0 \le x < \omega.$$

Then, assuming that $x_1 = x_2 = x$,

$$
\begin{aligned}
\overset{\circ}{e}_{x_1 x_2} &= \int_0^{\omega - x} {}_t p_{x_1}\, {}_t p_{x_2}\, dt \\
&= \frac{\omega - x}{k + m + 1}.
\end{aligned}
$$

Example

Suppose a female aged 20 is subject to

$$l_x = (80 - x)^2, \quad 0 \le x \le 80$$

and a male aged 20 is subject to

$$l_x = (80 - x)^3, \quad 0 \le x \le 80.$$

Then the complete expectation of the joint-life status is given by $\dfrac{80 - 20}{2 + 3 + 1}$, or 10 years.

Special Mortality Laws

I. de Moivre's Law

$$
\overset{\circ}{e}_{xx} = \frac{1}{3}(\omega - x)
$$

$$
\overset{\circ}{e}_{\overline{xx}} = \frac{2}{3}(\omega - x)
$$

$$
\overset{\circ}{e}_{xy} = {}_{y-x}p_x \overset{\circ}{e}_{yy} + {}_{y-x}q_x \overset{\circ}{e}_y \quad (x < y)
$$

$$
{}_\infty q^1_{xy} = \frac{1}{2}\, {}_{y-x}p_x \quad (x < y)
$$

$$
\mathrm{VAR}[T(xx)] = \frac{(\omega - x)^2}{18}
$$

$$
\mathrm{VAR}[T(\overline{xx})] = \frac{(\omega - x)^2}{18}
$$

$$
\mathrm{COV}[T(xx), T(\overline{xx})] = \frac{(\omega - x)^2}{36}
$$

II. Constant Force of Mortality (Note that $xy \equiv xx$.)

$$\overset{\circ}{e}_{xy} = \frac{1}{2\mu}$$

$$\overset{\circ}{e}_{\overline{xy}} = \frac{3}{2\mu}$$

$$e_{xy} = \frac{p_{xy}}{q_{xy}}$$

$$\text{VAR}[T(xy)] = \frac{1}{4\mu^2}$$

$$\text{VAR}[T(\overline{xy})] = \frac{5}{4\mu^2}$$

$$\text{VAR}[K(xy)] = \frac{p_{xy}}{(q_{xy})^2}$$

$$\text{COV}[(xy), T(\overline{xy})] = \frac{1}{4\mu^2}$$

$$\text{MEDIAN OF } T(xy) = \frac{\ln 2}{\mu_{xy}}$$

$$\overline{A}_{xy} = \frac{2\mu}{2\mu + \delta}$$

$$\overline{a}_{xy} = \frac{1}{2\mu + \delta}$$

$$A_{xy} = \frac{q_{xy}}{q_{xy} + i}$$

$$\ddot{a}_{xy} = \frac{1 + i}{q_{xy} + i}$$

$${}^2\overline{A}_{xy} = \frac{\mu}{\mu + \delta}$$

$${}^2\overline{a}_{xy} = \frac{1}{2\mu + 2\delta}$$

$${}^2A_{xy} = \frac{q_{xy}}{q_{xy} + 2i + i^2}$$

$$\overline{A}{}^1_{xy} = \frac{\mu}{2\mu + \delta}$$

$$\overline{A}{}^2_{xy} = \frac{\mu}{2\mu + \delta} \cdot \frac{\mu}{\mu + \delta}$$

$$\overline{A}_{\overline{xy}} = \frac{2\mu}{2\mu + \delta} \cdot \frac{\mu}{\mu + \delta}$$

III. Uniform Distribution of Deaths

$$q_{xy}^{1} = q_x \left(1 - \frac{1}{2}q_y\right)$$

$$q_{xy}^{2} = \frac{1}{2}q_x q_y$$

$$\overline{A}_{xy} = \frac{i}{\delta}A_{xy} + \frac{i}{\delta}\left(1 - \frac{2}{\delta} + \frac{2}{i}\right)\sum_{0}^{\infty} v^{k+1} {}_{k|}q_x {}_{k|}q_y$$

$$\bar{a}_{xy} = \alpha(\infty)\ddot{a}_{xy} - \beta(\infty) - \frac{i}{\delta^2}\left(1 - \frac{2}{\delta} + \frac{2}{i}\right)\sum_{0}^{\infty} v^{k+1} {}_{k|}q_x \cdot {}_{k|}q_y$$

$${}_{t}p_{xy}\mu_{x+t:y+t} = q_{xy} + (1 - 2t)q_{\overline{xy}}, \quad 0 \le t \le 1$$

Derivatives

$$\frac{\partial}{\partial t} {}_{t}p_{xy} = - {}_{t}p_{xy}\mu_{x+t:y+t}$$

$$\frac{\partial}{\partial t} {}_{t}p_{\overline{xy}} = - {}_{t}p_x\mu_{x+t} - {}_{t}p_y\mu_{y+t} + {}_{t}p_{xy}\mu_{x+t:y+t}$$

$$\frac{\partial}{\partial x} \mathring{e}_{xy} = \mu_x \mathring{e}_{xy} - {}_{\infty}q_{xy}^{1}$$

$$\frac{\partial}{\partial x} \mathring{e}_{xx} = 2\mu_x \mathring{e}_{xx} - 1$$

$$\frac{\partial}{\partial x} \bar{a}_{xy} = \mu_x \bar{a}_{xy} - \overline{A}_{xy}^{1}$$

$$\frac{\partial}{\partial x} \bar{a}_{xx} = 2\mu_x \bar{a}_{xx} - \overline{A}_{xx}$$

Exercises

8–1   Given: μ_x is constant for all x.

$\mathring{e}_{20:50} = K$

$COV[T(30:40), T(\overline{50:60})] = 100$

$v^3 = e^{-\frac{1}{2K}}$

Find: $\bar{a}_{55:65}$.

A) 8   B) $\frac{60}{7}$ C) $\frac{120}{13}$ D) 15   E) $\frac{120}{7}$

8-2   A table is known to follow Makeham's Law; $\mu_{20} = .0098$, $\mu_{40} = .0138$, and $\mu_{60} = .0338$. Find $\bar{A}^{\,1}_{20:40}$ using linear approximations in the following table:

x	c^x	$\bar{a}_{xx}$	$\bar{A}_{xx}$
33	14.2	9.50	.62
34	15.4	8.75	.65

A) .1591   B) .1593   C) .1595   D) .1597   E) .1599

8-3   Which of the following is/are true?

I. $_{n|}\bar{a}_{\overline{xy}} = {}_{n|}\bar{a}_x + {}_{n|}\bar{a}_y - {}_{n|}\bar{a}_{xy}$

II. $_{n|}\bar{a}_{\overline{xy}} = v^n {}_n p_{xy}\,\bar{a}_{\overline{x+n:y+n}}$

III. $_{n|}\bar{a}_{\overline{xy}} = v^n {}_n p_{\overline{xy}}\,\bar{a}_{\overline{x+n:y+n}}$

A) None   B) I only   C) II only   D) III only   E) I and III

8-4   Given: $_{n|}q_x = .050$; $_{n|}q_y = .080$; $_{n|}q_{xy} = .100$

Which is/are true?

I. The probability that neither (x) nor (y) will die in the $(n+1)$ st year is .126.

II. The probability that $\overline{xy}$ will fail in the $(n+1)$ st year is $_{n+1}q_x \cdot {}_{n|}q_y + {}_{n+1}q_y \cdot {}_{n|}q_x$.

III. The probability that exactly one of (x) and (y) will die in the $(n+1)$ st year is .100.

A) None   B) I only   C) II only   D) III only   E) More than one
                                                                              is correct

8-5   A joint and survivor life annuity-immediate pays $\$K$ annually as long as both (x) and (y) survive, reducing to $600 at the death of (y) or $1,000 at the death of (x). The net single premium for the annuity is $36,750. If $a_x = 20$, $a_y = 15$, and $a_{xy} = 7.5$, find K.

A) 1300   B) 1600   C) 2000   D) 2400   E) 2900

8-6   If de Moivre's Law is assumed, $\mathrm{COV}[T(xx), T(\overline{xx})] = 36$, for a specific x. Find μ_x.

A) $\frac{1}{1296}$ B) $\frac{1}{126}$ C) $\frac{1}{36}$ D) $\frac{1}{6}$ E) Cannot be
                                                                                                    determined

8-7   Simplify $A - B$, where

$A = $ Pr[at least one death of (x) and (y) occurs in the $(n+1)$st year from now]

$B = $ Pr[the second death of (x) and (y) occurs in the $(n+1)$st year from now]

A) 0   B) $_{n|}q_{xy}$ C) $_{n|}q_{\overline{xy}} - _{n|}q_{xy}$ D) $_{n|}q_{xy} - _{n|}q_{\overline{xy}}$

E) $_{n|}q_{xy} - _{n|}q_x \, _{n|}q_y$

8-8   Given: μ and δ are positive constants; $.25 < \mu < \delta < .50$.

$$I = \bar{A}_{xy}$$
$$II = \bar{A}_{\overline{xy}}$$
$$III = \bar{A}^{\,1}_{xy}$$
$$IV = \bar{A}^{\,2}_{xy}$$
$$V = \bar{a}_x - \bar{a}_{xx}$$

Which of the following is correct?

A) $IV < II < III < I < V$ B) $IV < III < II < I < V$

C) $IV < II < III < V < I$ D) $IV < II < V < III < I$

E) There is not sufficient information to conclude any of the above.

8-9   The probability that (25) dies at least 5 years before the death of (20) is $\frac{13}{28}$. If $\mu_x = \dfrac{1}{\omega - x}$, $0 < x < \omega$, find ω.

A) 88   B) 90   C) 92   D) 94   E) 96

8-10   Given: $f_X(x)$ is constant, $0 \le x < \omega$

$\qquad\qquad e_{70} = 15$

Evaluate $\overset{\circ}{e}_{\overline{20:30}}$ to the nearest integer.

A) 49   B) 50   C) 51   D) 52   E) 53

8-11   Let Q be the future lifetime random variable whose expected value is $\overset{\circ}{e}_{xy:\overline{20|}}$. If $\mu = .01$ for all ages, find $\mathrm{VAR}[Q]$.

A) $5000 - 7000e^{-.4} - (\overset{\circ}{e}_{xy:\overline{20|}})^2$

B) $5000 - 7400e^{-.4} - (\overset{\circ}{e}_{xy:\overline{20|}})^2$

C) $5000 - 7400e^{-.4} + 400e^{-.2} - (\overset{\circ}{e}_{xy:\overline{20|}})^2$

D) $5000 - 7400e^{-.4} + 20e^{-.2} - (\overset{\circ}{e}_{xy:\overline{20|}})^2$

E) $5000e^{-.4} - (\overset{\circ}{e}_{xy:\overline{20|}})^2$

8-12   If $\mu_x = \frac{1}{100-x}$, $0 < x < 100$, and $_nq^1_{50:60} = \frac{3}{10}$, find n.

A) 10   B) 20   C) 25   D) 30   E) 40

8-13   If $\overset{\circ}{e}_{xy} = 1$ for all x, y, find the probability that (20) and (50) will die within 30 years of each other.

A) e^{-15} B) e^{-30} C) $1 - e^{-15}$ D) $1 - e^{-30}$ E) $e^{-15} - e^{-30}$

8-14   If $l_x = (100 - x)^2$, $0 \leq x \leq 100$, evaluate $\text{COV}[T(40:40), T(\overline{40:40})]$.

A) 8   B) 10   C) 25   D) 64   E) 100

8-15   Let Z equal the present value random variable for an insurance of 1 payable at the instant of the second death of (20) and (30). If $\mu = .02$ for all ages and $\delta = .08$, find the probability that the present value of the claim is within one standard deviation of its expected value.

A) .68   B) $\dfrac{2 \cdot 5^{3/4} - 5^{1/2}}{5}$ C) e^{-4} D) $5^{-1/2}$ E) $5^{-1/4}$

8-16   Let $s(x) = e^{\frac{1-\phi^x}{\ln\phi}}$. If $_\infty q^1_{20:21} = \frac{1}{3}$, find ϕ.

A) 2   B) 3   C) 4   D) 5   E) 6

8-17   Assume $l_x = \omega - x$, $0 \leq x \leq \omega$. If $\text{VAR}[T(\overline{20:20})] = 200$, find ω.

A) 65   B) 70   C) 75   D) 80   E) 85

8-18   Given: $100 \cdot s(x) + x = 100$, $0 \leq x \leq 100$.

Find the probability that (30) will die within the 20-year period following the death of (40).

A) $\frac{1}{7}$ B) $\frac{3}{7}$ C) $\frac{23}{84}$ D) $\frac{4}{7}$ E) $\frac{6}{7}$

8-19   Given: $s(x) = \dfrac{2}{2^{(e^{2x}+x)}}$; $x : x + 2 \equiv x + t : x + t$. Find $2t$.

A) $\ln \dfrac{1+e}{2}$ B) $\ln \dfrac{1+e^2}{2}$ C) $\ln \dfrac{1+e^4}{2}$ D) $\ln \dfrac{1+e^8}{2}$ E) 2

8-20   Given: $\mu_x = Bc^x, \quad x \geq 0$

$$_\infty q_{20:51}^{\;\;\;2} = \tfrac{2}{7}$$

Find c.

A) 1.025   B) 1.030   C) 1.035   D) 1.040   E) 1.045

8-21   Let $R = \bar{a}_{\overline{T(30,40)|}}, \quad 0 \leq T(30,40) \leq 10$

$\qquad\qquad = 0, \qquad\quad 10 < T(30,40)$

If $\mu = .03$ and $\delta = .04$, find $E[R]$.

A) 10   B) $10(1 - e^{-1})$ C) $10 + 15e^{-1}$ D) $10 + 15e^{-1} - 25e^{-.6}$
E) $10 + 15e^{-1} - 25e^{-.6} + 25e^{-.2}$

8-22   Given: $\mu_x = \dfrac{3}{100 - x}, \quad 0 \leq x < 100$

Find $E[T(\overline{65 : 65})]$.

A) 5   B) 10   C) $12\tfrac{1}{2}$ D) 20   E) 30

8-23   If $\mu_x = \frac{1}{200 - 2x}, \quad 0 \leq x < 100$, find $\mathring{e}_{60:60}$.

A) 8   B) 10   C) 20   D) $\dfrac{40}{3}$ E) 30

8-24   The median of $T(xy)$ is 17.325 years for all x and y. If $ln\,2 = .693$, find the
probability that (40) will be alive 10 years after the death of (30).

A) $1 - \tfrac{1}{2}e^{-.2}$ B) $\tfrac{3}{2}e^{-.2}$ C) $\tfrac{1}{2}e^{-.2}$ D) $\tfrac{1}{2}$ E) $\tfrac{1}{2}e^{-.52}$

8-25   An annuity of 1 per annum is paid continuously as long as either (15) or (30) is alive
beyond age 40, but no payments are to be made if the life aged 15 dies prior to attaining
age 20.

Find the actuarial present value of the annuity.

A) $_5p_{15}\,_{10|}\bar{a}_{20:30}$
B) $_5p_{15}\,_{10|}\bar{a}_{30} + \,_{25|}\bar{a}_{15}$
C) $_5p_{15}\,_{10|}\bar{a}_{30} + \,_{25|}\bar{a}_{15} - \,_{5|}\bar{a}_{15:30}$
D) $_5p_{15}\,_{10|}\bar{a}_{30} + \,_{25|}\bar{a}_{15} - \,_{10|}\bar{a}_{15:30}$
E) $_5p_{15}\,_{10|}\bar{a}_{30} + \,_{25|}\bar{a}_{15} - \,_{25|}\bar{a}_{15:30}$

8-26   If $\mu_x = 2(\tfrac{1}{2})^{2x+3}, \quad x \geq 0$, find the probability that (30) will die before (28).

A) $\tfrac{1}{17}$ B) $\tfrac{1}{5}$ C) $\tfrac{1}{2}$ D) $\tfrac{4}{5}$ E) $\tfrac{16}{17}$

8-27   Let $Z = v^{T(y)}, T(x) \le T(y)$
            $\qquad = 0, \quad T(x) > T(y)$

If $\mu = \delta$, find $VAR[Z]$.

A) $\frac{1}{36}$ B) $\frac{1}{18}$ C) $\frac{1}{12}$ D) $\frac{1}{6}$ E) $\frac{1}{3}$

8-28   A 2 year deferred $1000 joint whole life policy with claim paid at death is issued to (40) and (50). If $\mu = .25$ and $\delta = .10$, find the probability that the present value of the claim is between $200 and $300.

A) .00032   B) .00211   C) .00243   D) .10000   E) Cannot be determined

8-29   Using $A_{30:40} = \frac{1}{3}$ and $i = 100\%$, evaluate $A_{31:41}$.

x	l_x
30	30
31	25
40	20
41	16

A) .10   B) .30   C) .40   D) .50   E) .75

8-30   A continuous annuity to (x), (y), and (z) pays as follows:
    I. $2000 per annum while all are alive
    II. $1500 per annum while only two are alive
    III. $1200 per annum while only one is alive
    IV. $1000 per annum after all are dead.

Find the net single premium, given:

$$\bar{a}_x + \bar{a}_y + \bar{a}_z = 30$$
$$\bar{a}_{xy} + \bar{a}_{xz} + \bar{a}_{yz} = 20$$
$$\bar{a}_{xyz} = 5$$
$$\delta = .02$$

A) $23,500   B) $28,500   C) $58,500   D) $63,500   E) $78,500

8-31   Given: $\mu_x = A + 3^{.2x}, \quad x \geq 0$

$\quad\quad\quad _\infty q_{20:30}^{\;\;\;2} = .15$

$\quad\quad\quad \overset{\circ}{e}_{20:30} = 30$

Find A.

A) $\frac{1}{540}$ B) $\frac{1}{480}$ C) $\frac{1}{325}$ D) $\frac{1}{125}$ E) $\frac{1}{32}$

8-32   Assuming de Moivre's Law, find the probability that a woman aged x will have a future lifetime at least three times as long as her twin sister.

A) 0   B) $\frac{1}{6}$ C) $\frac{1}{4}$ D) $\frac{1}{2}$ E) Cannot be determined

8-33   Let $T(x)$ and $T(y)$ be uniformly distributed in the next year of age. Given that both (x) and (y) will die within the next year, find the probability that exactly one of them will be alive at time t, $0 \leq t \leq 1$.

A) $(1-t)^2$ B) $t(1-t)$ C) $2t(1-t)$ D) $t(2-t)$ E) $t^2(1-t)$

8-34   Given: $_{10}q_{30} = .08$

$\quad\quad\quad\quad _{10}q_{40} = .10$

The probability that the deaths of (30) and (40) are no more than ten years apart is $.45$.

Find the probability that (50) will be alive at the death of (30).

A) .10   B) .20   C) .25   D) .30   E) .40

8-35   Given: $\mu_x = .06c^x, \quad x \geq 0$

$\quad\quad\quad \bar{A}^{\;1}_{20:30} = \frac{1}{2}\bar{A}_{20:30} = \frac{3}{8}$

Find $\bar{A}^{\;2}_{20:30}$.

A) .225   B) .333   C) .375   D) .500   E) Cannot be determined

8-36   Given: $q_x = \frac{x}{100}, \quad x = 0, 1, 2, \ldots, 100$

$\quad\quad\quad$ Deaths are uniformly distributed over each year of age.

If $q^1_{40:y} = .344$, find y.

A) 25   B) 28   C) 30   D) 32   E) 35

8-37   Which of the following represent the probability that the second death of (50) and (60) will occur between 10 and 20 years from now?

   I. $_{10|10}q_{50} + {_{10|10}}q_{60} - {_{20}}p_{50}\,{_{20}}q_{60}$

   II. $_{20}q_{\overline{50:60}} - {_{10}}q_{\overline{50:60}}$

   III. $_{10|10}q_{\overline{50:60}} - {_{10|10}}q_{50} \cdot {_{10|10}}q_{60}$

   A) All   B) All but I   C) All but II   D) All but III   E) Some other
                                                                                combination

8-38   Given: $Z = 0, \quad T(xy) \le m$
   $$= v^{T(xy)}, \quad T(xy) > m$$
   $$\mu = \delta = .05.$$

   If the 84th percentile of the distribution of Z is 0.3, find m.

   A) 10   B) 12   C) 14   D) 16   E) 20 $\ln 2$

8-39   Given $_{10}q^1_{30:20} - {_{10}}q^2_{30:20} = \frac{1}{5}$

   Assuming de Moivre's Law, find $\overset{\circ}{e}_{25:25}$.

   A) 15   B) $17\frac{1}{2}$ C) 20   D) $22\frac{1}{2}$ E) 25

8-40   Given: $\bar{a}_{15} = 17$ $\bar{a}_{15:\overline{25}|} = 15$
           $\bar{a}_{50} = 13$ $\bar{a}_{50:\overline{25}|} = 11$
           $\bar{a}_{15:50} = 12$ $\bar{a}_{15:50:\overline{25}|} = 8$

   Find the net single premium for a $1 continuous life annuity to a boy aged 15, with payments beginning when he reaches age 40 or at the death of his father, now aged 50, whichever occurs first.

   A) 3   B) 5   C) 7   D) 9   E) 11

8-41   Jones, aged 50, is subject to de Moivre's Law with $\omega = 90$. Smith, aged 80, is subject to a constant force of mortality of .5.

   Find the probability that Smith outlives Jones.

   A) 0   B) .01   C) .02   D) .04   E) .05

8-42   An annuity anticipates continuous payments according to the following conditions. Upon the death of (x), (y) will receive payments of $7 per annum for life. Upon the death of (y), (x) will receive payments of $8 per annum until the end of the fifth contract year and $4 per annum thereafter.

If both lives survive for five years, payments of $10 per annum begin at that time. When the first death occurs, the size of the payments decreases as indicated above. Find the net single premium, given:

$$\bar{a}_x = 15 \qquad \bar{a}_{x:\overline{5|}} = 4$$
$$\bar{a}_y = 12 \qquad \bar{a}_{y:\overline{5|}} = 3$$
$$\bar{a}_{xy} = 10 \qquad \bar{a}_{xy:\overline{5|}} = 2$$

A) 120   B) 121   C) 122   D) 123   E) 124

8-43   Find the probability that (30) will die in the fifteenth year following the year of death of (40).

Assume $s(x) = \frac{100-x}{100}$, $0 \le x \le 100$.

A) $\frac{9}{700}$ B) $\frac{11}{840}$ C) $\frac{23}{1680}$ D) $\frac{1}{70}$ E) $\frac{1}{60}$

8-44   If $\mu_x = A + Bc^x$ for all x, the status $y:y+5$ is equivalent to the status ww. If $\mu_x = B'c^x$ for all x, the status $y:y+5$ is equivalent to w'. If $c^5 = 2$, find $w' - w$.

A) 0   B) $\frac{1}{5}$ C) 1   D) 2   E) 5

8-45   Given: $_tq_{20} = .02t, \quad 0 \le t \le 1$

$_tq_{20:40} = .06t - .0008t^2, \quad 0 \le t \le 1$

Find $q^1_{20:40}$.

A) .0004   B) .0196   C) .0200   D) .0396   E) .0400

8-46   It is required to determine the probability that (20) will die during the five-year period following the death of (30).

Actuary A determines this probability using de Moivre's Law with $\omega = 100$. Actuary B determines it using a constant force of mortality.

If B's result is twice that of A, what constant force did B assume? Given: $ln\,2 = .69$, $ln\,3 = 1.1$.

A) .056   B) .060   C) .064   D) .068   E) .072

Answers to Chapter Eight Exercises

8–1	B.		8–17	D.		8–32	B.
8–2	C.		8–18	C.		8–33	C.
8–3	B.		8–19	C.		8–34	A.
8–4	A.		8–20	B.		8–35	A.
8–5	E.		8–21	D.		8–36	B.
8–6	C.		8–22	C.		8–37	D.
8–7	E.		8–23	C.		8–38	E.
8–8	C.		8–24	C.		8–39	A.
8–9	B.		8–25	E.		8–40	D.
8–10	C.		8–26	A.		8–41	E.
8–11	A.		8–27	B.		8–42	C.
8–12	B.		8–28	B.		8–43	B.
8–13	C.		8–29	D.		8–44	E.
8–14	D.		8–30	C.		8–45	B.
8–15	B.		8–31	B.		8–46	A.
8–16	A.						

Solutions

8–1.

Key Formulas:

$$\text{COV}[T(xy), T(\overline{xy})] = \frac{1}{4\mu^2}$$

$$\overset{\circ}{e}_{xy} = \frac{1}{2\mu}$$

Thus,

$$100 = \frac{1}{4\mu^2}$$

$$\therefore \mu = .05$$

and

$$K = \frac{1}{.10} = 10.$$

Then, since $v = e^{-\delta}$, we have

$$e^{-3\delta} = e^{-.05}$$

$$\therefore \delta = \frac{1}{60}$$

Finally, since $\bar{a}_{xy} = \frac{1}{2\mu+\delta}$, we have

$$\bar{a}_{55:65} = \frac{1}{\frac{1}{10} + \frac{1}{60}} = \frac{60}{7}$$

8-2.

Key Formula:

$$\bar{A}^{\,1}_{20:40} = \frac{1}{1+c^{20}}\,\bar{A}_{20:40} + A\left(1 - \frac{2}{1+c^{20}}\right)\bar{a}_{20:40}$$

Accordingly, we need c^{20}, $\bar{A}_{20:40}$, and $\bar{a}_{20:40}$. Solving the equations

$$.0098 = A + Bc^{20}$$
$$.0138 = A + Bc^{40}$$
$$.0338 = A + Bc^{60},$$

we obtain

$$A = .0088$$
$$B = .0002$$
$$c^{20} = 5$$

Since $c^{w} = \dfrac{c^{20} + c^{40}}{2}$ when $ww \equiv 20:40$, we obtain

$$c^{w} = 15.$$

Interpolating linearly in the given table, we obtain

$$\bar{a}_{20:40} = 9.00$$
$$\bar{A}_{20:40} = .64.$$

Finally,

$$\bar{A}^{\,1}_{20:40} = \frac{1}{6}(.64) + .0088\left(1 - \frac{2}{6}\right)9$$

$$= \underline{.15946\dot{}}$$

NOTE: Due to the form of the given values, it is not necessary to solve for w.

8-3.

    I. True from basic principles.

    II. False, because the right hand side requires *both* lives to survive n years.

    III. False (and, in fact, meaningless) because $_{n}p_{\overline{xy}}$ permits the case that one of (x) and (y) dies within n years, while $\bar{a}_{\overline{x+n:y+n}}$ requires *both* to be alive after n years.

    $\therefore$ <u>I only</u>

8–4.

    I.   The required probability is

$$(1 - {}_{n|}q_x)(1 - {}_{n|}q_y).$$

Thus, we have

$$(.95)(.92) = .874$$

and, accordingly, I is false.

    II. The required probability is

$${}_{n|}q_{\overline{xy}}.$$

However, rather than pursuing an algebraic approach, II is seen to be false because each of the two terms includes the case in which both (x) and (y) die in the $(n + 1)$ st year. Accordingly, there is duplication, as that case is counted twice.

A correct expression would be

$${}_{n+1}q_x \cdot {}_{n|}q_y + {}_{n+1}q_y \cdot {}_{n|}q_x - {}_np_{xy}q_{\overline{x+n:y+n}}$$

    III. The required probability is

$$({}_{n|}q_x)(1 - {}_{n|}q_y) + ({}_{n|}q_y)(1 - {}_{n|}q_x)$$

Thus, we have

$$(.05)(.92) + (.08)(.95) = .122$$

and, accordingly, III is false.

$$\therefore \underline{\text{None}}$$

8–5.

The net single premium is written most simply as

$$600a_x + 1000a_y + (K - 1600)a_{xy}.$$

Setting this equal to 36,750, we have

$$K = \underline{2900}.$$

A longer, but similar approach involves setting the net single premium equal to

$$Aa_x + Ba_y + Ca_{xy}$$

and using an undetermined coefficients technique. If (x) only is alive, the payment should be \$600. Similarly, if (y) only is alive, the payment should be \$1000 and, if both are alive, the payment should be K. This generates the simultaneous equations

$$A = 600$$
$$B = 1000$$
$$A + B + C = K$$

Since C is now seen to be $K - 1600$, the net single premium is

$$600a_x + 1000a_y + (K - 1600)a_{xy}$$

This technique of undetermined coefficients is often valuable for questions which are more complex than this one.

8–6.

Key Formula:
$$\mathrm{COV}[T(xx), T(\overline{xx})] = \frac{(\omega - x)^2}{36} \quad \text{(DML)}$$

Thus, $\omega - x = 36$.

Since $\mu_x = \dfrac{1}{\omega - x}$, we have $\mu_x = \dfrac{1}{\underline{\underline{36}}}$.

8–7.

This question may be solved by a diagrammatic enumeration of cases. The cases listed above the diagram are those included in "A," while those below the diagram are included in "B." The top case, for example, represents that in which (y) dies in the $(n + 1)$st year, and (x) dies *after* that year.

```
                              y          x
                              x          y
                             yx
                             xy
                      y      x
                      x      y
        ─────────────────────────────────
        0                    n      n + 1
                      x      y
                      y      x
                             xy
                             yx
```

Setting identical cases against each other, and subtracting B from A, we have

```
                              y              x
                              x              y
        ─────────────────────────────────────
        0                     n         n + 1
```

This pair of cases is represented by those in which the *first* death (but not both deaths) occurs in the $(n + 1)$ st year, or

$$\underline{\underline{{}_{n|}q_{xy} - {}_{n|}q_x\,{}_{n|}q_y.}}$$

Alternate Solution: Since

$$A = {}_{n|}q_x + {}_{n|}q_y - {}_{n|}q_x\,{}_{n|}q_y$$

and

$$B = {}_{n|}q_{\overline{xy}} = {}_{n|}q_x + {}_{n|}q_y - {}_{n|}q_{xy},$$

the result follows.

8–8.

Step One

$$\overline{A}_{xy}^{\,2} = \frac{1}{2}\overline{A}_{\overline{xy}} \qquad\qquad \therefore \text{IV} < \text{II}$$

Step Two

$$\overline{A}_{\overline{xy}} = \frac{2\mu}{2\mu + \delta} \cdot \frac{\mu}{\mu + \delta}$$

$$\overline{A}_{xy}^{\,1} = \frac{\mu}{2\mu + \delta}$$

But $\dfrac{2\mu}{\mu + \delta} < 1 \qquad\qquad \therefore \text{II} < \text{III}$

Step Three

$$\bar{a}_x - \bar{a}_{xx} = \frac{1}{\mu + \delta} - \frac{1}{2\mu + \delta}$$

$$= \frac{\mu}{(\mu + \delta)(2\mu + \delta)}$$

$$\overline{A}_{xy}^{\,1} = \frac{\mu}{2\mu + \delta}$$

But $\dfrac{1}{\mu + \delta} > 1 \qquad\qquad \therefore \text{III} < \text{V}$

Step Four

$$\overline{A}_{xy} = \frac{2\mu}{2\mu + \delta}$$

$$\bar{a}_x - \bar{a}_{xx} = \frac{\mu}{(\mu + \delta)(2\mu + \delta)}$$

But $2(\mu + \delta) > 1 \qquad\qquad \therefore \text{V} < \text{I}$

$$\therefore \underline{\text{IV} < \text{II} < \text{III} < \text{V} < \text{I}}$$

NOTE: Although several relationships here are obvious, such as $III > IV$, $I > II$, and $I > III$, the question depends in part upon the magnitudes of μ and δ and their relation to each other.

8–9.

The required event may be restated as "(20) dies more than five years after the death of (25)."

Accordingly, we have

$$_5p_{20} \, _\infty q^2_{25:25} = \frac{13}{28}$$

Since $_\infty q^2_{25:25} = \frac{1}{2}$,

$$_5p_{20} = \frac{13}{14} = \frac{\omega - 25}{\omega - 20}$$

$$\therefore \omega = \underline{\underline{90}}$$

8–10.

Key Concept:

De Moivre's law is assumed since the density of X is constant. Thus $\overset{\circ}{e}_{70} = 15\frac{1}{2}$, and $\omega = 101$.

$$\overset{\circ}{e}_{20} = \frac{81}{2}$$

$$\overset{\circ}{e}_{30} = \frac{71}{2}$$

$$\overset{\circ}{e}_{20:30} = {_{10}p_{20}}\,\overset{\circ}{e}_{30:30} + {_{10}q_{20}}\,\overset{\circ}{e}_{30} \qquad (DML)$$

$$= \frac{71}{81} \cdot \frac{71}{3} + \frac{10}{81} \cdot \frac{71}{2}$$

$$= \frac{12212}{486}$$

$$\therefore \overset{\circ}{e}_{\overline{20:30}} = \frac{81}{2} + \frac{71}{2} - \frac{6106}{243}$$

$$= 50.87$$

$$\doteq \underline{\underline{51}}$$

8–11.

NOTE: From the form of the answers, it is clear that we need only find the second moment of Q, where

$$Q = T(xy), \quad 0 \le T(xy) \le 20$$

$$= 20, \quad T(xy) > 20$$

$$\therefore E[Q^2] = \int_0^{20} t^2 \, _tp_{xy}\mu_{x+t:y+t} \, dt + 400 \cdot {_{20}p_{xy}}$$

Integrating by parts, we have

$$E[Q^2] = 2 \int_0^{20} t \, {}_t p_{xy} \, dt$$

$$= 2 \int_0^{20} te^{-.02t} \, dt$$

$$= 5000 - 7000e^{-.4}$$

Finally,

$$\mathrm{VAR}[Q] = \underline{\underline{5000 - 7000e^{-.4} - (\mathring{e}_{xy:\,\overline{20|}})^2}}$$

8–12.

Method One

$$
{}_n q^{1}_{50:60} = \int_0^n {}_t p_{50:60} \mu_{50+t} \, dt
$$

$$
= q_{50} \int_0^n (1 - t q_{60}) \, dt
$$

$$
= q_{50} \left[n - \frac{1}{2} n^2 q_{60} \right]
$$

$$
= \frac{1}{50} \left(n - \frac{1}{80} n^2 \right)
$$

Setting equal to $\frac{3}{10}$, and solving, we obtain

$$n = \underline{\underline{20}}.$$

Method Two

Key Identity:

$$
{}_\infty q^{1}_{50:60} = {}_n q^{1}_{50:60} + {}_n p_{50:60} \, {}_\infty q^{1}_{50+n:60+n}
$$

Using de Moivre relationships,

$$
{}_\infty q^{1}_{50:60} = \frac{2}{5}
$$

$$
{}_n p_{50:60} = \frac{(50 - n)(40 - n)}{(50)(40)}
$$

$$
{}_\infty q^{1}_{50+n:60+n} = \frac{20 - \frac{1}{2}n}{50 - n}
$$

Solving for n,

$$n = \underline{\underline{20}}.$$

Method Three

Under de Moivre's Law,

$$_nq_{50:60}^{\;1} = {}_nq_{50} \cdot {}_{n/2}p_{60} = {}_nq_{50}(1 - {}_{n/2}q_{60})$$
$$= \frac{n}{50}\left(1 - \frac{n}{80}\right) = \frac{3}{10}$$

Solving,

$$n = \underline{\underline{20}}.$$

8–13.

Key Concept: Since $\overset{\circ}{e}_{xy}$ is independent of x and y, the force of mortality must be constant. Specifically,

$$\mu = \frac{1}{2}.$$

Desired Probability:

$$1 - \left({}_{30}p_{20} \; {}_{\infty}q_{50:50}^{\;2} + {}_{30}p_{50} \; {}_{\infty}q_{80:20}^{\;2}\right)$$
$$= 1 - \left({}_{30}p_{20} + {}_{30}p_{50}\right)\frac{1}{2}$$
$$= 1 - {}_{30}p_{20}$$
$$= \underline{\underline{1 - e^{-15}}}$$

NOTE: With a high force of mortality, it is clear that the answer to this question must be numerically very large, i.e., close to 1. Thus, only choices C and D are realistic possibilities.

8–14.

Key Formula:

$$\text{COV}[T(xx), T(\overline{xx})] = \left(\overset{\circ}{e}_x - \overset{\circ}{e}_{xx}\right)^2$$

Key Fact: Since $\mu_x = \frac{2}{100-x}$, we know that $\overset{\circ}{e}_x = \frac{100-x}{3}$ and $\overset{\circ}{e}_{xx} = \frac{100-x}{5}$.

Thus, we have

$$\left(\frac{100-x}{3} - \frac{100-x}{5}\right)^2$$

Since $x = 40$,

$$\text{COV}[T(40:40), T(\overline{40:40})] = (20 - 12)^2 = \underline{\underline{64}}$$

8-15.

In order to find the desired probability, we need the expected value and variance of the present value random variable Z, where

$$Z = v^{T(\overline{xy})}, \quad T \geq 0$$

$$E[Z] = \overline{A}_{\overline{xy}} = \frac{2\mu}{2\mu + \delta} \cdot \frac{\mu}{\mu + \delta} = \frac{1}{15}$$

$$\text{VAR}[Z] = {}^2\overline{A}_{\overline{xy}} - (\overline{A}_{\overline{xy}})^2$$

$$= \frac{2\mu}{2\mu + 2\delta} \cdot \frac{\mu}{\mu + 2\delta} - \left(\frac{1}{15}\right)^2$$

$$= \frac{4}{225}$$

Now we want to determine

$$\Pr\left[\frac{1}{15} - \frac{2}{15} \leq Z \leq \frac{1}{15} + \frac{2}{15}\right], \text{ or}$$

$$\Pr\left[Z \leq \frac{1}{5}\right].$$

Let h be that time until death of the second of the two lives such that, if the second death occurs at duration h, the present value of the claim is $\frac{1}{5}$.

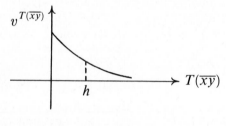

We must determine ${}_hp_{\overline{xy}} = 2e^{-.02h} - e^{-.04h}$. We know that $v^h = e^{-.08h} = \frac{1}{5}$.

Thus, ${}_hp_{\overline{xy}} = 2(\frac{1}{5})^{1/4} - (\frac{1}{5})^{1/2} = \frac{2 \cdot 5^{3/4} - 5^{1/2}}{5}$.

8-16.

Key Observation: Since $s(x) = e^{\frac{1 - \phi^x}{\ln\phi}}$, we have

$$\ln s(x) = \frac{1 - \phi^x}{\ln\phi} \text{ and}$$

$$-\frac{d}{dx}\ln s(x) = \mu_x = \phi^x.$$

Thus we are dealing with a Gompertz curve with $c = \phi$.

Key Formula:
$$_\infty q^1_{20:\overline{21}|} = \frac{1}{1+c} \qquad (GL)$$

$$\therefore \frac{1}{1+\phi} = \frac{1}{3}$$
$$\phi = \underline{\underline{2}}$$

8–17.

Key Formula:
$$VAR[T(\overline{xx})] = \frac{(\omega - x)^2}{18} \qquad (DML)$$

Thus $\dfrac{(\omega - 20)^2}{18} = 200$.

$$\therefore \omega = \underline{\underline{80}}$$

8–18.

The required probability is

$$_\infty q^2_{30:\overline{40}|} - {}_{20}p_{30}\,{}_\infty q^2_{50:\overline{40}|}$$

Since we are given de Moivre's Law with $\omega = 100$,

$$_\infty q^2_{30:\overline{40}|} = {}_{30}p_{30} = \frac{4}{7}$$
$$_\infty q^2_{50:\overline{40}|} = {}_{25}q_{40} = \frac{5}{12}$$
$$_{20}p_{30} = \frac{5}{7}$$

The final result, then, is

$$\frac{4}{7} - \frac{5}{7} \cdot \frac{5}{12} = \underline{\underline{\frac{23}{84}}}$$

8–19.

Key Observation: Since $s(x) = 2^{1-e^{2x}-x}$, we have

$$\ln s(x) = (1 - e^{2x} - x)\ln 2, \text{ and}$$
$$-\frac{d}{dx}\ln s(x) = \mu_x = (2e^{2x} + 1)\ln 2.$$

Thus, we are given Makeham's Law with $A = \ln 2$, $B = 2\ln 2$, and $c = e^2$.

Key Formula: If $x : x+2 \equiv x+t : x+t$,

$$1 + c^2 = 2c^t$$

$$\therefore t = \frac{\ln \dfrac{1+c^2}{2}}{\ln c}$$

Therefore,

$$t = \frac{\ln \dfrac{1+e^4}{2}}{2} \; ;$$

$$\therefore 2t = \ln\left(\frac{1+e^4}{2}\right)$$

8–20.

Key Formula: $${}_\infty q_{20:51}^{\;2} = {}_\infty q_{20:51}^{\;1} = \frac{1}{1+c^{31}} \qquad (GL)$$

Solving,

$$c^{31} = 2.5$$

From interest tables, we find

$$(1.03)^{31} = 2.5001$$

Thus, $c \doteq \underline{1.03}$.

NOTE: The answer is 1.029998932, correct to nine decimals.

8–21.

The expected value $E[R]$ is given by

$$E[R] = \bar{a}_{30:40:\,\overline{10|}} - {}_{10}p_{30:40}\,\bar{a}_{\overline{10|}}$$

Using the constant force assumption,

$$\bar{a}_{30:40:\,\overline{10|}} = \bar{a}_{30:40}(1 - {}_{10}E_{30:40})$$
$$= 10(1 - e^{-1})$$
$${}_{10}p_{30:40} = e^{-.6}$$

Since $\bar{a}_{\overline{10|}} = \dfrac{1 - e^{-.4}}{.04}$, we have

$$E[R] = 10(1 - e^{-1}) - 25e^{-.6}(1 - e^{-.4})$$
$$= \underline{\underline{10 - 25e^{-.6} + 15e^{-1}}}$$

8-22.

Key Formulas:

$$\overset{\circ}{e}_x = \frac{100 - x}{4}$$

$$\overset{\circ}{e}_{xx} = \frac{100 - x}{7}$$

$$\overset{\circ}{e}_{\overline{xx}} = 2\overset{\circ}{e}_x - \overset{\circ}{e}_{xx}$$

$$\therefore \overset{\circ}{e}_{\overline{65:65}} = 2\left(\frac{35}{4}\right) - \frac{35}{7} = 12\tfrac{1}{2}$$

8-23.

Since $\mu_x = \dfrac{1/2}{100 - x}$, we have

$$\overset{\circ}{e}_{xx} = \frac{100 - x}{1 + 1}.$$

Thus $\overset{\circ}{e}_{60:60} = \underline{\underline{20}}$.

8-24.

Key Concept:

Since the median of $T(xy)$ is independent of x and y, μ must be constant.

Accordingly,

$$_{17.325}p_{xy} = \frac{1}{2}$$

$$e^{-34.65\mu} = \frac{1}{2}$$

$$34.65\mu = ln\,2$$

$$\mu = .02$$

The desired probability is given by

$$_{10}p_{40}\ _{\infty}q^2_{50:30}$$

$$= e^{-.2}\left(\frac{1}{2}\right)$$

NOTE: Alternatively, to find the constant force, we could have recalled that the median of $T(xy)$ is $\dfrac{ln\,2}{\mu_{xy}}$.

Thus $17.325 = \dfrac{.693}{2\mu}$; $\mu = .02$.

8–25.

A helpful approach to a problem of this nature is to determine the present value of each recipient independently, and then to remove the present value of any resulting duplication of payments.

In this question, the present value of the payments to (30) is

$$_{10|}\bar{a}_{30} \cdot {}_5p_{15}$$

since (30) may receive no payments if (15) dies before age 20. Similarly, the present value of the payments to (15) is

$$_{25|}\bar{a}_{15}.$$

Since *both* of these quantities anticipate that payments will be made at any time in the future while both are alive beyond age 40, we must subtract

$$_{25|}\bar{a}_{15:30}.$$

The desired actuarial present value, therefore, is

$$\underline{{}_{10|}\bar{a}_{30}\,{}_5p_{15} + {}_{25|}\bar{a}_{15} - {}_{25|}\bar{a}_{15:30}}$$

NOTE: A less desirable, but somewhat informative, approach is to set up and evaluate the following:

$$\int_0^{15} v^{10+t} {}_{10+t}p_{30}\,{}_5p_{15}\,dt + \int_0^{\infty} v^{25+t}[{}_{25+t}p_{15} + {}_{25+t}p_{30}({}_5p_{15} - {}_{25+t}p_{15})]\,dt$$

8–26.

Key Fact:

The force of mortality follows Gompertz' Law, with $c = \frac{1}{4}$. Specifically,

$$\mu_x = \frac{1}{4}\left(\frac{1}{4}\right)^x$$

Key Formula:

$$_{\infty}q^1_{30:28} = \frac{c^2}{1 + c^2} \qquad (GL)$$

Thus, $_{\infty}q^1_{30:28} = \underline{\underline{\frac{1}{17}}}$.

NOTE: Even though c must be greater than 1 in Gompertz' Law in order for the force of mortality to satisfy definitional requirements, the fact that it is less than 1 in this question does not invalidate the solution.

8–27.

Key Concept: Z is the present value random variable whose expected value is

$$\overline{A}_{xy}^{2}.$$

The variance of Z, then, is

$$^{2}\overline{A}_{xy}^{2} - (\overline{A}_{xy}^{2})^{2}.$$

Using constant force relationships, we have

$$^{2}\overline{A}_{xy}^{2} = \frac{\mu}{2\mu + 2\delta} \cdot \frac{\mu}{\mu + 2\delta} = \frac{1}{12}$$

and

$$\overline{A}_{xy}^{2} = \frac{\mu}{2\mu + \delta} \cdot \frac{\mu}{\mu + \delta} = \frac{1}{6}$$

Finally, $\text{VAR}[Z] = \frac{1}{12} - (\frac{1}{6})^{2} = \underline{\frac{1}{18}}$.

8–28.

Let h be that duration until the first death, such that failure at that time generates a claim whose present value is 30% of the face amount.

Let j be that duration until the first death, such that failure at that time generates a claim whose present value is 20% of the face amount.

Referring to the following diagram, the desired probability is seen to be $_{h}p_{xy} - _{j}p_{xy}.$

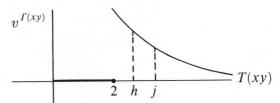

We know that

$$v^{h} = e^{-.1h} = .3$$

and

$$v^{j} = e^{-.1j} = .2.$$

Thus

$$_{h}p_{xy} = e^{-.5h} = (.3)^{5}$$

and

$$_{j}p_{xy} = e^{-.5j} = (.2)^{5},$$

giving a final answer of

$$_{h}p_{xy} - _{j}p_{xy} = (.3)^{5} - (.2)^{5} = \underline{.00211}.$$

8–29.

Key Recursion Formula:
$$A_{xy} = vq_{xy} + vp_{xy}A_{x+1:y+1}$$

Since $p_{30:40} = \frac{25}{30} \cdot \frac{16}{20} = \frac{2}{3}$, and $v = \frac{1}{2}$, we have
$$\frac{1}{3} = \frac{1}{2} \cdot \frac{1}{3} + \frac{1}{2} \cdot \frac{2}{3}A_{31:41}.$$
$$\therefore A_{31:41} = \underline{\underline{\frac{1}{2}}}.$$

8–30.

This question may be restated to indicate that there is a $1000 continuous perpetuity beginning now, along with annuities of $1000, $500, and $200, respectively, for the first three cases specified. Accordingly, one component of the answer is

$$1000\bar{a}_{\overline{\infty}|}, \text{ or } 50{,}000.$$

The remainder of the question may be written as
$$200(\bar{a}_x + \bar{a}_y + \bar{a}_z) + 100(\bar{a}_{xy} + \bar{a}_{xz} + \bar{a}_{yz}) + 100\bar{a}_{xyz},$$
which produces the value
$$200(30) + 100(20) + 100(5), \text{ or } 8500.$$
The total present value, then, is
$$\$50{,}000 + \$8{,}500 = \underline{\underline{\$58{,}500}}$$

NOTE: An alternative approach to this question, *after* the $1000 perpetuity has been stripped away, is that of undetermined coefficients. Using the form
$$A(\bar{a}_x + \bar{a}_y + \bar{a}_z) + B(\bar{a}_{xy} + \bar{a}_{xz} + \bar{a}_{yz}) + C\bar{a}_{xyz},$$
and the equations
$$3A + 3B + C = 1000$$
$$2A + B = 500$$
$$A = 200$$
we obtain $A = 200$, $B = 100$, $C = 100$, as before.

Although Chapter Eight limits multiple life problems to those involving only two lives, this question was included to illustrate important techniques.

8–31.

**Key Formula
(Makeham):**
$$_{\infty}q^1_{20:30} = \frac{1}{1+c^{10}} + A\left(1 - \frac{2}{1+c^{10}}\right)\overset{\circ}{e}_{20:30}$$

Since we have Makeham's Law with $c^5 = 3$, we solve, obtaining

$$.15 = \frac{1}{1+9} + A\left(1 - \frac{2}{1+9}\right)30$$

$$\therefore A = \underline{\underline{\frac{1}{480}}}$$

8–32.

The desired probability is given by

$$\int_0^{\frac{\omega-x}{3}} {}_tp_x\mu_{x+t} \cdot {}_{3t}p_x \, dt.$$

Applying de Moivre relationships, we have

$$q_x \int_0^{\frac{\omega-x}{3}} \left(1 - \frac{3t}{\omega-x}\right) dt$$

$$= q_x\left(\frac{\omega-x}{3}\right) - \frac{3}{(\omega-x)^2} \cdot \frac{(\omega-x)^2}{18}$$

$$= \frac{1}{3} - \frac{1}{6}$$

$$= \underline{\underline{\frac{1}{6}}}$$

NOTE: This question may be generalized, i.e., if we had wanted the probability that the woman will have a future lifetime at least n times as long as her twin sister, the answer would have been $\frac{1}{2n}$.

8–33.

This question may be symbolically stated as follows:

Pr[exactly one alive at duration t | both dead at $t = 1$]

$$= \frac{\text{Pr[one dies between now and time } t\text{; the other dies between time } t \text{ and year-end]}}{\text{Pr[both dead at } t = 1]}$$

$$= \frac{{}_tq_x({}_tp_y - p_y) + {}_tq_y({}_tp_x - p_x)}{q_xq_y}$$

Imposing the UDD assumption, we have

$$\frac{tq_x(1-t)q_y + tq_y(1-t)q_x}{q_xq_y}$$

$$= \underline{\underline{2t - 2t^2}}$$

8–34.

Key Formula: $.55 = {}_{10}p_{30} \cdot {}_{\infty}q^2_{40:40} + {}_{10}p_{40} \cdot {}_{\infty}q^2_{50:30}$

Then,

$$.55 = (.92)(\tfrac{1}{2}) + (.90) \, {}_\infty q^2_{50:30}$$

$${}_\infty q^2_{50:30} = \underline{.10}$$

8–35.

Key Concept: This force *appears* to follow Gompertz' Law. If so, then

$$\bar{A}^{\,1}_{20:30} = \frac{1}{1 + c^{10}} \bar{A}_{20:30} = \frac{1}{2} \bar{A}_{20:30}$$

implies that $c = 1$. Accordingly, μ_x is a constant; $\mu_x = .06$.

Key Formulas:

$$\bar{A}^{\,2}_{xy} = \frac{\mu}{2\mu + \delta} \cdot \frac{\mu}{\mu + \delta}$$

$$\bar{A}_{xy} = \frac{2\mu}{2\mu + \delta}$$

Thus

$$\bar{A}_{20:30} = \frac{.12}{.12 + \delta} = \frac{3}{4} \Rightarrow \delta = .04$$

Finally,

$$\bar{A}^{\,2}_{20:30} = \frac{.06}{.12 + .04} \cdot \frac{.06}{.06 + .04}$$

$$= \underline{.225}$$

8–36.

Key Formula: $$q^1_{40:y} = q_{40}\left(1 - \frac{1}{2}q_y\right) \qquad (UDD)$$

Thus,

$$.344 = (.4)\left(1 - \frac{1}{2} \cdot \frac{y}{100}\right)$$

$$y = \underline{28}$$

8–37.

A quite direct way to write the required probability is

$$_{10}p_{\overline{50:60}} - {}_{20}p_{\overline{50:60}}.$$

By realizing that $p = 1 - q$, we see that II is correct.

Another simple form of the required probability is

$$_{10|10}q_{\overline{50:60}},$$

and thus III is false.

It remains to determine if I is correct. Expanding $_{10|10}q_{\overline{50:60}}$, we have

$$_{10|10}q_{50} + {}_{10|10}q_{60} - {}_{10|10}q_{50:60}$$

This equals I only if $_{10|10}q_{50:60} = {}_{20}p_{50}\,{}_{20}q_{60}$

But

$$_{10|10}q_{50:60} = {}_{10}p_{50:60}\,{}_{10}q_{60:70}$$
$$= {}_{20}p_{50}(1 - {}_{10}p_{60:70})$$
$$= {}_{20}p_{50}(1 - {}_{20}p_{60})$$
$$= {}_{20}p_{50}\,{}_{20}q_{60}.$$

Thus I is correct.

$\therefore$ **All but III** .

8–38.

The definition of Z given here is that for the present value random variable for an m-year deferred joint whole life insurance to (xy) paid at the instant of the first death.

Let h be that time of failure of (xy) such that the present value of the associated claim will be exceeded 16% of the time, i.e.,

$$_{m}p_{xy} - {}_{h}p_{xy} = .16,$$

as is evident from the accompanying diagram:

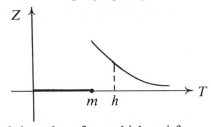

Thus we must find the value of m which satisfies

$$e^{-.1m} - e^{-.1h} = .16,$$

where $v^{h} = e^{-.05h} = .3$.

Finally,

$$e^{-.1m} - (.3)^{2} = .16$$
$$\therefore e^{-.1m} = .25$$
$$\therefore .1m = ln\,4 = 2ln\,2$$
$$\therefore m = \underline{20\,ln\,2}$$

8–39.

Key Identity: $_{10}q_{30:20}^{\;\;\;1} - {}_{10}q_{30:20}^{\;\;\;2} = {}_{10}q_{30}\,{}_{10}p_{20} = {}_{10}p_{20} - {}_{20}p_{20}$

Using de Moivre relationships, we have

$$\frac{1}{5} = \frac{10}{\omega - 20}.$$
$$\therefore \omega = 70$$

Finally,

$$\overset{\circ}{e}_{25:50} = \frac{45}{3} = \underline{\underline{15}}$$

8–40.

The net single premium for this benefit is represented by

$$\bar{a}_{15} - \bar{a}_{15:50:\,\overline{25}|}\,,$$

since (15) will receive payments for life except that, during the first 25 years, there will be no payments if (50) is alive.

Thus we have

$$17 - 8 = \underline{\underline{9}}$$

8–41.

The desired probability is given by

$$\int_0^{40} {}_t p_{50:80}\mu_{50+t}\,dt.$$

Applying the appropriate mortality laws, we have

$$\frac{1}{40}\int_0^{40} e^{-\frac{1}{2}t}\,dt$$
$$= \frac{1}{40}(2)(1 - e^{-20})$$
$$= \frac{1 - e^{-20}}{20}$$

Since e^{-20} is negligible, we have a final result which is essentially $\underline{\underline{.05}}$.

8–42.

This question is approached by undetermined coefficients and an analysis of cases. The net single premium is given by

$$A\bar{a}_x + B\bar{a}_y + C\bar{a}_{xy} + D\bar{a}_{x:\,\overline{5}|} + E\bar{a}_{y:\,\overline{5}|} + F\bar{a}_{xy:\,\overline{5}|}.$$

The following tabulation summarizes the approach:

Persons Alive	Duration	Stipulated Payment	Equation
x, y	< 5	0	$A + B + C + D + E + F = 0$
x	< 5	8	$A + D = 8$
y	< 5	7	$B + E = 7$
x, y	> 5	10	$A + B + C = 11$
x	> 5	4	$A = 4$
y	> 5	7	$B = 7$

Solving the system, we have

$$\begin{aligned} A &= 4 & D &= 4 \\ B &= 7 & E &= 0 \\ C &= -1 & F &= -14 \end{aligned}$$

Thus the net single premium is given by

$$4\bar{a}_x + 7\bar{a}_y - \bar{a}_{xy} + 4\bar{a}_{x:\overline{5|}} - 14\bar{a}_{xy:\overline{5|}}.$$

Evaluating, we have <u>122</u>.

8–43.

The desired probability is given by the following:

$$\int_0^{55} {}_t p_{40}\mu_{40+t}\left({}_{14+t}p_{30} - {}_{15+t}p_{30}\right) dt$$

Note that a key component is the determination of the upper limit of the integral.

Imposing de Moivre relationships, we have

$$\frac{1}{60}\int_0^{55}\frac{1}{70}\,dt$$
$$= \frac{1}{60}\cdot\frac{1}{70}\cdot 55$$
$$= \underline{\frac{11}{840}}$$

8–44.

Key Relationships:

$$c^y + c^{y+5} = 2c^w$$
$$c^y + c^{y+5} = c^{w'}$$

Thus, $\qquad 2c^w = c^{w'}$

$$\therefore \ln 2 + w\ln c = w'\ln c$$
$$\therefore w' - w = \frac{\ln 2}{\ln c}.$$

Since $c^5 = 2$,

$$5 \ln c = \ln 2,$$

and

$$w' - w = \underline{\underline{5}}.$$

8–45.

Key Formula:
$$_t q_{20:40} = {_t q_{20}} + {_t q_{40}} - {_t q_{20}} \, {_t q_{40}}$$

Therefore,

$$.06t - .0008t^2 = .02t + {_t q_{40}}(1 - .02t)$$

$$\therefore {_t q_{40}} = \frac{.04t - .0008t^2}{1 - .02t}$$

$$= .04t.$$

Thus, we are told that the UDD assumption is given for both lives. Accordingly,

$$q_{20:40}^1 = q_{20}\left(1 - \frac{1}{2}q_{40}\right)$$

$$= (.02)\left(1 - \frac{1}{2}(.04)\right)$$

$$= \underline{.0196}$$

8–46.

The desired probability is

$$_\infty q_{20:30}^2 - {_5 p_{20}} \, {_\infty q_{25:30}^2}$$

Actuary A's determination produces

$$_{35}p_{20} - {_5 p_{20}} \, {_{35}p_{25}}$$

$$= \frac{45}{80} - \frac{40}{80}$$

$$= \frac{1}{16},$$

while Actuary B's produces

$$\frac{1}{2} \, {_5 q_{20}}$$

$$= \frac{1}{2}(1 - e^{-5\mu}).$$

Finally,

$$\frac{1}{2}(1 - e^{-5\mu}) = \frac{1}{8}$$

$$1 - e^{-5\mu} = \frac{1}{4}$$

$$e^{-5\mu} = \frac{3}{4}$$

$$5\mu = ln\,4 - ln\,3 = .28$$

$$\therefore \mu = \underline{.056}$$

Chapter Nine

Supplementary Concepts

1. As this is largely a notational chapter, we begin with sets of equivalences which indicate relationships between "statistical" and "actuarial" expressions.

    a) $f(t, j) = {}_t p_x^{(T)} \mu_{x+t}^{(j)}$

    b) $\int_0^t f(s, j)\, ds = {}_t q_x^{(j)}$

    c) $\int_0^\infty f(s, j)\, ds = h(j) = {}_\infty q_x^{(j)}$

    d) $\sum_{j=1}^m f(t, j) = g(t) = {}_t p_x^{(T)} \mu_{x+t}^{(T)}$

    e) $h(j \mid T = t) = \dfrac{\mu_{x+t}^{(j)}}{\mu_{x+t}^{(T)}}$

2. The following development is useful in gaining an understanding of the often elusive relationship between probabilities of decrement and absolute rates of decrement. The first expression in this development may be interpreted as follows: of $l_x^{(T)}$ lives, the number expected to succumb to cause 1 before age $x + 1$ (if decrements attributable to cause 2 are eliminated in the double-decrement model) is the theoretical sum of two quantities:

    a) those who would have succumbed to cause 1 if both causes were operable, and

    b) those who would have succumbed to decrement 2 if it had been operable but who, since decrement 2 is *not* operable, subsequently succumb to decrement 1 before year end.

    Accordingly, we have

    $$l_x^{(T)} q_x^{\prime(1)} = d_x^{(1)} + \int_0^1 l_{x+t}^{(T)} \mu_{x+t}^{(2)} {}_{1-t} q_{x+t}^{\prime(1)} \, dt$$

    $$\doteq d_x^{(1)} + d_x^{(2)} q_x^{\prime(1)} \int_0^1 (1 - t)\, dt$$

    $$\doteq d_x^{(1)} + \frac{1}{2} d_x^{(2)} q_x^{\prime(1)}$$

    $$\therefore q_x^{\prime(1)} \doteq \frac{d_x^{(1)}}{l_x^{(T)} - \frac{1}{2} d_x^{(2)}} = \frac{q_x^{(1)}}{1 - \frac{1}{2} q_x^{(2)}}$$

    With the introduction of the symbol

    $$q_x^{(-j)} = 1 - q_x^{(j)},$$

this formula may be generalized to

$$q_x'^{(j)} \doteq \frac{q_x^{(j)}}{1 - \frac{1}{2}q_x^{(-j)}}.$$

Although these formulas are not considered to be "standard approximations" in *Actuarial Mathematics*, the fact remains that they are widely used in practice. Even more importantly, the approximation

$$q_x'^{(1)} \doteq \frac{d_x^{(1)}}{l_x^{(T)} - \frac{1}{2}d_x^{(2)}}$$

reflects the interpretation that the aggregate exposure in the calculation of an absolute rate of decrement is the total number of lives in the double-decrement table at the beginning of the year of age, reduced by one-half year (the second half) for those who succumb to cause 2 before year end.

Note that this reduction of one-half year may be modified if the stated assumptions so indicate. For example, if the assumption is that decrements due to cause 2 occur at the end of three-fourths of the year of age, we would have

$$q_x'^{(1)} \doteq \frac{q_x^{(1)}}{1 - \frac{1}{4}q_x^{(2)}}$$

3.   In a similar manner, interpretation of the central rate $m_x^{(j)}$ is possible. Consider the following excerpt from a triple-decrement table:

x	$l_x^{(T)}$	$d_x^{(1)}$	$d_x^{(2)}$	$d_x^{(3)}$
30	1000	10	20	40
31	930			

$$q_{30}^{(1)} = \frac{10}{1000} \text{ (exactly)}$$

$$q_{30}'^{(1)} \doteq \frac{10}{1000 - \frac{1}{2}(20) - \frac{1}{2}(40)} \text{ (from Paragraph 2 above)}$$

$$m_{30}^{(1)} \doteq \frac{10}{1000 - \frac{1}{2}(10) - \frac{1}{2}(20) - \frac{1}{2}(40)} = \frac{10}{\frac{1}{2}(1000) + \frac{1}{2}(930)}$$

This format aids substantially in reaching the conclusion that $m_x^{(j)} \geq q_x'^{(j)} \geq q_x^{(j)}$. Note that the denominator of the central rate includes a deduction of one-half year for the decrement being measured, as well as for the competing decrements. As before, the one-half unit subtractions may be modified if the assumptions warrant.

It must again be emphasized that these expressions for absolute and central rates would not be categorized as "standard" in *Actuarial Mathematics*.

4. Note the following relationships between individual decrements and the "total" decrement:

$$\sum_{j=1}^{m} \mu_x^{(j)} = \mu_x^{(T)}$$

$$\sum_{j=1}^{m} q_x^{(j)} = q_x^{(T)}$$

$$\sum_{j=1}^{m} m_x^{(j)} = m_x^{(T)}$$

$$\sum_{j=1}^{m} q_x'^{(j)} \text{ and } \sum_{j=1}^{m} m_x'^{(j)} \text{ are both meaningless.}$$

5. Most of the working formulas involving probabilities, absolute rates, and central rates are based upon simplifying assumptions and are therefore approximations. A major exception is the *exact* formula

$$p_x^{(T)} = p_x'^{(1)} p_x'^{(2)} \cdots p_x'^{(m)}$$

and its offshoots

$$q_x^{(T)} = q_x'^{(1)} + q_x'^{(2)} - q_x'^{(1)} q_x'^{(2)} \text{ (double decrement)},$$

$$q_x^{(T)} = q_x'^{(1)} + q_x'^{(2)} + q_x'^{(3)} - q_x'^{(1)} q_x'^{(2)} - q_x'^{(1)} q_x'^{(3)} - q_x'^{(2)} q_x'^{(3)}$$
$$+ q_x'^{(1)} q_x'^{(2)} q_x'^{(3)} \text{ (triple decrement)},$$

and so on.

6. If forces of decrement are given, and the desired quantity is an absolute rate, then all of the forces other than that for the desired decrement should be ignored.

For example, suppose

$$\mu_{x+t}^{(1)} = .01, \ t \geq 0$$

$$\mu_{x+t}^{(2)} = \frac{1}{100 - x - t}, \ 0 \leq t < 100 - x.$$

Then $p_x'^{(1)} = e^{-.01}$, and $p_x'^{(2)} = \dfrac{99 - x}{100 - x}$ are both easily found by appealing to single-decrement theory. However, determinations of $q_x^{(1)}$ and $q_x^{(2)}$ each require consideration of both forces. Accordingly,

$$q_x^{(1)} = \int_0^1 {}_t p_x^{(T)} \mu_{x+t}^{(1)} \, dt$$

$$= \int_0^1 e^{-.01t} \frac{100 - x - t}{100 - x} (.01) \, dt$$

$$= 1 - \frac{99 - x}{100 - x} e^{-.01} - \frac{100}{100 - x} (1 - e^{-.01})$$

and

$$q_x^{(2)} = \int_0^1 {}_t p_x^{(T)} \mu_{x+t}^{(2)} dt$$

$$= \frac{1}{100 - x} \int_0^1 e^{-.01t} dt$$

$$= \frac{100}{100 - x}(1 - e^{-.01})$$

Note that $q_x^{(2)}$ is much easier to find than $q_x^{(1)}$ because of the fact that decrement 2 is uniformly distributed in its single-decrement table.

7.   The development of a double-decrement table, based upon two familiar forces of decrement, serves to illustrate many of the concepts of multiple decrement theory.

Let $\mu_x^{(1)} = 1$ for all $x \geq 0$

$$\mu_x^{(2)} = \frac{1}{90 - x}, \ 0 \leq x < 90$$

$$l_{87}^{(T)} = 1000$$

Some of the key results are as follows (all numbers of lives are rounded to the nearest integer):

$$p_{87}^{(T)} = e^{-1} \cdot \frac{2}{3}; \ p_{88}^{(T)} = e^{-1} \cdot \frac{1}{2}; \ p_{89}^{(T)} = e^{-1} \cdot 0 = 0$$

$$l_{88}^{(T)} = 245; \ l_{89}^{(T)} = 45; \ l_{90}^{(T)} = 0$$

$$q_{87}^{(1)} = \int_0^1 e^{-t} \frac{3 - t}{3} dt = \frac{2 - e^{-1}}{3} \doteq .544$$

$$q_{88}^{(1)} = \int_0^1 e^{-t} \frac{2 - t}{2} dt = \frac{1}{2} = .500$$

$$q_{89}^{(1)} = \int_0^1 e^{-t} \frac{1 - t}{1} dt = e^{-1} \doteq .368$$

$$q_{87}^{(2)} = \int_0^1 e^{-t} \frac{3 - t}{3} \cdot \frac{1}{3 - t} dt = \frac{1}{3}(1 - e^{-1}) \doteq .211$$

$$q_{88}^{(2)} = \int_0^1 e^{-t} \frac{2 - t}{2} \cdot \frac{1}{2 - t} dt = \frac{1}{2}(1 - e^{-1}) \doteq .316$$

$$q_{89}^{(2)} = \int_0^1 e^{-t} \frac{1 - t}{1} \cdot \frac{1}{1 - t} dt = 1 - e^{-1} \doteq .632$$

Depicting the results in tabular form, we have

x	$l_x^{(T)}$	$d_x^{(1)}$	$d_x^{(2)}$
87	1000	544	211
88	245	123	77
89	45	17	28
90	0		

Note that more decrements occur due to cause 1 than to cause 2 at tabular ages 87 and 88, but that the opposite occurs at tabular age 89. This is because the force of decrement for cause 2 first exceeds that for cause 1 at *exact* age 89. Thus, for all subsequent years of age, more decrements are expected due to cause 2.

8.   An especially interesting and informative application of multiple decrement theory is illustrated by problems in which the distribution of the decrements (in their associated single-decrement tables) is hypothesized. Often, these hypotheses include distributions which are continuous as well as those which are discrete.

Example

Assume that decrements 1 and 2 are uniformly distributed in their associated single-decrement tables. Assume that, in its associated single-decrement table, two-thirds of decrement 3 occurs after the first four months of the year of age and the remainder occurs nine months after the beginning of the year of age. It is desired to find each of the probabilities $q_x^{(1)}$, $q_x^{(2)}$, and $q_x^{(3)}$.

Use of the following diagram is helpful:

$$
\begin{array}{ccccc}
& \frac{2}{3}\text{ of \#3} & & \frac{1}{3}\text{ of \#3} & \\
& \downarrow & & \downarrow & \\
\hline
x & x+\frac{1}{3} & & x+\frac{3}{4} & x+1
\end{array}
$$

Let us first consider $q_x^{(3)}$. This simply involves an analysis of the situation at the two specific ages at which that decrement can occur. Since both competing decrements are uniformly distributed, one-third of each will have occurred at age $x + 1/3$ and three-fourths of each will have occurred at age $x + 3/4$.

Accordingly,

$$
\begin{aligned}
q_x^{(3)} = {} & \frac{2}{3}q_x'^{(3)}\left(1 - \frac{1}{3}q_x'^{(1)}\right)\left(1 - \frac{1}{3}q_x'^{(2)}\right) \\
& + \frac{1}{3}q_x'^{(3)}\left(1 - \frac{3}{4}q_x'^{(1)}\right)\left(1 - \frac{3}{4}q_x'^{(2)}\right).
\end{aligned}
$$

Determination of probabilities for the continuously-operating decrements involves a different approach. The three subintervals of the year of age must be considered separately. Specifically, the *midpoints* of those subintervals are of primary importance due to the assumptions of *uniform* distribution. At age $x + \frac{13}{24}$, for example, $\frac{13}{24}$ of decrements 1 and 2 will have occurred while two-thirds of decrement three will have occurred.

Therefore,

$$
\begin{aligned}
q_x^{(1)} = {} & \frac{1}{3}q_x'^{(1)}\left(1 - \frac{1}{6}q_x'^{(2)}\right) \\
& + \frac{5}{12}q_x'^{(1)}\left(1 - \frac{13}{24}q_x'^{(2)}\right)\left(1 - \frac{2}{3}q_x'^{(3)}\right) \\
& + \frac{1}{4}q_x'^{(1)}\left(1 - \frac{7}{8}q_x'^{(2)}\right)(1 - q_x'^{(3)}).
\end{aligned}
$$

Clearly, $q_x^{(2)}$ is found by exactly the same analysis.

It is important to recognize that questions of this type should be solved without integration wherever possible. Integration, however, is required in any instance in which at least three decrements are competing *continuously* with each other.

Special Decrement Laws

I. Uniform Distribution of Decrements in the Multiple Decrement Tables

$$_tq_x^{(j)} = t \cdot q_x^{(j)}, \; 0 \le t \le 1, \; j = 1, 2, \ldots, m$$

$$q_x^{(j)} = \mu_x^{(j)}; \; q_x^{(T)} = \mu_x^{(T)}$$

$$p_x'^{(j)} = (p_x^{(T)})^{\frac{q^{(j)}}{q_x^{(T)}}}$$

$$\mu_{x+t}^{(j)} = \frac{q_x^{(j)}}{1 - tq_x^{(T)}}; \; \mu_{x+t}^{(T)} = \frac{q_x^{(T)}}{1 - tq_x^{(T)}}$$

$$m_x^{(j)} = \frac{q_x^{(j)}}{1 - \frac{1}{2}q_x^{(T)}}; \; m_x^{(T)} = \frac{q_x^{(T)}}{1 - \frac{1}{2}q_x^{(T)}}$$

$$q_x^{(j)} = \frac{m_x^{(j)}}{1 + \frac{1}{2}m_x^{(T)}}; \; q_x^{(T)} = \frac{m_x^{(T)}}{1 + \frac{1}{2}m_x^{(T)}}$$

II. Constant Forces of Decrement

$$\mu_{x+t}^{(j)} = \mu_x^{(j)}, \; 0 \le t \le 1$$

$$\frac{q_x^{(j)}}{q_x^{(T)}} = \frac{\mu_x^{(j)}}{\mu_x^{(T)}} = h(j)$$

$$p_x'^{(j)} = (p_x^{(T)})^{\frac{q_x^{(j)}}{q_x^{(T)}}}$$

$$m_x^{(j)} = m_x'^{(j)} = \mu_x^{(j)}$$

T and J are independent random variables.

III. Uniform Distribution of Decrements in the Associated Single-Decrement Tables

Two decrements:

$$_tq_x'^{(j)} = t \cdot q_x'^{(j)}, \; 0 \le t \le 1, \; j = 1, 2, \ldots, m$$

$$q_x^{(1)} = q_x'^{(1)} \left(1 - \tfrac{1}{2}q_x'^{(2)}\right)$$

Three decrements:

$$q_x^{(1)} = q_x'^{(1)} \left(1 - \tfrac{1}{2}q_x'^{(2)} - \tfrac{1}{2}q_x'^{(3)} + \tfrac{1}{3}q_x'^{(2)} q_x'^{(3)}\right)$$

Derivatives

$$\frac{\partial}{\partial t} {}_t q_x^{(j)} = {}_t p_x^{(T)} \mu_{x+t}^{(j)}$$

$$\frac{\partial}{\partial t} {}_t q_x^{(T)} = {}_t p_x^{(T)} \mu_{x+t}^{(T)}$$

$$\frac{d}{dx} l_x^{(T)} = -l_x^{(T)} \mu_x^{(T)}$$

$$\frac{d}{dx} l_x^{(j)} = -l_x^{(T)} \mu_x^{(j)}$$

$$\frac{d}{dx} l_x'^{(j)} = -l_x'^{(j)} \mu_x^{(j)}$$

$$\frac{\partial}{\partial x} {}_t p_x'^{(j)} = -{}_t p_x'^{(j)} \mu_{x+t}^{(j)}$$

$$\frac{\partial}{\partial x} {}_t q_x^{(j)} = {}_t p_x^{(T)} \mu_{x+t}^{(j)} + {}_t q_x^{(j)} \mu_x^{(T)} - \mu_x^{(j)}$$

$$\frac{\partial}{\partial x} {}_t q_x^{(T)} = {}_t p_x^{(T)} \mu_{x+t}^{(T)} - {}_t p_x^{(T)} \mu_x^{(T)}$$

Exercises

9-1 Given that the forces of decrement are constant over the year of age, and

$$q_x^{(1)} = q_x^{(2)} = \frac{12}{49},$$

find $q_x'^{(1)}$ for the associated single decrement table. Assume only two decrements.

A) $\frac{2}{7}$ B) $\frac{2\sqrt{6}}{7}$ C) $\frac{5}{7}$ D) $\frac{2\sqrt{2}}{7}$ E) $\frac{12}{43}$

9-2 Given: $\mu_{x+s}^{(1)} = \frac{s}{100}$, $s \geq 0$

$\mu_{x+s}^{(2)} = \frac{1}{20}$, $s \geq 0$

${}_k p_x^{(T)} = e^{-3}$ for some k; there are only two decrements.

Find $\mu_{x+k}^{(1)}$.

A) $\frac{1}{5}$ B) $\frac{1}{10}$ C) $\frac{1}{15}$ D) $\frac{1}{20}$ E) $\frac{3}{20}$

9-3   The force of decrement is constant for each of m causes of decrement.
Which of the following is/are true?

$\quad$ I: $E[T \mid J = j] = E[T]$
$\quad$ II: $E[J \mid T = t] = E[J]$
$\quad$ III: $f(t, j) = g(t)h(j)$

A) All $\qquad$ B) I, II only $\qquad$ C) I, III only $\qquad$ D) II, III only $\qquad$ E) Fewer than two
$\qquad\qquad\qquad\qquad\qquad\qquad\qquad\qquad\qquad\qquad\qquad\qquad\qquad\qquad\qquad$ are correct

9-4   Given: $\mu_{x+t}^{(j)} = \dfrac{j}{150}$, $j = 1, 2, 3$

Find $E(T \mid J = 3)$.

A) 3 $\qquad$ B) $12\frac{1}{2}$ $\qquad$ C) 25 $\qquad$ D) $37\frac{1}{2}$ $\qquad$ E) 50

9-5   Three decrements are under study. In the associated single decrement models, decrements due to cause 1 are uniformly distributed in each year of age, decrements due to cause 2 occur only at mid-year, and decrements due to cause 3 occur only at the end of each year of age.

Find $q_x^{(1)}$.

A) $q_x'^{(1)}(1 - q_x'^{(2)})$ $\qquad\qquad\qquad$ B) $q_x'^{(1)}(1 - \frac{1}{2}q_x'^{(2)})(1 - \frac{1}{2}q_x'^{(3)})$

C) $\frac{1}{2}q_x'^{(1)}[2 - \frac{1}{2}q_x'^{(2)}]$ $\qquad\qquad\quad$ D) $\frac{1}{2}q_x'^{(1)}[2 - q_x'^{(2)}]$

E) $q_x'^{(1)}(1 - \frac{1}{4}q_x'^{(2)})$

9-6   Given: $l_x'^{(j)} = (100 - x)^{j+1}$, $j = 1, 2$, $0 \le x \le 100$.

Evaluate ${}_{40}q_{20}^{(T)}$.

A) $\frac{7}{8}$ $\qquad$ B) $\frac{15}{16}$ $\qquad$ C) $\frac{31}{32}$ $\qquad$ D) $\frac{63}{64}$ $\qquad$ E) $\frac{127}{128}$

9-7   Assuming that $q_x^{(j)} = \frac{3}{4}m_x^{(j)}$ for all j, and that the total decrement is uniformly distributed within the multiple decrement model, determine the value of $m_x^{(T)} - q_x^{(T)}$.

A) $\frac{1}{3}$ $\qquad$ B) $\frac{1}{4}$ $\qquad$ C) $\frac{1}{5}$ $\qquad$ D) $\frac{1}{6}$ $\qquad$ E) Cannot be
$\qquad\qquad\qquad\qquad\qquad\qquad\qquad\qquad\qquad\qquad\qquad\qquad\qquad\qquad\qquad$ determined

9–8   Given: $\mu_x^{(k)} = \dfrac{1}{3k(180-x)}$, $k = 1, 2$

Find the probability that, in a double decrement model, (20) will succumb to neither decrement prior to age 90.

A) $\frac{7}{32}$ B) $\frac{9}{32}$ C) $\frac{9}{16}$ D) $\frac{\sqrt{7}}{4}$ E) $\frac{3}{4}$

9–9   Given: $\mu_{x+t}^{(1)} = \dfrac{1}{90-x-t}$, $t \le 90 - x$

            $\mu_{x+t}^{(2)} = \frac{1}{2}$, $t \ge 0$

Find the complete double decrement table expectation of (87).

A) $\frac{1}{2}$ B) $\frac{4e^{-3/2}}{3}$ C) $\frac{4e^{-3/2}+2}{3}$ D) $\frac{3}{2}$ E) 2

9–10   Given: $q_x'^{(2)} = \frac{1}{9}$, $m_x^{(T)} = \frac{3}{7}$

If there are only two decrements, each of which is uniformly distributed in its associated single decrement table, find $p_x'^{(1)}$.

A) $\frac{3}{52}$ B) $\frac{75}{116}$ C) $\frac{100}{137}$ D) $\frac{50}{87}$ E) $\frac{225}{274}$

9–11   In associated single decrement tables 1, 2, and 3, decrements are uniformly distributed over the year of age from 64 to 65. However, all lives attaining age 65 in table 3 are immediately removed due to decrement 3. Of 100,000 lives at age 64 subject to the related triple decrement table, how many are ultimately removed due to decrement 3?

Given: $q_{64}'^{(1)} = .06$; $q_{64}'^{(2)} = .10$; $_tq_{64}'^{(3)} = .3t$, $0 \le t < 1$.

A) 27,660   B) 84,600   C) 85,000   D) 86,880   E) 88,626

9–12   Consider five absolute rates of decrement $q_x'^{(j)}$, $j = 1, 2, 3, 4, 5$. In the single decrement tables, decrements 1, 2, 3, and 4 are equal to each other and are uniformly distributed over the year of age, while decrement 5 can only occur at the end of the year of age. If it is known that

$$\left(\lim_{t\to 1^-} {}_tp_x^{(T)} \right) - \left(\lim_{t\to 1^+} {}_tp_x^{(T)} \right) = .05$$

and

$$\frac{\lim_{t\to 1^+} {}_tp_x^{(T)}}{\lim_{t\to 1^-} {}_tp_x^{(T)}} = .20,$$

find $p_x'^{(1)}$.

A) $\frac{1}{6}$ B) $\frac{1}{5}$ C) $\frac{1}{4}$ D) $\frac{1}{3}$ E) $\frac{1}{2}$

9–13   Decrement 1 is uniformly distributed in each year of age in its associated single decrement table, while decrement 2 occurs in equal proportions at the mid-year and the year-end of age in its associated single decrement table; $q_x^{\prime(2)} = .04$. There are only two decrements.

If $l_x^{(T)} = 10,000$ and $d_x^{(T)} = 592$, find $d_x^{(1)}$.

A) 198   B) 200   C) 202   D) 204   E) 206

9–14   Given: $\mu_x^{(T)} = \dfrac{1}{100 - x}$, $0 \le x < 100$
$\mu_x^{(1)} = .01$, $0 \le x$
$l_x^{(T)} = l_x^{(1)} + l_x^{(2)}$, $0 \le x$

Find $h(2 \mid T = 20)$ for a person now aged 40.

A) .2   B) .4   C) .5   D) .6   E) .8

9–15   An insurance policy to (30) is scheduled to pay $4 upon death if death is accidental and occurs within 25 years. Further, an additional $1 is paid regardless of cause of death and regardless of when death occurs. The force of accidental death at all ages is .01, and the force of death for all other causes at all ages is .05. Find the net single premium if $\delta = .10$.

A) $\dfrac{4e^4 - 1}{8e^4}$ B) $\dfrac{5e^4 - 2}{8e^4}$ C) $\dfrac{9e^4 - 4}{16e^4}$ D) $\dfrac{10e^4 - 5}{16e^4}$ E) None of the above

9–16   If $\dfrac{\mu_{x+t}^{(1)}}{\mu_{x+t}^{(T)}} = \dfrac{1}{10}$, $t \ge 0$, find $E[T \mid J = 1]$.

A) .1   B) 1   C) 10   D) 100   E) Cannot be determined

9–17   Given the following forces of decrement: $\mu_{x+t}^{(1)} = 1$, $t > 0$
$\mu_{x+t}^{(2)} = \dfrac{t}{20 - t}$, $0 \le t < 20$
$\mu_{x+t}^{(3)} = \dfrac{1}{20 - t}$, $0 \le t < 20$

Find $E[T]$ in the resulting triple decrement table.

A) $\dfrac{10}{7}$ B) $\dfrac{5}{4}$ C) $\dfrac{10}{9}$ D) 1   E) $\dfrac{10}{11}$

9–18   Consider a double decrement table. If $h(1) = h(2)$ and $g(t) = \frac{1}{60}$, $0 \le t \le 60$, find $E[T|J = 2]$.

    A) 10   B) 20   C) 30   D) 40   E) Cannot be determined

9–19   It is known that decrement 1 is uniformly distributed over each year of age in its associated single decrement table; $q_x'^{(1)} = .10$. In its associated single decrement table, decrement 2 occurs only at the end of the first three months and at the end of the first ten months of the year of age, with equal proportions occurring at each of these points; $q_x'^{(2)} = .12$.

If $l_x^{(T)} = 1000$, find the number of decrements in the double decrement table, as a result of decrement 2, in the second half of the year of age from x to $x+1$.

    A) 48   B) 50   C) 52   D) 55   E) 58

9–20   Given: $q_x^{(T)} = .60$, $_rp_x'^{(1)} = .80$, $q_x^{(1)} = .30$.

There are only two decrements, each of which is uniformly distributed over each year of age in the double decrement table.

Find r.

    A) $\frac{1}{3}$ B) $\frac{2}{5}$ C) $\frac{1}{2}$ D) $\frac{3}{5}$ E) $\frac{2}{3}$

9–21   Given: $\mu_x^{(1)} = 10\,ln(2x + 4) - .2x$, $0 \le x \le 80$

Which of the following is/are true?
    I. $m_{45}^{(1)} > m_{45}'^{(1)}$
    II. $m_{48}^{(1)} > m_{48}'^{(1)}$
    III. $m_{50}^{(1)} > m_{50}'^{(1)}$

    A) All   B) I, III   C) II, III   D) I, II   E) III only

9–22   The forces of decrement $\mu_x^{(1)}$ and $\mu_x^{(2)}$ are each constant for all x. Given the following table, evaluate $\dfrac{\mu_{61}^{(T)}}{\mu_{61}^{(2)}}$.

x	$l_x^{(T)}$	$d_x^{(1)}$	$d_x^{(2)}$
60	100,000	63,348	31,674
61	4,978	3,153	1,577
62	248		

    A) 1.5   B) 2.0   C) 2.5   D) 3.0   E) 3.5

9-23   The absolute rates $q_x'^{(1)}$ and $q_x'^{(2)}$ are each equal to $\frac{1}{2}$; each of these decrements is uniformly distributed in its single decrement table. In its associated single-decrement table, decrement 3 occurs in equal proportions at ages $x + \frac{1}{3}$, $x + \frac{2}{3}$, and $x + 1$; $q_x'^{(3)} = .9$.

Of 240 persons aged x in the corresponding triple-decrement table, how many are expected to succumb to decrement 3 prior to age $x + 1$?

A) 67   B) 86   C) 98   D) 100   E) 108

9-24   A table in n decrements shows that $q_x'^{(1)} = \frac{2}{5}$ and $q_x^{(T)} = \frac{16}{25}$. If the decrements are uniformly distributed in the multiple-decrement table, find $m_x^{(1)}$.

A) $\frac{7}{17}$ B) $\frac{8}{17}$ C) $\frac{1}{2}$ D) $\frac{9}{17}$ E) $\frac{10}{17}$

9-25   Deaths and withdrawals are each uniformly distributed in their single-decrement tables; $q_{65}'^{(d)} = .10$ and $q_{65}'^{(w)} = .09$. Find the error in the number of retirements between ages 65 and 66 in the appropriate triple-decrement table if retirements are assumed to occur uniformly when, in fact, all occur at midyear. It is known that $l_{65}^{(T)} = 1,000,000$ and $l_{66}^{(T)} = 573,300$.

A) 200   B) 225   C) 250   D) 275   E) 300

9-26   Given: $\,_t p_{20}'^{(j)} = e^{-\frac{tj}{2}}$, $0 \le t \le 1$, $j = 1, 2, 3, 4$

Find $q_{20}^{(2)}$ in a table with the four decrements referenced above.

A) $\dfrac{1 - e^{-5}}{5}$ B) $\dfrac{1 - e^{-4}}{4}$ C) $\dfrac{1 - e^{-3}}{3}$ D) $\dfrac{1 - e^{-2}}{2}$ E) $1 - e^{-1}$

9-27   A life aged 5 is subject to two decrements described by

$$\mu_x^{(1)} = \frac{1}{30 - x}, \qquad\qquad 5 \le x < 30$$
$$\mu_x^{(T)} = \frac{50 - 2x}{600 - 50x + x^2}, \qquad 5 \le x < 20$$

The probability is .052 that (5) will succumb to decrement 2 during the k th year from now.

Find k.

A) 5   B) 6   C) 7   D) 8   E) 9

9-28   You are given two forces of decrement: $\mu_x^{(1)} = ln3, \quad 0 \le x$

$$\mu_x^{(2)} = \frac{2}{\omega - x}, \qquad 0 \le x < \omega$$

For a life aged 50, the joint density $f(2, 1)$ is $\dfrac{9\,ln3}{121}$.

Find $q_{50}^{\prime(2)}$.

A) $\frac{21}{121}$ B) $\frac{60}{121}$ C) $\frac{61}{121}$ D) $\frac{100}{121}$ E) None of
                                                                                       these

9-29   Given: $\mu_{65+t}^{(1)} = \dfrac{1}{6-t}, \quad 0 \le t < 6$

$\mu_{65+t}^{(2)} = .05 \quad , \quad 0 \le t$

$\mu_{65+t}^{(3)} = .15 \quad , \quad 0 \le t$

If it is known that (65) has left the triple-decrement table prior to age 70, what is the
probability that his exit was due to decrement 1?

A) $\frac{1}{3}$ B) $\frac{1}{2}$ C) $\frac{5}{6}$ D) $\frac{5e-5}{6e-1}$ E) $\frac{5e}{6e-1}$

9-30   Given: $_tq_x^{(j)} = \frac{1}{11}(2^j - 1)(1 - e^{-2t})$, $j = 1, 2, 3$, $0 \le t \le 1$

Find $\mu_{x+1/3}^{(2)}$.

A) $\frac{5}{13}$ B) $\frac{6}{13}$ C) $\frac{7}{13}$ D) $\frac{6}{11}$ E) $\frac{7}{11}$

9-31   Given: $\mu_x^{(j)} = \dfrac{j}{20}$, $x \ge 0$, $j = 1, 2, 3, \ldots, m$

$l_{65}^{(T)} = 1800$

$l_{65}^{(2)} = 100$

Find m.

A) 6   B) 7   C) 8   D) 9   E) 10

9–32   Given: $\mu_x^{(1)} = \dfrac{1}{80-x}$, $0 \le x < 80$

$\mu_x^{(T)} = \dfrac{82-x}{160-2x}$, $0 \le x < 80$

If it is known that (50) left the double decrement table at age K last birthday, it is impossible to predict whether the reason for leaving was decrement 1 or decrement 2. Find K.

A) 52   B) 54   C) 65   D) 76   E) 78

9–33   Given: $_{1/3}q_x^{(T)} = .68$; $_{1/3}q_x^{\prime(1)} = 3 \cdot {}_{1/3}q_x^{\prime(2)}$

Find $_{1/3}p_x^{\prime(1)} + {}_{1/3}p_x^{\prime(2)}$.

A) .2   B) .4   C) .6   D) 1.0   E) 1.2

9–34   Given: $f(k,1) = f(k,2) = \frac{1}{12}(\frac{5}{6})^k$, $k = 0,1,2,\ldots$
Find $E[K]$, given that there are only two decrements.

A) 3   B) 4   C) 5   D) 6   E) 7

9–35   Given: $\mu_x^{(1)} = \dfrac{1}{1+x}$, $x \ge 0$

$\mu_x^{(2)} = \dfrac{2}{1+x}$, $x \ge 0$

$l_0^{(T)} = 300$

Find $m_2^{(1)}$, assuming only two decrements.

A) $\frac{37}{126}$ B) $\frac{37}{105}$ C) $\frac{37}{84}$ D) $\frac{37}{63}$ E) $\frac{37}{42}$

9–36   In their associated single decrement tables, decrements 1 and 2 are distributed as follows:
$$_tq_x^{\prime(1)} = t^2 \cdot q_x^{\prime(1)}, \quad 0 \le t \le 1$$
$$_tq_x^{\prime(2)} = t \cdot q_x^{\prime(2)}, \quad 0 \le t \le 1$$

If $q_x^{\prime(1)} = q_x^{\prime(2)} = .03$, and $l_x^{(T)} = 10,000$, how many more decrements are expected between ages x and $x+1$ for decrement 2 than for decrement 1? Assume that there are only two decrements.

A) 0   B) 1   C) 2   D) 3   E) 4

9-37 Given: $q_x^{\prime(1)} = .1$; $q_x^{\prime(2)} = .3$; only two decrements exist.

Let $A = m_x^{(T)}$, assuming that each decrement is uniformly distributed in its associated single-decrement table.

Let $B = m_x^{(T)}$, assuming that each decrement is uniformly distributed in the double-decrement table.

Find $\dfrac{A}{B}$.

A) $\frac{81}{82}$ B) $\frac{162}{163}$ C) 1   D) $\frac{163}{162}$ E) $\frac{82}{81}$

9-38 In its associated single-decrement table, decrement 1 occurs in equal proportions at the end of the first four months and at the end of the first ten months of the year of age. In its associated single-decrement table, decrement 2 occurs in equal proportions at the beginning and the end of the year of age.

If $q_x^{(1)} = .3$ and $q_x^{(2)} = .4$, find $q_x^{\prime(1)}$.

A) .30   B) .35   C) .40   D) .45   E) .50

9-39 In their associated single-decrement tables, decrements 1, 2, and 3 all follow de Moivre's Law with $\omega = 65$.

Find $q_{62}^{(1)}$ in the triple-decrement table.

A) $\frac{19}{81}$ B) $\frac{7}{27}$ C) $\frac{23}{81}$ D) $\frac{25}{81}$ E) $\frac{1}{3}$

9-40 Given: $m_x^{\prime(j)} = \dfrac{j}{10}$, $j = 1, 2$.

Find $m_x^{(T)}$ for the double-decrement table, assuming a uniform distribution of decrements in the associated single-decrement tables.

A) $\frac{90}{301}$ B) $\frac{180}{601}$ C) $\frac{1}{3}$ D) $\frac{180}{599}$ E) $\frac{90}{299}$

9-41 Given: $\mu_x^{(1)} = .1$, $\quad x \geq 0$

$\mu_x^{(2)} = \dfrac{1}{50 - x}$, $\quad 0 \leq x < 50$.

Find $h(1)$ for a life aged 20, if only two decrements exist.

A) $\frac{1}{3}$ B) $\frac{2}{3}$ C) $\frac{1}{3}(2 + e^{-3})$ D) $\frac{1}{3}(1 - e^{-3})$ E) $\frac{1}{2}(1 + e^{-2})$

9–42   Given: $l_{30}^{(T)} = 2500$

$\mu_{30+t}^{(1)} = \frac{1}{4} ln5, \quad t \geq 0$

$\mu_{30+t}^{(2)} = \frac{3}{4} ln5, \quad t \geq 0$

Find: $d_{33}^{(1)}$, if only two decrements exist.

A) 1   B) 4   C) 8   D) 16   E) 64

9–43   Given: $\mu_x^{(1)} = \frac{1}{10-x}, \quad 0 \leq x < 10$

$\mu_x^{(1)} + \mu_x^{(2)} = \mu_x^{(T)} = \frac{34-3x}{(140-24x+x^2)}, \quad 0 \leq x < 10$

$q_k^{\prime(2)} = .36$

Find k.

A) 6   B) 7   C) 8   D) 9   E) 10

9–44   You are given the following portion of a double-decrement table:

x	$l_x^{(T)}$	$d_x^{(1)}$	$d_x^{(2)}$
1	10000	4698	1759
2	3543	1596	831
3	1116	460	393
4	263	78	185

If $\mu_x^{(1)} = K$, $1 \leq x \leq 5$, and $\mu_x^{(2)} = \frac{1}{5-x}$, $1 \leq x < 5$, find K.

A) .66   B) .68   C) .70   D) .73   E) .75

9–45   You are asked to construct a double-decrement table based upon an initial group of 1000 lives aged 30. Given the following values, find the probability that a life aged 31 will ultimately succumb to decrement 2.

$d_{31}^{(1)} = 100; \quad {}_2p_{30}^{(T)} = .50; \quad {}_{2|}q_{31}^{(2)} = .10;$

$d_x^{(2)} = (x-29)d_x^{(1)}, \quad x = 30, 31, 32, \ldots$

$\omega = 34$

A) .650   B) .680   C) .725   D) .825   E) .850

9–46 Given the following double-decrement table, in which each decrement is uniformly distributed over each year of age, find $q_{60}^{\prime(1)} + {}_{1|}q_{60}^{\prime(1)}$.

x	$l_x^{(T)}$	$d_x^{(1)}$	$d_x^{(2)}$
60	1000	10	30
61	960	30	30

A) .04   B) .05   C) .06   D) .07   E) .08

9–47 Given: $m_x^{\prime(j)} = \dfrac{6}{10j^2 - 60j + 107}$, $j = 1, 2, 3$; There are only three decrements.

If decrements are uniformly distributed in their associated single-decrement tables, find $q_x^{(2)}$.

A) .077   B) .162   C) .171   D) .183   E) .200

Answers to Chapter Nine Exercises

9–1	A.	9–17	E.	9–33	E.
9–2	A.	9–18	E.	9–34	C.
9–3	A.	9–19	D.	9–35	A.
9–4	C.	9–20	D.	9–36	D.
9–5	D.	9–21	C.	9–37	D.
9–6	C.	9–22	D.	9–38	C.
9–7	D.	9–23	D.	9–39	A.
9–8	E.	9–24	B.	9–40	B.
9–9	C.	9–25	B.	9–41	C.
9–10	C.	9–26	A.	9–42	B.
9–11	D.	9–27	B.	9–43	D.
9–12	E.	9–28	A.	9–44	E.
9–13	A.	9–29	D.	9–45	C.
9–14	D.	9–30	D.	9–46	A.
9–15	B.	9–31	C.	9–47	B.
9–16	E.	9–32	E.		

Solutions

9–1.

Key Formula:
$$p_x'^{(j)} = (p_x^{(T)})^{\frac{q_x^{(j)}}{q_x^{(T)}}}$$

Since $q_x^{(T)} = \frac{24}{49}$ and $p_x^{(T)} = \frac{25}{49}$, we have

$$p_x'^{(1)} = \left(\frac{25}{49}\right)^{1/2} = \frac{5}{7}$$

$$q_x'^{(1)} = \underline{\underline{\frac{2}{7}}}$$

9–2.

Key Formula:
$$_k p_x^{(T)} = {_k p_x'^{(1)}} \, {_k p_x'^{(2)}}$$

Since $_k p_x'^{(1)} = e^{-\int_0^k \frac{s}{100} ds} = e^{-\frac{1}{200}k^2}$, and

$$_k p_x'^{(2)} = e^{-\frac{1}{20}k},$$

we have
$$_kp_x^{(T)} = e^{-k(\frac{1}{20} + \frac{1}{200}k)} = e^{-3}.$$

Solving, $k = 20$.

Finally, $\mu_{x+20}^{(1)} = \underline{\underline{\frac{1}{5}}}$.

9–3.

All three of these statements are correct. This is most easily seen by recognizing that the random variables T and J are independent under the constant force assumption.

9–4.

Since $\mu_{x+t}^{(T)} = \sum_{j=1}^{3} \mu_{x+t}^{(j)}$, we have
$$\mu_{x+t}^{(T)} = \frac{1}{25}.$$

Also, since T and J are independent, we have
$$E[T|J = 3] = E[T].$$

Finally, $E[T] = \frac{1}{\mu^{(T)}} = \underline{\underline{25}}$

9–5.

Key Concept: Since decrement 3 can occur only at the end of the year of age, it is not in competition with decrement 1. Thus, in the determination of $q_x^{(1)}$, decrement 3 may be disregarded.

From the assumptions, we have
$$q_x^{(1)} = \tfrac{1}{2}q_x'^{(1)} + \tfrac{1}{2}q_x'^{(1)}(1 - q_x'^{(2)})$$
$$= \underline{\underline{\tfrac{1}{2}q_x'^{(1)}(2 - q_x'^{(2)})}}$$

It is instructive to determine the other probabilities as well.
$$q_x^{(2)} = q_x'^{(2)}(1 - \tfrac{1}{2}q_x'^{(1)})$$
$$q_x^{(3)} = q_x'^{(3)}(1 - q_x'^{(1)})(1 - q_x'^{(2)})$$

Finally, as a check, it should be verified that
$$q_x^{(1)} + q_x^{(2)} + q_x^{(3)} = q_x^{(T)} = q_x'^{(1)} + q_x'^{(2)} + q_x'^{(3)}$$
$$- q_x'^{(1)}q_x'^{(2)} - q_x'^{(1)}q_x'^{(3)} - q_x'^{(2)}q_x'^{(3)}$$
$$+ q_x'^{(1)}q_x'^{(2)}q_x'^{(3)}.$$

9–6.

Key Concept: The entire hypothesis deals with single-decrement tables. Thus, we need the single-decrement probabilities $_{40}p_x'^{(1)}$ and $_{40}p_x'^{(2)}$, from which we determine $_{40}p_x^{(T)}$ as their product.

$$l_x'^{(1)} = (100 - x)^2$$

$$\therefore \; _{40}p_{20}'^{(1)} = \left(\frac{40}{80}\right)^2 = \frac{1}{4}$$

$$l_x'^{(2)} = (100 - x)^3$$

$$\therefore \; _{40}p_{20}'^{(2)} = \left(\frac{40}{80}\right)^3 = \frac{1}{8}$$

Finally,

$$_{40}p_{20}^{(T)} = \frac{1}{4} \cdot \frac{1}{8} = \frac{1}{32}, \text{ and}$$

$$_{40}q_{20}^{(T)} = \underline{\underline{\frac{31}{32}}}.$$

9–7.

Key Concept: Under the assumption of a uniform distribution of decrements in the multiple-decrement table, the ratio $\dfrac{q_x^{(j)}}{m_x^{(j)}}$ is independent of the decrement j. That is,

$$\frac{q_x^{(j)}}{m_x^{(j)}} = 1 - \frac{1}{2}q_x^{(T)} \text{ for all } j.$$

Accordingly, we see that

$$\frac{3}{4} = 1 - \frac{1}{2}q_x^{(T)}, \text{ and thus}$$

$$q_x^{(T)} = \frac{1}{2}.$$

Since $q_x^{(T)} = \frac{3}{4}m_x^{(T)} = \frac{1}{2}$, we have

$$m_x^{(T)} - q_x^{(T)} = \frac{2}{3} - \frac{1}{2} = \underline{\underline{\frac{1}{6}}}$$

9–8.

Key Formula:
$$\mu_x^{(T)} = \mu_x^{(1)} + \mu_x^{(2)}$$

Here, $\mu_x^{(T)} = \dfrac{1/2}{180 - x}$.

At this point, the question ceases to involve the multiple-decrement concepts, if the student considers "T" to represent a single decrement.

Finally,

$$_{70}p_{20}^{(T)} = \left(\frac{90}{160}\right)^{1/2} = \underline{\underline{\frac{3}{4}}}.$$

9–9.

The complete multiple-decrement table expectation, often represented by $E[T]$ or $\overset{\circ}{e}_x^{(T)}$, is given by

$$E[T] = \int_0^\infty {}_tp_x^{(T)}\, dt.$$

Here we have

$$_tp_{87}^{\prime(1)} = \frac{3 - t}{3}, \quad 0 \le t \le 3$$
$$\text{and}$$
$$_tp_{87}^{\prime(2)} = e^{-\frac{1}{2}t}, \quad t \ge 0.$$

Since it is impossible for a person to attain age 90 in the double-decrement table, the upper limit must equal three. Now,

$$E[T] = \overset{\circ}{e}_{87}^{(T)} = \int_0^3 \frac{3 - t}{3} e^{-\frac{1}{2}t}\, dt.$$

Integrating by parts,

$$E[T] = \underline{\underline{\frac{2}{3} + \frac{4}{3}e^{-3/2}}}.$$

NOTE: If decrement #1 were the only decrement operating, the expectation would be 1.5 years. Clearly, then, the result must be less than 1.5. Similarly, it must be less than 2, the expectation if only decrement 2 were operating.

9–10.

Key Formula:

$$m_x^{(T)} = \frac{q_x^{(T)}}{\int_0^1 {}_tp_x^{(T)}\,dt}$$

Using this formula, and incorporating the assumption of uniformly distributed decrements in the single-decrement tables, we have

$$m_x^{(T)} = \frac{q_x^{(T)}}{\int_0^1 (1 - tq_x'^{(1)})(1 - tq_x'^{(2)})\,dt}$$

$$= \frac{q_x'^{(1)} + q_x'^{(2)} - q_x'^{(1)}q_x'^{(2)}}{1 - \frac{1}{2}q_x'^{(1)} - \frac{1}{2}q_x'^{(2)} + \frac{1}{3}q_x'^{(1)}q_x'^{(2)}}$$

$$\frac{3}{7} = \frac{q_x'^{(1)} + \frac{1}{9} - \frac{1}{9}q_x'^{(1)}}{1 - \frac{1}{2}q_x'^{(1)} - \frac{1}{18} + \frac{1}{27}q_x'^{(1)}}$$

Solving, $q_x'^{(1)} = \dfrac{37}{137}$.

$$\therefore p_x'^{(1)} = \underline{\frac{100}{137}}$$

9–11.

Key Concepts:

Integration is required here, since three decrements are competing with each other in a continuous manner.

Decrement 3 removes lives continuously throughout the year of age. In addition, it removes all surviving lives instantaneously at yearend. Note that $q_{64}'^{(3)} = 1$ is implied, but that $\lim\limits_{t \to 1} {}_tq_{64}'^{(3)} = .3$.

Thus, we have

$$q_{64}^{(3)} = \int_0^1 {}_tp_{64}'^{(1)}\,{}_tp_{64}'^{(2)}\,{}_tp_{64}'^{(3)}\,\mu_{64+t}^{(3)}\,dt + p_{64}'^{(1)}\,p_{64}'^{(2)}\,p_{64}'^{(3)}$$

$$= q_{64}'^{(3)} \int_0^1 {}_tp_{64}'^{(1)}\,{}_tp_{64}'^{(2)}\,dt + p_{64}'^{(1)}\,p_{64}'^{(2)}\,p_{64}'^{(3)}$$

$$= .3 \int_0^1 (1 - .06t)(1 - .10t)\,dt + (.94)(.90)(.70)$$

$$= .8688$$

Thus, there are $\underline{86880}$ lives who exit due to decrement 3. It should be verified that the numbers exiting due to decrements 1 and 2 are 4860 and 8260, respectively.

Note that the solution ostensibly uses a value of .70 for $p_{64}'^{(3)}$. This represents the effect of decrement 3 up until the instant of attainment of age 65. In fact, $p_{64}'^{(3)} = 0$. This concept is expanded in the next problem.

9–12.

Key Concept: Since decrement 5 may only occur at a single instant (exact age $x+1$), the left-hand and right-hand limits are unequal.

Specifically, we have

$$\lim_{t \to 1^-} {}_t p_x^{(T)} = p_x'^{(1)} p_x'^{(2)} p_x'^{(3)} p_x'^{(4)}$$

and

$$\lim_{t \to 1^+} {}_t p_x^{(T)} = p_x'^{(1)} p_x'^{(2)} p_x'^{(3)} p_x'^{(4)} p_x'^{(5)}.$$

Thus $p_x'^{(5)} = .2$

Now,

$$p_x'^{(1)} p_x'^{(2)} p_x'^{(3)} p_x'^{(4)} (1 - p_x'^{(5)}) = .05.$$

Letting $p_x'^{(1)} = p_x'^{(2)} = p_x'^{(3)} = p_x'^{(4)} = K$, we have

$$K^4(1 - p_x'^{(5)}) = .05$$

$$K^4 = \frac{1}{16}$$

$$K = \underline{\underline{\frac{1}{2}}}$$

9–13.

Key Formula:
$$p_x^{(T)} = p_x'^{(1)} p_x'^{(2)}$$

Here, $p_x^{(T)} = .9408$ and $p_x'^{(2)} = .96$. Thus $p_x'^{(1)} = .98$ and $q_x'^{(1)} = .02$.

Using the given assumptions, we have

$$q_x^{(1)} = \frac{1}{2} q_x'^{(1)} + \frac{1}{2} q_x'^{(1)} \left(1 - \frac{1}{2} q_x'^{(2)}\right)$$

$$= .0198$$

$$d_x^{(1)} = \underline{198}$$

It should be verified independently, i.e., by finding $q_x^{(2)}$ directly, that $d_x^{(2)} = 394$.

9-14.

Key Formula:

$$h(j|T = t) = \frac{\mu_{x+t}^{(j)}}{\mu_{x+t}^{(T)}}$$

Thus, we have

$$h(2|T = 20) = \frac{\mu_{60}^{(2)}}{\mu_{60}^{(T)}}$$

$$= \frac{\frac{1}{40} - \frac{1}{100}}{\frac{1}{40}} = \underline{\underline{.6}}$$

9-15.

Key Concept: The easy component of the question is the second; i.e., that in which the cause of death is irrelevant. No integration is required because of the constant total force of death.

Component #1:

$$NSP = 4\int_0^{25} v^t \, {}_t p_{30}^{(T)} \, \mu_{30+t}^{(ad)} \, dt$$

$$= 4\int_0^{25} e^{-.10t} e^{-.06t}(.01) \, dt$$

$$= \frac{1}{4}(1 - e^{-4})$$

Component #2:

$$NSP = \frac{\mu^{(T)}}{\mu^{(T)} + \delta} = \frac{.06}{.16} = \frac{3}{8}$$

The total net single premium is

$$\frac{1}{4}(1 - e^{-4}) + \frac{3}{8}, \text{ or } \underline{\underline{\frac{5e^4 - 2}{8e^4}}}$$

9-16.

Key Concept: The ultimate probability that (x) will succumb to decrement 1 is 0.1. This does not necessarily mean, however, that any of the forces of decrement are constant.

Since the density $f(t, 1)$ is given by

$$f(t, 1) = {}_tp_x^{(T)}\mu_{x+t}^{(1)}$$
$$= \frac{1}{10}{}_tp_x^{(T)}\mu_{x+t}^{(T)}$$
$$= \frac{1}{10}g(t),$$

we have

$$E[T|J = 1] = \int_0^\infty \frac{\frac{t}{10}g(t)}{h(1)}\, dt$$
$$= \int_0^\infty tg(t)\, dt$$
$$= \overset{\circ}{e}_x^{(T)}.$$

However, since none of the forces are known, it is <u>impossible</u> to evaluate $\overset{\circ}{e}_x^{(T)}$.

9–17.

Key Concept:

As the question involves the expectation based upon the totality of decrements, and since $\mu^{(T)}$ is directly available, this question should ultimately be treated as a single-decrement problem.

Adding the $\mu_x^{(j)}$ values, we have

$$\mu_{x+t}^{(T)} = \frac{21}{20 - t}$$

If $\mu_{x+t}^{(T)}$ had been $\dfrac{1}{20 - t}$, we would have obtained $E[T] = \dfrac{20}{1 + 1} = 10$.

Since, however, $\mu_{x+t}^{(T)} = \dfrac{21}{20 - t}$, we have

$$E[T] = \frac{20}{1 + 21} = \underline{\underline{\frac{10}{11}}}.$$

9–18.

Key Concepts:

The fact that the *ultimate* probabilities of succumbing to decrement 1 and decrement 2 are equal in no way implies that the *distributions* of the decrements are identical.

Since $g(t)$ is constant, the *total* decrement is uniformly distributed. Thus $\overset{\circ}{e}_x^{(T)} = 30$.

Key Formula: $E[T] = \Pr[J = 1] \cdot E[T|J = 1] + \Pr[J = 2] \cdot E[T|J = 2]$

Since the ultimate probabilities are equal, we have

$$30 = \frac{1}{2}[E[T|J = 1] + E[T|J = 2]]$$
$$\therefore E[T|J = 1] + E[T|J = 2] = 60.$$

At this point, the solution dead-ends. For example,

$$f(t, 1) = \frac{60 - t}{3600} \text{ and}$$
$$f(t, 2) = \frac{t}{3600}$$

satisfy the question's hypotheses, but so would

$$f(t, 1) = \frac{t}{3600} \text{ and}$$
$$f(t, 2) = \frac{60 - t}{3600}$$

Therefore, the answer <u>cannot be determined</u>.

9–19.

Key Concept: All of the decrements occurring due to cause 2, in the second half of the year of age, occur at exact age $x + \frac{10}{12}$.

Using the given assumptions, we have as the required number of decrements

$$1000 \left(\frac{1}{2} q_x^{\prime(2)} \right) \left(1 - \frac{10}{12} q_x^{\prime(1)} \right)$$
$$= \underline{\underline{55}}$$

It should be verified that, over the entire year of age, 94.5 and 113.5 decrements are expected as a result of causes 1 and 2 respectively.

9–20.

Key Formula:

$$_rp_x^{\prime(1)} = (_rp_x^{(T)})^{\frac{q_x^{(1)}}{q_x^{(T)}}} \qquad \text{(UDDMDT)}$$

Thus, $.8 = (1 - rq_x^{(T)})^{1/2} = (1 - .6r)^{1/2}$

$$\therefore r = \underline{\underline{\frac{3}{5}}}$$

NOTE: An alternate solution reflects the fact that both decrements are identically distributed *and* equal in magnitude, making them equivalent and thus interchangeable.

$$\therefore {}_r p_x^{(T)} = {}_r p_x'^{(1)} \, {}_r p_x'^{(2)} = ({}_r p_x'^{(1)})^2 = .64$$

$$\therefore 1 - {}_r q_x^{(T)} = .64$$

$$r = \frac{3}{5}$$

9–21.

Key Concept:

If $\mu_x^{(j)}$ is a decreasing function of age, $m_x'^{(j)} < m_x^{(j)}$, and vice versa. We must identify those ages at which $\frac{d}{dx}\mu_x^{(j)}$ is positive.

$$\mu_x^{(1)} = 10\,ln(2x + 4) - .2x$$

$$\therefore \frac{d}{dx}\mu_x^{(1)} = \frac{20}{2x + 4} - \frac{1}{5} > 0$$

$$\therefore x < 48$$

Thus, at ages under 48, $m_x'^{(1)} > m_x^{(1)}$.

Accordingly, I is false and III is true. In addition, II is true because the symbol m_{48} refers to ages *between* 48 and 49.

9–22.

Key Formula:

When forces of decrement are constant,

$$\frac{\mu_x^{(j)}}{\mu_x^{(T)}} = \frac{q_x^{(j)}}{q_x^{(T)}}.$$

Thus, $\dfrac{\mu_{61}^{(T)}}{\mu_{61}^{(2)}} = \dfrac{q_{61}^{(T)}}{q_{61}^{(2)}} = \dfrac{d_{61}^{(T)}}{d_{61}^{(2)}} = \dfrac{4730}{1577}$

$$= \underline{3.0}$$

9-23.

The following diagram and statement of assumptions should be helpful.

$$\begin{array}{cccc} \vdash & \vdash & \vdash & \vdash \\ x & x+\tfrac{1}{3} & x+\tfrac{2}{3} & x+1 \end{array}$$

#1: uniform

#2: uniform

#3: $\dfrac{1}{3}$ at $x+\dfrac{1}{3}$, $\dfrac{1}{3}$ at $x+\dfrac{2}{3}$, $\dfrac{1}{3}$ an instant before $x+1$

Looking at the three points at which decrement 3 can operate, we have

$$
\begin{aligned}
q_x^{(3)} &= \frac{1}{3}q_x'^{(3)}\left(1-\frac{1}{3}q_x'^{(1)}\right)\left(1-\frac{1}{3}q_x'^{(2)}\right) \\
&\quad + \frac{1}{3}q_x'^{(3)}\left(1-\frac{2}{3}q_x'^{(1)}\right)\left(1-\frac{2}{3}q_x'^{(2)}\right) \\
&\quad + \frac{1}{3}q_x'^{(3)}(1-q_x'^{(1)})(1-q_x'^{(2)}) \\
&= (.3)[(5/6)^2 + (2/3)^2 + (1/2)^2] \\
&= .41\dot{6}
\end{aligned}
$$

Thus, $240(.41\dot{6}) = \underline{100}$ decrements are expected.

Alternatively,

$$
\begin{aligned}
q_x^{(1)} &= \frac{1}{6}\cdot\frac{11}{12} + \frac{1}{6}\cdot\frac{3}{4}\cdot\frac{7}{10} + \frac{1}{6}\cdot\frac{7}{12}\cdot\frac{4}{10} = .2791\dot{6} \\
q_x^{(2)} &= q_x^{(1)} = .2791\dot{6} \\
q_x^{(3)} &= q_x^{(T)} - q_x^{(1)} - q_x^{(2)} \\
&= 1 - \left(\frac{1}{2}\right)\left(\frac{1}{2}\right)\left(\frac{1}{10}\right) - 2(.2791\dot{6}) = .41\dot{6}
\end{aligned}
$$

9-24.

Key Formulas:

$$p_x'^{(1)} = (p_x^{(T)})^{\frac{q_x^{(1)}}{q_x^{(T)}}}$$
$$\text{and}$$
$$m_x^{(1)} = \frac{q_x^{(1)}}{1 - \frac{1}{2}q_x^{(T)}}.$$

Accordingly,

$$\frac{3}{5} = \left(\frac{9}{25}\right)^{\frac{q_x^{(1)}}{16/25}}$$

$$\therefore q_x^{(1)} = \frac{8}{25}$$

$$\therefore m_x^{(1)} = \frac{8/25}{1 - \frac{1}{2}(16/25)} = \underline{\frac{8}{17}}$$

9–25.

Given:

$$p_{65}^{(T)} = .5733$$
$$p_{65}^{\prime(d)} = .90$$
$$p_{65}^{\prime(w)} = .91$$
$$\therefore p_{65}^{\prime(r)} = .70$$
$$\therefore q_{65}^{\prime(r)} = .30$$

Case I: Retirements at midyear:

$$d_{65}^{(r)} = 1,000,000 \left(1 - \frac{1}{2}(.1)\right)\left(1 - \frac{1}{2}(.09)\right)(.3)$$
$$= 272,175$$

Case II: Retirements uniform:

$$d_{65}^{(r)} = 1,000,000 \int_0^1 {}_t p_{65}^{\prime(d)} \, {}_t p_{65}^{\prime(w)} \, {}_t p_{65}^{\prime(r)} \, \mu_{65+t}^{(r)} \, dt$$

$$= 1,000,000 q_{65}^{\prime(r)} \int_0^1 (1 - t q_{65}^{\prime(d)})(1 - {}_t q_{65}^{\prime(w)}) \, dt$$

$$= 1,000,000(.30) \int_0^1 (1 - .1t)(1 - .09t) \, dt$$

$$= 272,400$$

$$\therefore 272,400 - 272,175 = \underline{225}$$

9–26.

Key Concept: Although no specific assumption appears to be stated with regard to distribution of decrements, it is easy to deduce that each force of decrement is constant.

Specifically,

$$\mu_{x+t}^{(j)} = \frac{-\frac{\partial}{\partial t}\,{}_tp_x'^{(j)}}{{}_tp_x'^{(j)}} = -\frac{\partial}{\partial t}\,ln\,{}_tp_x'^{(j)}.$$

Here, $\mu_{20+t}^{(j)} = j/2$ for $0 \le t \le 1$ and $j = 1,2,3,4$

$$\mu_{20}^{(2)} = 1$$
$$\mu_{20}^{(T)} = 5$$
$$q_{20}^{(T)} = 1 - p_{20}^{(T)} = 1 - e^{-1/2}e^{-1}e^{-\frac{3}{2}}e^{-2}$$
$$= 1 - e^{-5}$$

Finally, since

$$q_{20}^{(2)} = q_{20}^{(T)}\,\frac{\mu_{20}^{(2)}}{\mu_{20}^{(T)}},$$

we have

$$q_{20}^{(2)} = \frac{1}{5}(1 - e^{-5})$$

9–27.

The following equation must be solved for k:

$$\int_{k-1}^{k} {}_tp_5^{(T)}\,\mu_{5+t}^{(2)}\,dt = .052.$$

Since $\mu_x^{(1)} + \mu_x^{(2)} = \mu_x^{(T)}$, we have

$$\mu_x^{(2)} = \frac{1}{20-x} \text{ and } \mu_x^{(1)} = \frac{1}{30-x},$$

both of which represent uniform distributions within the associated single-decrement tables. Accordingly,

$$_tp_5^{(T)} = {}_tp_5'^{(1)}\,{}_tp_5'^{(2)} = \frac{15-t}{15}\cdot\frac{25-t}{25}.$$

Finally, solving

$$\int_{k-1}^{k} \frac{(15-5)(25-t)}{375}\cdot\frac{1}{15-t}\,dt = .052$$

produces $k = \underline{6}$.

9–28.

Key Formula:
$$_tp_{50}^{(T)} = \,_tp_{50}^{\prime(1)} \,_tp_{50}^{\prime(2)}$$

Thus,

$$f(2,1) = \,_2p_{50}^{(T)}\mu_{52}^{(1)} = \left(\frac{1}{3}\right)^2 \left(\frac{\omega - 52}{\omega - 50}\right)^2 \ln 3 = \frac{9\ln 3}{121},$$

which produces

$$\left(\frac{\omega - 52}{\omega - 50}\right)^2 = \frac{81}{121}$$

$$\therefore \frac{\omega - 52}{\omega - 50} = \frac{9}{11}$$

$$\therefore \omega = 61$$

Finally,

$$q_{50}^{\prime(2)} = 1 - p_{50}^{\prime(2)} = 1 - \left(\frac{10}{11}\right)^2$$

$$= \underline{\underline{\frac{21}{121}}}$$

9–29.

Key Formula: The required conditional probability is given by

$$\frac{_5q_{65}^{(1)}}{_5q_{65}^{(T)}}.$$

Since $_5q_{65}^{(1)} = \int_0^5 \frac{1}{6}e^{-.2t}\,dt = \frac{5}{6}(1 - e^{-1})$ and $_5q_{65}^{(T)} = 1 - \,_5p_{65}^{(T)} = 1 - \frac{1}{6}e^{-1}$, we have

$$\frac{_5q_{65}^{(1)}}{_5q_{65}^{(T)}} = \frac{\frac{5}{6}(1 - e^{-1})}{1 - \frac{1}{6}e^{-1}} = \underline{\underline{\frac{5(e-1)}{6e-1}}}$$

9–30.

Key Formulas:
$$\mu_{x+t}^{(j)} = \frac{\frac{\partial}{\partial t}\,_tq_x^{(j)}}{_tp_x^{(T)}}$$

$$_tq_x^{(T)} = \sum_j \,_tq_x^{(j)}$$

Thus $_tq_x^{(T)} = (1 - e^{-2t})$. Since

$$\frac{\partial}{\partial t}\,_tq_x^{(j)} = \frac{2}{11}(2^j - 1)e^{-2t},$$

we have

$$\mu_{x+t}^{(2)} = \frac{\frac{6}{11}e^{-2t}}{e^{-2t}} = \underline{\underline{\frac{6}{11}}}$$

9–31.

Key Concept: Since all forces are constant,

$$h(j) = \frac{\mu^{(j)}}{\mu^{(T)}}.$$

Thus, for a life aged 65,

$$h(2) = \frac{l_{65}^{(2)}}{l_{65}^{(T)}} = \frac{1}{18} = \frac{\mu^{(2)}}{\mu^{(T)}} = \frac{\frac{2}{20}}{\frac{m(m+1)}{2 \cdot 20}}$$

$$\therefore \underline{m = 8}$$

9–32.

Key Concept: If it is known that decrement occurred at a given age in a multiple-decrement table, the more likely decrement would be the one with the larger force at that given age.

Formally, then, we could set

$$h(1|T = 30) = \frac{f(30,1)}{g(30)} = \frac{1}{2}.$$

More directly, however, we should set

$$\mu_x^{(1)} = \mu_x^{(2)} = \frac{1}{2}\mu_x^{(T)}$$

and solve for x.

Thus $\dfrac{1}{80-x} = \dfrac{1}{2} \cdot \dfrac{82-x}{160-2x}$

$$\therefore \underline{x = 78}$$

9–33.

Key Concept: As no assumptions are given (or implied) regarding distribution of the decrements, the question must be solved in the absence of simplifying approximations. In almost all instances, this suggests the exact formula

$$_t p_x^{(T)} = {}_t p_x^{\prime(1)} \, {}_t p_x^{\prime(2)} \cdots {}_t p_x^{\prime(m)}.$$

Thus, set $_{1/3}q'^{(1)}_x = 3A$ and $_{1/3}q'^{(2)}_x = A$. Since $_{1/3}q^{(T)}_x = 1 - _{1/3}p^{(T)}_x = 1 - (1 - 3A)(1 - A) = .68$, we have $A = .2$.

Finally,

$$_{1/3}p'^{(1)}_x + _{1/3}p'^{(2)}_x = (1 - 3A) + (1 - A) = \underline{\underline{1.2}}$$

9–34.

Key Concept: Where as time of decrement is usually considered to be a continuous random variable, here the distribution of time of decrement is discrete.

Using actuarial notation, we have

$$_{k|}q^{(1)}_x = \frac{1}{12}\left(\frac{5}{6}\right)^k = _{k|}q^{(2)}_x$$

$$\therefore _{k|}q^{(T)}_x = \frac{1}{6}\left(\frac{5}{6}\right)^k, \quad k = 0, 1, 2, 3, \ldots$$

Thus K follows a geometric distribution, with $q^{(T)} = \frac{1}{6}$ and $p^{(T)} = 5/6$.

Accordingly,

$$E[K] = \frac{p}{q} = \underline{\underline{5}}$$

9–35.

Key Concept: Since the forces of decrement do not suggest any of the standard approximations (constant force or uniform distribution of either type), we must appeal to the definition of $m^{(j)}_x$, i.e.,

$$m^{(j)}_x = \frac{q^{(j)}_x}{\int_0^1 {}_t p^{(T)}_x \, dt}.$$

Since it is evident that $q^{(1)}_x = \frac{1}{3}q^{(T)}_x$, we need only find $_t p^{(T)}_x$.

We know that $\mu_x = \frac{1}{1+x}$ implies that $_x p_0 = \frac{1}{1+x}$. Thus, since we have

$$\mu^{(T)}_x = \frac{3}{1+x}$$

we know that

$$_x p^{(T)}_0 = \frac{1}{(1+x)^3} \quad \text{and}$$

$$_t p^{(T)}_x = \frac{(1+x)^3}{(1+x+t)^3}.$$

Now,

$$\int_0^1 {}_t p_2^{(T)} \, dt = \int_0^1 \frac{27}{(3+t)^3} \, dt = \frac{21}{32}.$$

Finally,

$$m_2^{(1)} = \frac{\frac{1}{3} \cdot \frac{37}{64}}{\frac{21}{32}} = \underline{\frac{37}{126}}$$

9–36.

Key Formula:

$$ {}_t p_x'^{(j)} \mu_{x+t}^{(j)} = -\frac{d}{dt} \, {}_t p_x'^{(j)} $$

Thus,

$$ {}_t p_x'^{(1)} \mu_{x+t}^{(1)} = 2t q_x'^{(1)} = .06t $$
$$ {}_t p_x'^{(2)} \mu_{x+t}^{(2)} = q_x'^{(2)} = .03 $$

We need the values of $q_x^{(2)}$ and $q_x^{(1)}$.

$$
\begin{aligned}
q_x^{(2)} &= \int_0^1 {}_t p_x'^{(1)} {}_t p_x'^{(2)} \mu_{x+t}^{(2)} \, dt \\
&= .03 \int_0^1 (1 - .03t^2) \, dt \\
&= .0297 \\
q_x^{(1)} &= \int_0^1 {}_t p_x'^{(1)} {}_t p_x'^{(2)} \mu_{x+t}^{(1)} \, dt \\
&= .06 \int_0^1 t(1 - .03t) \, dt \\
&= .0294
\end{aligned}
$$

Finally,

$$ 10{,}000(.0297 - .0294) = \underline{\underline{3}} $$

9–37.

Key Concept: This question illustrates the two similar, but distinct, types of assumptions regarding uniform distribution of decrements.

$$\frac{A}{B} = \frac{\dfrac{q_x^{(T)}}{\int_0^1 (1 - tq_x'^{(1)})(1 - tq_x'^{(2)})\,dt}}{\dfrac{q_x^{(T)}}{\int_0^1 (1 - tq_x^{(T)})\,dt}}$$

$$= \frac{\int_0^1 (1 - t(.37))\,dt}{\int_0^1 (1 - .1t)(1 - .3t)\,dt}$$

$$= \underline{\underline{\frac{163}{162}}}$$

9–38.

Key Concept: Unlike most problems of this type, here we are given the probabilities and required to find the absolute rates. An analysis of the diagram and the assumptions leads to two simultaneous equations.

$$\overset{}{\underset{x}{|}} \quad \overset{}{\underset{x + 1/3}{|}} \quad \overset{}{\underset{x + 5/6}{|}} \quad \overset{}{\underset{x + 1}{|}}$$

#1: Half at $x + 1/3$; half at $x + 5/6$
#2: Half at x; half at $x + 1$

$$q_x^{(1)} = \frac{1}{2}q_x'^{(1)}\left(1 - \frac{1}{2}q_x'^{(2)}\right) + \frac{1}{2}q_x'^{(1)}\left(1 - \frac{1}{2}q_x'^{(2)}\right)$$

$$= q_x'^{(1)} - \frac{1}{2}q_x'^{(1)}q_x'^{(2)}$$

$$q_x^{(2)} = \frac{1}{2}q_x'^{(2)} + \frac{1}{2}q_x'^{(2)}(1 - q_x'^{(1)})$$

$$= q_x'^{(2)} - \frac{1}{2}q_x'^{(1)}q_x'^{(2)}$$

Finally,

$$.3 = q_x'^{(1)} - \frac{1}{2}q_x'^{(1)}q_x'^{(2)}$$

$$.4 = q_x'^{(2)} - \frac{1}{2}q_x'^{(1)}q_x'^{(2)}$$

and

$$q_x'^{(1)} = \underline{\underline{.4}} \quad (q_x'^{(2)} = .5)$$

9–39.

Formal Approach:

$$_t p_{62}^{'(j)} = \frac{3-t}{3}, \ 0 \le t \le 3, \ j = 1,2,3$$

$$\mu_{62+t}^{(j)} = \frac{1}{3-t}, \ 0 \le t < 3, \ j = 1,2,3$$

$$q_{62}^{(1)} = \int_0^1 {}_t p_{62}^{'(1)} \, {}_t p_{62}^{'(2)} \, {}_t p_{62}^{'(3)} \, \mu_{62+t}^{(1)} \, dt$$

$$= \frac{1}{3} \int_0^1 \frac{(3-t)^2}{9} \, dt$$

$$= \underline{\underline{\frac{19}{81}}}$$

More Direct Approach:

$$q_{62}^{(1)} = \frac{1}{3} q_{62}^{(T)} = \frac{1}{3} \left(1 - \left(\frac{2}{3} \right)^3 \right) = \frac{19}{81}$$

9–40.

Key Formulas:

$$m_x^{(T)} = \frac{q_x^{(T)}}{\int_0^1 {}_t p_x^{(T)} \, dt} = \frac{q_x^{(T)}}{\int_0^1 (1 - t q_x^{'(1)})(1 - t q_x^{'(2)}) \, dt}$$

$$q_x^{'(j)} = \frac{m_x^{'(j)}}{1 + \frac{1}{2} m_x^{'(j)}}, \ j = 1,2$$

Thus, $q_x^{'(1)} = 2/21$

$q_x^{'(2)} = 2/11$

$\therefore p_x^{(T)} = \frac{19}{21} \cdot \frac{9}{11} = \frac{171}{231}$

$q_x^{(T)} = \frac{60}{231}$

Finally,

$$m_x^{(T)} = \frac{\dfrac{60}{231}}{\displaystyle\int_0^1 (1 - \frac{2t}{21})(1 - \frac{2t}{11}) \, dt}$$

$$= \underline{\underline{\frac{180}{601}}}$$

NOTE: Decrements are uniform in their single decrement tables; accordingly, $\mu^{(j)}$ increases with age. Thus,

$$m_x^{'(j)} > m_x^{(j)}.$$

In the case of two decrements, we have

$$m_x'^{(1)} > m_x^{(1)}$$

$$m_x'^{(2)} > m_x^{(2)}$$

$$\therefore m_x'^{(1)} + m_x'^{(2)} > m_x^{(T)}$$

$$\underline{\frac{3}{10} > m_x^{(T)}}$$

Thus, only answers A and B are possible.

9–41.

Key Concept: It is mathematically easier to find $h(j)$ for the decrement which is uniformly distributed (in its single-decrement table) than for the decrement whose force is constant.

$$h(2) = \int_0^{30} {}_t p_{20}'^{(1)} \, {}_t p_{20}'^{(2)} \, \mu_{20+t}^{(2)} \, dt$$

$$= \frac{1}{30} \int_0^{30} e^{-.1t} \, dt$$

$$= \frac{1}{3}(1 - e^{-3})$$

Thus, $h(1) = 1 - \frac{1}{3}(1 - e^{-3}) = \underline{\underline{\frac{1}{3}(2 + e^{-3})}}$

9–42.

Key Concept: Since $\mu^{(2)} = 3\mu^{(1)}$ for all ages greater than 30, we know that three times as many decrements will be attributable to decrement 2 as to decrement 1 in any interval of time.

$$\mu_{30+t}^{(T)} = \ln 5, \; t \geq 0$$

$$\therefore p_x^{(T)} = \frac{1}{5}, \; x \geq 30$$

$$\therefore l_{33}^{(T)} = 2500 \left(\frac{1}{5}\right)^3 = 20$$

$$l_{34}^{(T)} = 2500 \left(\frac{1}{5}\right)^4 = 4$$

$$\therefore d_{33}^{(T)} = 16$$

$$d_{33}^{(1)} = \frac{1}{4} d_{33}^{(T)} = \underline{\underline{4}}$$

9–43.

Key Concept: Since the question involves the absolute rate $q_k^{\prime(2)}$, only the force of decrement for cause 2 is relevant.

$$\mu_x^{(2)} = \mu_x^{(T)} - \mu_x^{(1)}$$

$$= \frac{2}{14 - x}$$

$$\therefore p_k^{\prime(2)} = \left(\frac{13 - k}{14 - k}\right)^2 = .64$$

$$\therefore \frac{13 - k}{14 - k} = .8$$

$$\underline{k = 9}$$

9–44.

Key Concept: Only row 1 (or any single row) of the decrement table need be considered.

$$p_1^{(T)} = .3543 = p_1^{\prime(1)} p_1^{\prime(2)}$$

$$= e^{-K} \cdot \frac{3}{4}$$

$$\therefore e^{-K} = .4724$$

In the absence of an adequate calculator, the solution is not complete. Continuing,

$$q_1^{(2)} = \int_0^1 {}_tp_1^{\prime(1)} \, {}_tp_1^{\prime(2)} \, \mu_{1+t}^{(2)} \, dt$$

$$= q_1^{\prime(2)} \int_0^1 e^{-Kt} \, dt$$

$$.1759 = \frac{1}{4} \cdot \frac{1}{K}(1 - e^{-K}) = \frac{.1319}{K}$$

$$\therefore K \doteq \underline{\underline{.75}}$$

9–45.

This question requires the construction of a portion of a double-decrement table from the given data. The following entries should be verified.

x	$l_x^{(T)}$	$d_x^{(1)}$	$d_x^{(2)}$
30	1000	100	100
31	800	100	200
32	500	100	300
33	100	20	80
34	0		

Thus, for a life aged 31,

$$h(2) = \frac{200 + 300 + 80}{800} = \underline{\underline{.725}}$$

9–46.

Key Formula:

$$p_x'^{(j)} = (p_x^{(T)})^{\frac{q_x^{(j)}}{q_x^{(T)}}}$$

Thus,

$$p_{60}'^{(1)} = (p_{60}^{(T)})^{\frac{q_{60}^{(1)}}{q_{60}^{(T)}}}$$
$$= (.96)^{1/4}$$

$$p_{61}'^{(1)} = (p_{61}^{(T)})^{\frac{q_{61}^{(1)}}{q_{61}^{(T)}}}$$
$$= \left(\frac{90}{96}\right)^{1/2}$$

Finally,

$$q_{60}'^{(1)} + {}_{1|}q_{60}'^{(1)} = q_{60}'^{(1)} + p_{60}'^{(1)} q_{61}'^{(1)}$$

$$= 1 - (.96)^{1/4} + (.96)^{1/4}\left(1 - \left(\frac{90}{96}\right)^{1/2}\right)$$

$$= \underline{\underline{.0416}}$$

9–47.

Key Formula:

$$q_x'^{(j)} = \frac{m'^{(j)}}{1 + \frac{1}{2}m_x'^{(j)}}$$

Thus $q_x'^{(1)} = \dfrac{1}{10}$

$q_x'^{(2)} = \dfrac{2}{10}$

$q_x'^{(3)} = \dfrac{3}{10}$

Now, $q_x^{(2)} = \displaystyle\int_0^1 {}_tp_x'^{(1)} \, {}_tp_x'^{(2)} \, {}_tp_x'^{(3)} \, \mu_{x+t}^{(2)} \, dt$

$= .2 \displaystyle\int_0^1 \left(1 - \frac{t}{10}\right)\left(1 - \frac{3t}{10}\right) dt$

$= \underline{.162}$

Chapter Ten

Supplementary Concepts

1. Two specific forms of salary scale functions are of special interest, both because of their prevalence in practice and because of their ease of application.

    First, consider discrete salary scale functions which are linear functions of age, i.e.,

    $$S_x = a + bx$$

    where x assumes integral values only. Then,

    $$_mZ_y = S_{y-m/2}$$

    regardless of whether m is even or odd. Similarly,

    $$_m\tilde{Z}_y = S_{y-m/2-1/2}.$$

    Second, consider discrete salary scale functions that are geometric functions of age, i.e.,

    $$S_x = (1+i)^x$$

    where x assumes integral values only. Then,

    $$_mZ_y = S_y(\tfrac{1}{2m})(\ddot{a}_{\overline{m}|i} + a_{\overline{m}|i})$$

    Similarly,

    $$_m\tilde{Z}_y = S_y(\tfrac{1}{m})a_{\overline{m}|i}$$

2. The descriptive terms such as excess-type, step-rate, offset, and add-on plans are significant and should be comprehended. However, actuarial present values of retirement benefits are most easily determined from basic principles, a careful reading of the benefit description, and a clear understanding of the symbols $R(x,h,t)$ and $R(x,h,k+\tfrac{1}{2})$. Such problems are easily categorized into a) those involving employee salaries for an entire working lifetime (career average plans) and b) all others.

    The following diagram is helpful with category (b) above:

    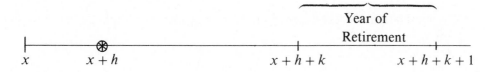

The usual simplifying assumptions lead to the actuarial present value

$$\sum v^{k+1/2} \, {}_k p^{(T)}_{x+h} q^{(r)}_{x+h+k} R(x,h,k+1/2) \bar{a}^r_{x+h+k+1/2}$$

or, in commutation symbols,

$$\sum \frac{{}^a\bar{C}^{\,r}_{x+h+k}}{D^{(T)}_{x+h}} R(x,h,k+1/2)$$

The limits of summation, as well as the specific substitution for $R(x,h,k+1/2)$, are determined not by rote but with a careful analysis of the verbal description of the benefit prescribed. Similar comments are valid with respect to the actuarial present value of employee contributions.

Analysis of career average plans is more complex because of their very nature. Let us assume that the annualized pension is f times the aggregate lifetime earnings of the employee. The following diagram, indicating both a "year of earnings" and a subsequent "year of retirement" is helpful:

Usual simplifying assumptions lead to the following actuarial present value, taking into consideration only the one year of earnings and the one year of retirement as indicated:

$$v^{k+1/2} \, {}_k p^{(T)}_{x+h} q^{(r)}_{x+h+k} \bar{a}^r_{x+h+k+1/2} \cdot \frac{f(AS)_{x+h}}{S_{x+h}} (S_{x+h+j})$$

or

$$\frac{{}^a\bar{C}^{\,r}_{x+h+k}}{{}^S D^{(T)}_{x+h}} \cdot f(AS)_{x+h} \cdot S_{x+h+j}$$

Now, realizing that all years of earnings contribute to the ultimate retirement benefit, we sum over the variable j. Further realizing that one-half a year's salary will be earned in the year of retirement, we obtain the following actuarial present value still limited to the single year of retirement as indicated in the diagram:

$$v^{k+1/2} \, {}_k p^{(T)}_{x+h} q^{(r)}_{x+h+k} \bar{a}^r_{x+h+k+1/2} \cdot \frac{f(AS)_{x+h}}{S_{x+h}} (S_{x+h} + S_{x+h+1} + \cdots + S_{x+h+k-1} + \tfrac{1}{2} S_{x+h+k})$$

or

$$\frac{{}^a\bar{C}^{\,(r)}_{x+h+k}}{{}^S D^{(T)}_{x+h}} \cdot f(AS)_{x+h} (S_{x+h} + S_{x+h+1} + \cdots + S_{x+h+k-1} + \tfrac{1}{2} S_{x+h+k})$$

Finally, summation of these expressions over k produces the total actuarial present value, as desired.

3.   Similar observations, regarding an appeal to basic principles, may be reiterated for plans incorporating disability and/or withdrawal benefits. A particularly simple and logical technique is available where a return of contribution benefit is provided upon participant withdrawal prior to vesting of retirement benefits. Let us assume that participant contributions, improved at a rate of interest equal to the valuation rate of interest, are returned to the withdrawing employee.

With regard to past contributions, whose value at age $x + h$ is $(ATPC)_{x+h}$, we must simply realize that the actuarial present value of the return benefit to an active employee is $(ATPC)_{x+h}$ multiplied by the probability that he will actually exit the employee group via the decrement of withdrawal. This is because the rate of growth of these past contributions is exactly offset by the discount factor associated with the valuation rate of interest.

A similar analysis can be made for the actuarial present value of the return of a participant's "current year" contribution, again improved with interest at the valuation rate. For those who withdraw after age $x + 1$, the actuarial present value of the refund is the amount contributed times the probability of the withdrawal. For those who withdraw between ages x and $x + 1$, thus making only 50% of the scheduled annual contribution, the actuarial present value of the refund is only half as great. It is vital to realize, in each of these cases, that the actuarial present values just described must be multiplied by $v^{1/2}$ to reflect the assumption of mid-year contributions.

For example, consider an employee aged 40 whose accumulated past contributions total \$1000, who expects to contribute \$100 during the current year, and who is subject to the following multiple-decrement model:

x	$l_x^{(T)}$	$l_x^{(w)}$
40	10,000	2,000
41	7,000	1,200

The actuarial present value of the withdrawal benefit outlined above consists of three components:

$$\text{a)} \quad 1000 \frac{2000}{10,000} = 200$$

$$\text{b)} \quad 100 \frac{1200}{10,000} v^{1/2} = 12 v^{1/2}$$

$$\text{c)} \quad 50 \frac{800}{10,000} v^{1/2} = 4 v^{1/2}$$

for a total of $200 + 16 v^{1/2}$.

4. With regard to commutation functions, most such definitions in this chapter are straightforward and predictable. An important distinction, however, must be made between ${}^{Sa}\overline{M}_x^r$ and ${}^{S'a}\overline{M}_x^r$. The first of these is a sum of ${}^a\overline{C}_y$ functions, each weighted by the salary scale function at the appropriate age, i.e.,

$$ {}^{Sa}\overline{M}_x^r = S_x {}^a\overline{C}_x^r + S_{x+1} {}^a\overline{C}_{x+1}^r + S_{x+2} {}^a\overline{C}_{x+2}^r + \cdots . $$

The second of these is also a sum of ${}^a\overline{C}_y$ functions, but each is weighted by the single salary scale function S_{x-1}, i.e.,

$$ {}^{S'a}\overline{M}_x^r = S_{x-1} {}^a\overline{C}_x^r + S_{x-1} {}^a\overline{C}_{x+1}^r + S_{x-1} {}^a\overline{C}_{x+2}^r + \cdots $$

Whereas these symbols, and the corresponding functions ${}^{Sa}\overline{R}_x^r$ and ${}^{S'a}\overline{R}_x^r$ appear quite similar, they are in fact quite dissimilar. The single prime in the left hand superscript alone accounts for the difference between the future service actuarial present value for final salary pensions

$$\frac{f(AS)_{x+h}}{{}^{S}D^{(T)}_{x+h}} \cdot {}^{Sa}\bar{R}^{r}_{x+h+1}$$

and that for career average pensions

$$\frac{f(AS)_{x+h}}{{}^{S}D^{(T)}_{x+h}} \cdot {}^{S'a}\bar{R}^{r}_{x+h+1}.$$

If we assume an increasing salary scale, the former exceeds the latter, possibly by a substantial amount.

5.   Chapter Ten is unique in the text in that it contains very little to be memorized and relatively few new concepts. It constantly appeals to basic principles and notation of earlier chapters and its mastery is heavily dependent upon the student's ability to reduce verbose benefit descriptions to actuarial notation. This chapter does not require the same degree of concentrated and frequent attention which other chapters demand. It does, however form the basis of a vitally important actuarial area. It is difficult to master because of the necessary wordiness of the problems but, in a very real sense, it is the text's most elementary chapter.

Exercises

NOTE: Salary scale functions are assumed to be defined only on the positive integers unless otherwise indicated.

10–1   Find i, if $S_y = (1 + i)^{-y}$ and $\dfrac{{}_{20}\tilde{Z}_{45}}{S_{25}} = .7662$.

A) .015   B) .020   C) .025   D) .030   E) .035

10–2   If $S_x = 30 + .1x$, evaluate $\displaystyle\sum_{m=1}^{20} ({}_{m}\tilde{Z}_{60} - {}_{m}Z_{60})$.

A) −35   B) −1   C) 0   D) 1   E) 35

10–3   Employees A and B are each aged 40, are earning identical salaries, and plan to retire in the year of age between 60 and 61. Find the ratio of their expected 10-year final average salaries, if they are subject to the following salary scales:

$$^{A}S_X = (1.04)^{x-40}$$

$$^{B}S_X = 1 + .04(x - 40)$$

A) 1.04   B) 1.09   C) 1.13   D) 1.16   E) 1.20

10-4   Joe, hired at age 25 at a $30,000 salary, is permitted to participate in an employer-sponsored pension plan. The employer contributes 1% of Joe's salary each year throughout his tenure with the company. Contributions are made continuously.

If $\delta = .10$, ${}_t p_{25}^{(T)} = e^{-.02t}$, $t \geq 0$, and $S_x = (1.1)^x$, find the actuarial present value of the contributions to be made on Joe's behalf.

Given: $e^{.12} = 1.1275$. (Answer to the nearest $10)

A) $11,570   B) $11,590   C) $11,610   D) $11,630   E) $11,650

10-5   The accumulated total past contributions to a pension plan by a participant now aged 40 is $10,000. Upon withdrawal, interest is credited at a rate equal to the valuation rate. There is no upper limit on the age at which decrements from the work force are permitted.

If $\mu_{40+t}^{(w)} = \frac{1}{4}\mu_{40+t}^{(T)} = .04$, for all t, and $(1.04)^{1/4} = 1.01$, find the actuarial present value of the return of contributions which were made prior to age 40.

A) $99   B) $100   C) $2475   D) $2500   E) $2525

10-6   A man now aged 66, earning $32,000 per year, is participating in a 2% career average pension plan. His total past salary is $300,000. Which of the following represents the actuarial present value of the pension benefit credited for service in the next year?

I. $\dfrac{1}{D_{66}^{(T)}}[320^a\overline{M}{}_{66}^r + 640^a\overline{M}{}_{67}^r]$

II. $\dfrac{1}{D_{66}^{(T)}}[6320^a\overline{C}{}_{66}^r + 640^a\overline{M}{}_{67}^r]$

III. $\dfrac{640}{D_{66}^{(T)}}{}^a\overline{M}{}_{67}^r + 320v^{1/2}q_{66}^r\bar{a}_{66\frac{1}{2}}^r$

IV. $\dfrac{1}{{}^SD_{66}^{(T)}}[320^{Sa}\overline{C}{}_{66}^r + 640^{Sa}\overline{M}{}_{67}^r]$

A) I only   B) II only   C) III only   D) IV only   E) More than one is correct.

10-7   Find the net single premium for a one-year coverage to (55) which will pay him a life annuity of $6000 if he should retire or become disabled within the next year. The probability of disability in the next year is triple that of retirement. The first annuity payment is at the date of decrement.

Given: $D_{55}^{(T)} = 200$; ${}^a\overline{C}{}_{55}^r = 320$; $\ddot{a}_{55\frac{1}{2}}^i = .16\ddot{a}_{55\frac{1}{2}}^r$

A) $806.40   B) $1420.80   C) $2960.00   D) $6080.00   E) $18,960.00

10-8   Let $\alpha = 2^{Za}\bar{R}^{r}_{40} + {}^{Za}\bar{M}^{r}_{39}$

$\beta = 2^{Sa}\bar{R}^{r}_{40} + {}^{Sa}\bar{M}^{r}_{39}$

$\gamma = 2^{S'a}\bar{R}^{r}_{40} + {}^{Sa}\bar{M}^{r}_{39}$

If the salary scale function is increasing, which of the following is true?

A) $\gamma < \beta < \alpha$ B) $\beta < \gamma < \alpha$ C) $\gamma < \alpha < \beta$ D) $\alpha < \gamma < \beta$ E) $\alpha < \beta < \gamma$

10-9   Employees A and B are each aged 40 with \$10,000 annual salaries. A's annual pension will be 50% of his final salary; B's will be 50% of his 5-year final average salary. Find the excess of the actuarial present value of A's annual pension over that of B.

Given: ${}^{S}D^{(T)}_{40} = 25,000$

${}^{a}\bar{R}^{r}_{40} = 260,000$

${}^{a}\bar{R}^{r}_{41} = 250,000$

$S_{x} = x + 5$

A) \$2500   B) \$4000   C) \$5000   D) \$6000   E) \$7500

10-10   A vested benefit in a pension plan consists of return of employee contributions with interest at 5%. Consider an employee aged 53, who entered at age 33, and who has \$40,000 in accumulated contributions.

Find the actuarial present value of the refund benefit attributable to past contributions. The valuation rate of interest is 6%.

Given: $D^{(T)}_{53} = 8000$ $\bar{C}^{w}_{52} = 800$

$D^{(T)}_{54} = 7000$ $\bar{C}^{w}_{53} = 700$

$D^{(T)}_{55} = 5000$ $\bar{C}^{w}_{54} = 600$

$\bar{C}^{w}_{x} = 0, \quad x \geq 55.$

A) \$6450   B) \$6650   C) \$6814   D) \$6983   E) \$7155

10-11 Jones is an employee aged 25, currently earning \$30,000, who annually contributes \$1,000 to a retirement plan in addition to 5% of his salary, beginning at age 30. Find the actuarial present value of his future contributions, if retirements occur on birthdays no later than age 70. The salary scale is linear; Jones' salary is expected to have doubled as of the attainment of age 45.

A) $\dfrac{1}{D_{25}^{(T)}}[2500\overline{N}_{25}^{(T)} + 75\overline{S}_{26}^{(T)}]$ 　　　 B) $\dfrac{1}{D_{25}^{(T)}}[2500\overline{N}_{30}^{(T)} + 75\overline{S}_{31}^{(T)}]$

C) $\dfrac{1}{D_{25}^{(T)}}[2875\overline{N}_{30}^{(T)}]$ 　　　　　　　 D) $\dfrac{1}{D_{25}^{(T)}}[2800\overline{N}_{30}^{(T)} + 75\overline{S}_{30}^{(T)}]$

E) $\dfrac{1}{D_{25}^{(T)}}[2800\overline{N}_{30}^{(T)} + 75\overline{S}_{31}^{(T)}]$

10-12 A salary scale is set so that annual raises of $i\%$ are put into effect on each employee's birthday.

For a person aged 40, find the ratio of his final five year average salary under conditions I and II, where I assumes retirement at age $65\frac{1}{2}$ and II assumes retirement at age 65.

A) 1 　　　　 B) $1 + \frac{1}{2}i$ 　　　 C) $(1 + \frac{1}{2}i)(1 + i)$ 　 D) $1 + i$ 　　 E) $1 + \frac{3}{2}i$

10-13 If the discrete salary scale function S_x is linear, which of the following equals ${}_m\tilde{Z}_y$?

A) ${}_{m-1}Z_y$ 　　　 B) ${}_{m+1}Z_y$ 　　　 C) ${}_mZ_{y-1}$ 　　　 D) ${}_mZ_{y+1}$ 　　　 E) ${}_mZ_{y+1/2}$

10-14 An employee aged 35 has an annual salary of \$20,000 and his accumulated past contributions to a retirement plan equal \$9,000. His retirement benefits are vested at age 40, after which no withdrawal benefits are payable. Find the actuarial present value of his withdrawal benefit attributable to past and current year contributions, if interest on contributions is credited at $j = i = .1025$. Contributions are made at the rate of 10% of salary.

Given: $l_{35}^{(T)} = 4500$ 　　　 $l_{40}^{(T)} = 3000$

　　　　　 $l_{35}^{(w)} = 500$ 　　　 $d_{35}^{(w)} = 20$

A) \$1139 　　　 B) \$1160 　　　 C) \$1187 　　　 D) \$1207 　　　 E) \$1218

10-15   Employee A, aged 25, is currently earning \$25,000 per year, while B is earning \$37,500. It is assumed that A will retire in the year of age between 65 and 66 and that B will retire on his 65th birthday. The retirement income rate is the same for both employees and equals k % of their respective five-year final average salaries. Given their salary scale functions, find B's current age.

$$^{A}S_{x} = 2 + .16x$$
$$^{B}S_{x} = 1 + .50x$$

A) 43   B) 44   C) 45   D) 46   E) 47

10-16   A 60-year old employee has \$1,000 in accumulated past contributions to a retirement plan. He is currently earning \$30,000 and contributes 10% of his salary each year. Upon withdrawal, contributions are returned at $j = .0404$ which also equals the valuation rate.

Find the actuarial present value of the return of his past and current year contributions.

Given:

k	$l_{60+k}^{(T)}$	$q_{60+k}^{(w)}$
0	1000	.05
1	800	.05
2	620	.10
3	450	.02
4	340	.05
5	250	.06
6	180	.05
7	90	.10
8	40	.05
9	0	

A) \$492   B) \$508   C) \$637   D) \$719   E) \$766

10-17   Given: $S_{x} = a + bx$
$$_{5}\tilde{Z}_{20} = 33,600$$
$$_{10}Z_{60} = 64,000$$
Find $a - b$.

A) 19,200   B) 19,600   C) 20,000   D) 20,400   E) 20,800

10-18 The annual retirement benefit formula for a defined benefit plan is 55% of three-year final average earnings less 75% of estimated PIA. The benefit is reduced proportionately if the employee has less than 35 years of service at retirement. Find the increase in the annual benefit if (60), who was hired at 40, retires two years from now rather than retiring today.

x	$(AS)_x$		x	$(PIA)_x$
57	$18,700		60	$7272
58	$20,000		61	$7572
59	$21,000		62	$8100
60	$21,840			

$$S_x = (1.05)^x, \quad x = 60, 61, \ldots$$

A) $604   B) $623   C) $978   D) $1046   E) $1057

10-19 A career average plan provides for a retirement pension of 2% of total salary. Retirements occur as assumed in *Actuarial Mathematics*, but any employees attaining age 63 must retire at that time. Assume only two decrements.

An employee aged 60 has total past salary of $750,000 and is currently earning $40,000. Find the actuarial present value of his benefit attributable to past contributions.

Given:

x	$d_x^{(r)}$	$d_x^{(d)}$	$\ddot{a}_{x+1/2}^r$
60	500	40	10.5
61	500	45	10.2
62	2000	50	9.8

$$l_{60}^{(T)} = 100,000$$
$$i = .0816$$
$$\ddot{a}_{63}^r = 9.4$$

(Answer to the nearest $100.)

A) $101,200   B) $103,900   C) $108,100   D) $111,800   E) $122,100

10-20 An excess-type plan requires contributions of 15% of salary in excess of H_k for year $k+1$. Contributions are made by a 55-year old employee until attainment of age 60. His current salary is $40,000. The actuarial present value of his contributions is $143.40. Find H_4.

k	S_{55+k}	$_{k+1/2}E_{55}^{(T)}$	H_k
0	.9800	.8910	$42,000
1	1.0094	.7990	$42,500
2	1.0388	.6675	$43,000
3	1.0780	.5040	$43,500
4	1.1270	.3200	

A) $43,600   B) $43,700   C) $43,800   D) $43,900   E) $44,000

10-21   Employee contributions to a pension plan are made at a flat rate of $c per annum. The actuarial present value of future contributions for an active employee aged 56 is $50,000. Contributions are made continuously.

From the following data, and using the uniform distribution of decrements assumption, determine c.

$$N_{56}^{(T)} = 42,000$$
$$N_{57}^{(T)} = 35,000$$
$$i = .0430$$
$$\delta = .0421$$

(Answer to the nearest $10.)

A) $8300   B) $8310   C) $8320   D) $9090   E) $9100

10-22   Employee A will receive, upon withdrawal, the accumulated value of his total past contributions with interest credited at 5%. Employee B receives a similar benefit, but with 4% interest. The actuarial present value of A's benefit is $9478.49. Find the corresponding figure for B, given:

Employee	Current Age	$ATPC$
A	58	45,000
B	58	40,000

$$\overline{C}_{58}^{(w)} = 400$$
$$\overline{C}_{59}^{(w)} = 500$$
$$\overline{C}_{x}^{(w)} = 0, \qquad x \geq 60.$$

A) $8340   B) $8345   C) $9115   D) $9380   E) $9390

10-23   Throughout a worker's lifetime, contributions are made at a rate of 3% of initial salary. The actuarial present value of the future contributions of an employee, now aged 50, is 20.305% of his current salary. At what age was he hired?

Given:

$$S_x = (1 + j)^x, \qquad x = 30, 31, 32, \ldots$$
$$\mu^{(T)} = \delta = j = .05$$

A) 34   B) 35   C) 42   D) 45   E) 46

10-24 Employees A and B are both age 50; A's current salary is $40,000. Assuming retirement of each between ages 65 and 66, the 10-year final average salary of A will be 146.25% of that of B. Find B's current salary, given that A's salary increases by 5% per year while B's will increase annually by 5% of his current salary; ${}^A S_{50} = {}^B S_{50}$.

(Answer to nearest $100.)

A) $14,400   B) $25,700   C) $27,300   D) $30,000   E) $64,200

10-25 A retirement benefit pays K per complete year of service beyond age 67. If the actuarial present value of this benefit for an employee aged 66 is $380, find K.

Given:

x	${}^{a}\bar{C}{}_{x}^{r}$	D_{x}^{T}
66	30	100
67	40	90
68	50	80
69	60	70
70	70	60

$(\omega = 71)$

A) 60   B) 70   C) 80   D) 90   E) 100

10-26 If $S_y = 1 + 2y$, $y \geq 0$, is a continuous salary scale function, evaluate ${}_{10}Z_{50}$.

A) 90   B) 90.5   C) 91   D) 91.5   E) 92

10-27 A 30-year old employee, hired five years ago and currently earning $15,000, is participating in a pension plan. His retirement annuity will be 1% of the first $20,000 of his final salary and 2% of the excess, all multiplied by number of years of service. Assume that his salary doubles every ten years. Find the annual income benefit rate, assuming retirement between ages 60 and 61.

A) $67,100   B) $77,000   C) $78,100   D) $91,000   E) $92,300

10-28 Given: $S_x = (1.04)^{2x}$, $x = 50, 50\frac{1}{2}, 51, \ldots$

Find: $\dfrac{{}_4Z_{60}}{S_{56}}$.

(All annuity values are at 4%.)

A) $\dfrac{1}{8}\left(\dfrac{1}{a_{\overline{2}|}} + \dfrac{1}{s_{\overline{8}|}}\right)s_{\overline{8}|}$ B) $\dfrac{1}{4}\dfrac{s_{\overline{8}|}}{s_{\overline{2}|}}$ C) $\dfrac{1}{4}\dfrac{s_{\overline{8}|}}{a_{\overline{2}|}}$ D) $\dfrac{1}{8}\ddot{s}_{\overline{8}|}$ E) $\dfrac{1}{8}s_{\overline{8}|}$

10–29   An employee aged 60 will make a contribution of $1000 to a pension plan in the current year; contributions in subsequent years increase by 6.09% per annum.

Find the actuarial present value of contributions made prior to age 65, using the assumptions in *Actuarial Mathematics* and the following:

$$i^{(2)} = .06$$

$$l^{(T)}_{60+t} = 100 - 10t, \quad 0 \leq t \leq 10.$$

A) $3500   B) $3535   C) $3641   D) $3750   E) $4000

10–30   Find the actuarial present value of future contributions to a pension plan for a man now aged 50. Contributions are expected to increase at a compound annual rate of 4% from the current year level of $1000. Let $i = .06$. Contributions are made in accordance with the assumptions in *Actuarial Mathematics*.

A) $971.29 $\dfrac{\overline{N}^{(T)}_{50}}{D^{T}_{50}}$ $@i = \dfrac{1}{52}$

B) $980.58 $\dfrac{\overline{N}^{(T)}_{50}}{D^{(T)}_{50}}$ $@i = \dfrac{1}{52}$

C) $1000 $\dfrac{\overline{N}^{(T)}_{50}}{D^{(T)}_{50}}$ $@i = .06$

D) $1000 $\dfrac{N^{(T)}_{50}}{D^{(T)}_{50}}$ $@i = .06$

E) $1000 $\dfrac{N^{(T)}_{50}}{D^{(T)}_{50}}$ $@i = \dfrac{1}{52}$

10–31   Mr. Jones, aged 35, has $50,000 in accumulated past contributions to a pension plan. Upon withdrawal, he will receive this lump sum, improved with interest at 5% per annum.

Find the actuarial present value of his withdrawal benefit, given:

$$i = .05$$

$$\mu^{(r)}_{35+t} = \frac{1}{2}\mu^{(i)}_{35+t} = \frac{1}{3}\mu^{(w)}_{35+t} = \frac{1}{4}\mu^{(d)}_{35+t}, \quad \text{for all } t.$$

A) $5000   B) $10,000   C) $15,000   D) $50,000   E) Cannot be determined

10-32   Retirements in a pension plan may occur only at exact age 65. Annual benefits, beginning at that time, equal 30% of the average annual salary over the last 5 years prior to retirement.

An employee, hired 15 years ago at age 30, is earning $20,000. Find the actuarial present value of his pension, if the continuous salary scale function is given by

$$S_{45+t} = 80 + 7t + 2t^2, \quad t \geq 0$$

A) $15 \, {}_5Z_{65} \, {}_{20}E_{45}^{(T)} \, \bar{a}_{65}^r$ B) $75 \, {}_5\tilde{Z}_{65} \, {}_{20}E_{45}^{(T)} \, \bar{a}_{65}^r$ C) $57,690 \, {}_{20}E_{45}^{(T)} \, \bar{a}_{65}^r$
D) $61,437.5 \, {}_{20}E_{45}^{(T)} \, \bar{a}_{65}^r$ E) None of these

10-33   In an excess-type plan, both the employer and the employee make contributions until the employee's attainment of age 65. Employees make contributions of 10% of the excess of their annual salary over H_k, where k is their age at the beginning of the year. The employer makes contributions of 1% of the excess. In addition, a new tax law provides that the employee's contributions in excess of $200 in any year are taxed at 50%.

An employee aged 62 is earning $25,000. Using the assumptions in *Actuarial Mathematics*, and the following table, find the after-tax actuarial present value of all contributions to be made on his behalf.

				H_x	
x	S_x	${}_{x-61\frac{1}{2}}p_{62}^{(T)}$	$v^{x-61\frac{1}{2}}$	Employee	Employer
62	1.0	.9	.97	23,000	26,000
63	1.1	.8	.91	25,300	27,300
64	1.2	.7	.86	27,600	28,700
65	1.3	.6	.81	30,000	30,000

A) $249   B) $414   C) $469   D) $489   E) $591

10-34   A pension benefit is defined as 60% of final salary, less 2% of final salary multiplied by a social insurance factor given by $(.2t + 15)$, where t is the exact number of years of service.

Starting salaries are $1000 per year of age; salaries then increase continuously by $1500 for each year of service. Retirements occur continuously between age 55 and 70.

An employee aged 50 was hired at age 35. He chooses his retirement date in order to maximize his pension. What pension will he receive?

A) $14,484.00   B) $14,496.00   C) $14,500.00   D $14,504.00   E) $14,504.17

10–35   The retirement annuity in a pension plan is defined to be the total number of years of service times 2% of the current social security wage base, plus the complete number of years of service times the greater of

   i) $1\frac{3}{4}\%$ of the three-year final average salary in excess of the wage base
        and
   ii) $1\frac{1}{4}\%$ of the final salary in excess of the wage base.

An employee now aged 60, whose starting salary five years ago was \$40,000, plans to retire between ages 65 and 66. If the wage base five years from now will be \$50,000, find his annual benefit at retirement.

Assume $S_x = (1.05)^x$.

(Answer to nearest \$100.)

A) \$11,900   B) \$12,200   C) \$12,300   D) \$12,400   E) \$12,500

10–36   A 50-year old is trying to decide between two job offers, each offering a beginning salary of \$40,000. He decides to make his choice solely on the basis of the pension he will receive upon retirement on his 60th birthday.

The plan of employer A provides for a 2% career average pension plan, and is based upon a salary scale function $S_x = 15 + .1x$.

The plan of employer B provides for a pension of k% of final five year average salary per year of service. Salaries are projected to increase by 5% on each birthday.

What value of k would make him unable to use the pension criterion to select an employer?

A) 1.40   B) 1.45   C) 1.50   D) 1.55   E) 1.60

10–37   Joe, age 20, accepts two jobs, each paying \$20,000 per year. Each provides a pension benefit of 40% of final salary. The first job offers a 5% raise on each birthday; the second offers a \$1000 raise on each birthday.

How many complete years must Joe work in order to earn a retirement pension of at least \$30,000 per year? Assume retirements in the middle of the year of age.

A) 12   B) 13   C) 14   D) 15   E) 16

10-38   The retirement benefit in a pension plan is a continuous whole life annuity of 2% of final salary times the total years of service. For a new employee aged 25, find the actuarial present value of his pension, per unit of starting salary, given:

  I) $S_x = 625e^{.1025+.1x}$, $x \geq 25$

  II) $\mu_x^{(r)} = \frac{1}{65-x}$, $45 \leq x < 65$
        $= 0$, otherwise

  III) $\mu_x^{(i)} = .01$, $25 \leq x < 65$

  IV) $\mu_x^{(w)} = \frac{1}{65-x}$, $25 \leq x < 45$

  V) $\mu_x^{(d)} = .04$, $25 \leq x < 65$

  VI) $\delta = .05$

  VII) The force of mortality for retired or disabled persons is .2, for all ages.

A) .25   B) .40   C) .50   D) .53   E) .56

10-39   A pension plan has one participant, aged 40, currently earning \$40,000. Contributions are made at the beginning of each year at the rate of 2% of current salary. If the salary scale $S_x = \frac{x}{40}$, $_tE_{40}^{(T)} = (1.05)^{-t}$, $t = 0, 1, 2, \ldots, 29$, calculate the actuarial present value of future contributions. Retirement is mandatory at age 70.

(All answers at $i = .05$.)

A) $\$1220 \, (a_{\overline{30}|} - 10v^{30})$ B) $\$1220 \, (\ddot{a}_{\overline{30}|} - 10v^{30})$ C) $\$1200 \, (\ddot{a}_{\overline{30}|} - 10v^{29})$

        D) $\$1200 \, (\ddot{a}_{\overline{30}|} - 10v^{30})$ E) $\$1220 \, a_{\overline{30}|} - \$12000v^{30}$

10-40   A pension plan provides a lump sum withdrawal benefit of \$25 for each complete year of service in addition to a death benefit of \$250. Given the following double-decrement table, find the total actuarial present value of the two benefits for an employee aged 57 who was hired at age 20. Retirement is mandatory upon the attainment of age 60.

Let $i = .05$. Benefits are payable at the end of the year of decrement.

x	$q_x^{(w)}$	$q_x^{(d)}$
57	.018	.016
58	.015	.018
59	.010	.020

A) \$38   B) \$41   C) \$44   D) \$46   E) \$48

10–41   Employees of a certain organization receive salary increases of 10% on each birthday. An employee now aged y will make contributions, at the beginning of each year, of 10% of his *starting* salary, throughout his working lifetime. The actuarial present value of his future contributions is 12.5% of his *current* salary.

Find, to the nearest integer, the number of years of *past* service of this employee, given

$$p_x^{(T)} = .9 \quad \text{for all integral } x$$
$$i = .1$$
$$ln2 = .693$$
$$ln1.1 = .095$$

A) 14   B) 15   C) 16   D) 17   E) 18

10–42   An employee, hired 20 years ago, is age 50 on January 1 of this year; his current salary is \$25,000. His salary is expected to increase by 5% on each May 1 and each September 1. His annual pension will be 2% of his two-year final average salary multiplied by his total years of service.

Find $R(30, 20, 10\frac{1}{2})$.

(Answer to nearest \$10.)

A) \$38,600   B) \$38,610   C) \$38,620   D) \$38,630   E) \$38,640

10–43   The income benefit rate in a retirement plan is $r\%$ of the three-year final average salary plus 20% of the career average salary of the retiree. The continuous salary scale function is given by

$$S_{40+t} = t + 20, \quad -10 \le t \le 20.$$

If the employee's annual pension will equal 102% of his current salary, find r. He is currently age 40, was hired at age 30, and will retire at exact age 60.

A) 20   B) 25   C) 30   D) 35   E) 40

10-44   Each employee contributes 5% of his earnings to fund a social insurance plan. Contributions, however, are waived on earnings which exceed a variable wage base.

An employee is exact age 44 on January 1, 1990 and will earn $70,000 in 1990. His contribution for 1990 will be $2000.

Based upon the following assumptions, find the actuarial present value as of January 1, 1990 of the contributions waived due to the existence of the wage base.

    i)   Contributions are made at midyear.

    ii)   Salaries increase by 6.08% on each birthday.

    iii)   The wage base increases by 4% annually.

    iv) $i = .04$.

    v)   Prior to mandatory retirement at age 65, there are no decrements.

(Answer to nearest $100.)

A) $30,900   B) $41,200   C) $44,300   D) $47,300   E) $57,600

Answers to Chapter Ten Exercises

10–1	D.	10–16	E.	10–31	C.
10–2	B.	10–17	A.	10–32	D.
10–3	C.	10–18	B.	10–33	C.
10–4	B.	10–19	D.	10–34	E.
10–5	D.	10–20	C.	10–35	D.
10–6	C.	10–21	E.	10–36	B.
10–7	B.	10–22	A.	10–37	D.
10–8	C.	10–23	C.	10–38	D.
10–9	C.	10–24	D.	10–39	C.
10–10	C.	10–25	E.	10–40	E.
10–11	D.	10–26	E.	10–41	C.
10–12	B.	10–27	C.	10–42	A.
10–13	B.	10–28	D.	10–43	E.
10–14	D.	10–29	C.	10–44	D.
10–15	D.	10–30	B.		

Solutions

10–1.

Key Concept: The standard formulas used for geometric salary scale functions are not applicable here, as this expression for S_y represents a *decreasing* salary scale. Accordingly, we should appeal to basic principles.

$$\frac{_{20}\tilde{Z}_{45}}{S_{25}} = \frac{S_{44} + S_{43} + S_{42} + \cdots + S_{25}}{20 S_{25}}$$

$$= \frac{1}{20}\left((1+i)^{-19} + (1+i)^{-18} + (1+i)^{-17} + \cdots + 1\right)$$

$$= \frac{1}{20}\ddot{a}_{\overline{20}|i} = .7662$$

$$\therefore \ddot{a}_{\overline{20}|i} = 15.324$$

Referring to interest tables, we have $i = \underline{\underline{.03}}$.

10–2.

Key Formulas:
$$_mZ_x = S_{x-m/2}$$
$$_m\tilde{Z}_x = S_{x-m/2-1/2}$$

Thus,
$$_mZ_{60} = S_{60-m/2} = 36 - .05m$$
$$\text{and}$$
$$_m\tilde{Z}_{60} = S_{60-m/2-1/2} = 35.95 - .05m$$

Finally,
$$\sum_{m=1}^{20}(\,_m\tilde{Z}_{60} - \,_mZ_{60}) = \sum_{m=1}^{20}(-.05) = \underline{\underline{-1}}$$

NOTE: Since $_mZ_x$ is larger than $_m\tilde{Z}_x$ for salary scales with positive slope, it should be clear that this question must have a negative answer.

10–3.

Key Concept: Since current salaries are identical, the year of retirement is the same, and the values of the salary scales are equal at age 40, we must only determine
$$\frac{^A_{10}Z_{60}}{^B_{10}Z_{60}}.$$
Thus, using the formulas for linear and geometric salary scales, we have
$$\frac{^A_{10}Z_{60}}{^B_{10}Z_{60}} = \frac{^AS_{60}(a_{\overline{10|}} + \ddot{a}_{\overline{10|}})}{20\,^BS_{55}}$$
$$= \frac{(1.04)^{20}}{20(1.6)}(a_{\overline{10|}.04} + \ddot{a}_{\overline{10|}.04}).$$

From interest tables, we have $\underline{1.13}$.

10–4.

Appealing to basic principles and a simple diagram, we have

Year of
Contribution

| 25 | 25 + k | 26 + k |

$$30,000(.01)(1.1)^k \bar{a}^{(T)}_{25+k:\,\overline{1}|}\, {}_kE^{(T)}_{25}$$

as the actuarial present value of the contributions for a single year of age.

Since $\mu^{(T)}_x + \delta = .12$, we have

$$\bar{a}^{(T)}_{25+k:\,\overline{1}|} = \bar{a}^{(T)}_{25}(1 - {}_1E^{(T)}_{25})$$
$$= \frac{1}{.12}(1 - e^{-.12})$$

and

$${}_kE^{(T)}_{25} = e^{-.12k}$$

Putting the pieces together, and summing, we have

$$\sum_{k=0}^{\infty} 300(1.1)^k \left(\frac{1}{.12}\right)\left(1 - e^{-.12}\right)e^{-.12k}$$
$$= 2500(1 - e^{-.12})\sum_{0}^{\infty}(1.1e^{-.12})^k$$
$$= 2500(1 - e^{-.12})\left(\frac{1}{1 - (1.1)e^{-.12}}\right)$$
$$= 2500\frac{e^{.12} - 1}{e^{.12} - 1.1}$$
$$= \underline{\underline{11,591}}$$

10-5.

Key Concept: Since the two interest rates are equal, and the probability that a current participant will exit via withdrawal is $1/4$, the actuarial present value of return of past contributions is simply their current value times $1/4$.

Accordingly, we have

$$10,000\left(\frac{1}{4}\right) = \underline{\underline{2500}}$$

Note that the *magnitude* of the forces was irrelevant; only their *ratio* is significant.

10-6.

Key Concept: This question, like many pension benefit problems of this type, is most efficiently handled by a basic principles approach. Mathematical formulas and summations are unnecessary.

In the upcoming year, the pension benefit will grow by \$640 if the employee works the entire year, and \$320 otherwise, according to standard assumptions on distribution of decrements. These can be treated in a manner similar to life insurance, with the benefit payable as an annuity upon retirement. Accordingly, one of the simpler forms of the correct answer is

$$\frac{320^a\bar{C}^r_{66} + 640^a\bar{M}^r_{67}}{D^{(T)}_{66}}.$$

Thus, answers I, II, and IV are clearly incorrect. Answer <u>III</u> is correct because

$$\frac{^a\bar{C}^r_{66}}{D^{(T)}_{66}} = v^{1/2} q^r_{66} \bar{a}^r_{66\frac{1}{2}}.$$

10-7.

Key Concept:

Since $^a\bar{C}^r_{55} = v^{55\frac{1}{2}} r_{55} \bar{a}^r_{55\frac{1}{2}}$ and

$$^a\bar{C}^i_{55} = v^{55\frac{1}{2}} i_{55} \bar{a}^i_{55\frac{1}{2}},$$

and the ratios $\dfrac{r_{55}}{i_{55}}$ and $\dfrac{\bar{a}^r_{55\frac{1}{2}}}{\bar{a}^i_{55\frac{1}{2}}}$ are given, we can find $^a\bar{C}^i_{55}$ from the given values.

Accordingly, $^a\bar{C}^i_{55} = {}^a\bar{C}^r_{55} \left(\dfrac{i_{55}}{r_{55}}\right) \left(\dfrac{\bar{a}^i_{55\frac{1}{2}}}{\bar{a}^r_{55\frac{1}{2}}}\right)$

$$= (320)(3)(.16)$$
$$= 153.6$$

Thus the actuarial present value of this benefit is

$$\frac{6000}{D^{(T)}_{55}}\left({}^a\bar{C}^r_{65} + {}^a\bar{C}^i_{65}\right) = \underline{1420.80}$$

10-8.

Key Concept:

When the appropriate denominator, $2D^{(T)}_{39}$, is supplied, we have the actuarial present values, respectively, of pensions based upon

    a) salary for the final m years of employment
    b) salary for the final year of employment
    c) salary for all years of employment

If salaries increase, the size of the pension is inversely proportional to the number of years of salary used in its determination. Thus $\underline{\gamma < \alpha < \beta}$.

10–9.

Key Concept:

Whereas the answer to this question is clearly $\dfrac{5000}{{}^S D_{40}^{(T)}}({}^{Sa}\overline{M}{}_{40}^{r} - {}^{za}\overline{M}{}_{40}^{r})$, the commutation symbols must be decomposed in order to incorporate the given salary scale function. Accordingly,

$$\frac{1}{5}({}^{Sa}\overline{M}{}_{40}^{r} - {}^{Za}\overline{M}{}_{40}^{r}) = \frac{1}{5}\sum_{k=0}^{\infty}({}^{Sa}\overline{C}{}_{40+k}^{r} - {}^{Za}\overline{C}{}_{40+k}^{r})$$

$$= \frac{1}{5}\sum_{0}^{\infty}(S_{40+k}{}^{a}\overline{C}{}_{40+k}^{r} - Z_{40+k}{}^{a}\overline{C}{}_{40+k}^{r})$$

$$= \frac{1}{5}\sum_{0}^{\infty}((45+k) - (42\tfrac{1}{2}+k)){}^{a}\overline{C}{}_{40+k}^{r}$$

$$= \frac{1}{2}{}^{a}\overline{M}{}_{40}^{r} = \underline{5000}$$

10–10.

Key Concept:

With the two relevant interest rates being unequal, a basic principles approach must be used. Since the commutation values indicate that all withdrawals occur before age 55, there are only two cases to consider for a life aged 53.

The actuarial present value, then, is

$$\frac{40,000}{D_{53}^{(T)}}(\overline{C}_{53}^{(w)}(1.05)^{1/2} + \overline{C}_{54}^{(w)}(1.05)^{3/2})$$

$$= 5(1.05)^{1/2}[700 + 600(1.05)]$$

$$= \underline{6814}$$

10–11.

This question primarily involves the determination of expected salaries at ages 30 and greater. Salaries increase by a total of $30,000 in 20 years. Since the salary scale is linear, the expected increase is $1500 per annum.

The following diagram indicates the expected salary pattern (above the line) and the expected contribution pattern (below the line).

		37,500		39,000		40,500		42,000	$\cdots$
✳									
25		30		31		32		33	
		2,875		2,950		3,025		3,100	$\cdots$

The contribution pattern leads immediately to the actuarial present value given by answer $\underline{D}$.

10–12.

The question is $\dfrac{_5Z_{65}}{_5\tilde{Z}_{65}}$. The salary scale $S_x = (1+i)^x$ produces

$$\frac{_5Z_{65}}{_5\tilde{Z}_{65}} = \frac{S_{65}(\frac{1}{10})(a_{\overline{5|}} + \ddot{a}_{\overline{5|}})}{S_{65}(\frac{1}{5})a_{\overline{5|}}}$$

$$= \frac{1}{2}(1 + (1+i))$$

$$= 1 + \frac{1}{2}i$$

10–13.

Key Concept:

Although this question could be solved quickly by an algebraic approach, it is more instructive to consider it diagrammatically. The symbol $_m\tilde{Z}_y$ refers to salaries earned between ages $y - m$ and y; the symbol $_{m+1}Z_y$ refers to salaries earned between ages $y - m - \frac{1}{2}$ and $y + \frac{1}{2}$. Since the second interval overlaps the first by an equal amount on each end, and since the salary scale is linear, the resulting average salaries are equal.

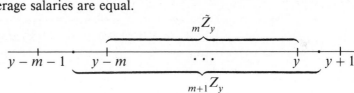

Accordingly, $_m\tilde{Z}_y = {}_{m+1}Z_y$.

10–14.

Key Concept:

The probability of (35)'s withdrawal after age 35 is $\frac{500}{4500}$, and the probability of his withdrawal after age 36 is $\frac{480}{4500}$. Thus the three components of the required actuarial present value are immediately available, i.e.,

$$9000\left(\frac{500}{4500}\right) + 2000\left(\frac{480}{4500}\right)v^{1/2} + 1000\left(\frac{20}{4500}\right)v^{1/2}$$

Since $v^{1/2} = \dfrac{1}{(1.1025)^{1/2}} = \dfrac{1}{1.05}$, we have

$$1000 + 217.78\left(\frac{1}{1.05}\right) = 1207.41$$

10–15.

Equating the two retirement income rates, we have

$$.01k(25,000)\frac{{}_5^AZ_{65}}{{}^AS_{65}} = .01k(37,500)\frac{{}_5^B\tilde{Z}_{65}}{{}^BS_x}.$$

Applying the given linear salary scales, we have

$$\frac{25,000}{6}{}^AS_{62\frac{1}{2}} = \frac{37,500}{1+.5x}{}^BS_{62}$$

$$\frac{25,000}{6}(12) = \frac{37,500}{1+.5x}(32)$$

$$\therefore x = \underline{\underline{46}}$$

10–16.

Key Technique: In order to determine the required probabilities for this familiar problem, construction of a portion of a decrement table is helpful.

x	60	61	62	63	64	65	66	67	68
w_x	50	40	62	9	17	15	9	9	2
$l_x^{(w)}$	213	163	123	61	52	35	20	11	2

Now, the three required components of the actuarial present value are

a) $1000(\frac{213}{1000})$

b) $3000v^{1/2}(\frac{163}{1000})$

c) $1500v^{1/2}(\frac{50}{1000})$

Since $v^{1/2} = \frac{1}{1.02}$, we have

$$213 + 564\left(\frac{1}{1.02}\right) = \underline{\underline{766}}$$

10–17.

Key Formulas:

$$_mZ_x = S_{x-m/2}$$
$$_m\tilde{Z}_x = S_{x-m/2-1/2}$$

$$\text{Thus,} \quad {}_5\tilde{Z}_{20} = S_{17} = a + 17b = 33,600$$
$$_{10}Z_{60} = S_{55} = a + 55b = 64,000.$$

Solving, $a = 20,000$; $b = 800$.

Finally, $a - b = \underline{\underline{19,200}}$.

10–18.

This is an elementary problem, requiring little more than a careful reading of the benefit description. The question may be symbolically stated as

$$R(40,20,2) - R(40,20,0).$$

Then,

$$R(40,20,0) = \left[.55\left(\frac{18,700 + 20,000 + 21,000}{3}\right) - .75(7272)\right]\frac{20}{35}$$

$$= 3137.71$$

$$R(40,20,2) = \left[.55\left(\frac{21,000 + 21,840 + 21,840(1.05)}{3}\right) - .75(8100)\right]\frac{22}{35}$$

$$= 3760.87$$

Finally,

$$3760.87 - 3137.71 = \underline{623.16}$$

10–19.

There are four points at which (60) is permitted to retire, specifically, at ages $60\frac{1}{2}$, $61\frac{1}{2}$, $62\frac{1}{2}$, and 63. The four components of the actuarial present value are found by discounting $\$750,000(.02)$ with the appropriate probabilities and discount factors, and then weighting with the appropriate annuities. We have, for the four cases,

a) $\quad 15,000\left(\frac{500}{100,000}\right)v^{1/2}(10.5)$

b) $\quad 15,000\left(\frac{500}{100,000}\right)v^{3/2}(10.2)$

c) $\quad 15,000\left(\frac{2000}{100,000}\right)v^{5/2}(9.8)$

d) $\quad 15,000\left(\frac{96,865}{100,000}\right)v^{3}(9.4)$

The ensuing arithmetic leads to an actuarial present value of $\underline{111,795}$.

10–20.

Key Concept:

Not until age 58 does the employee's salary exceed the H_k value for the appropriate year. Accordingly, contributions are made for a maximum of two years.

The actuarial present values of the contributions for those two years are, respectively,

$$(.504)\left[40,000\left(\frac{1.0780}{.9800}\right) - 43,500\right](.15) = 37.8$$

and

$$(.320)\left[40,000\left(\frac{1.1270}{.9800}\right) - H_4\right](.15) = 2208 - .048H_4.$$

Thus,

$$143.40 = 2245.8 - .048H_4$$
$$H_4 = \underline{\underline{43,800}}$$

10–21.

Key Approach:

We need to determine the actuarial present value $\bar{a}_{56}^{(T)}$, or $\dfrac{\overline{N}_{56}^{(T)}}{D_{56}^{(T)}}$.

Since only discrete annuity values are directly obtainable, we must use a formula analogous to the familiar approximation

$$\bar{a}_x = \alpha(\infty)\ddot{a}_x - \beta(\infty).$$

Specifically,

$$\begin{aligned}
\bar{a}_{56}^{(T)} &= \alpha(\infty)\ddot{a}_{56}^{(T)} - \beta(\infty) \\
&= \frac{id}{\delta^2} \cdot 6 - \frac{i-\delta}{\delta^2} \\
&= 5.493
\end{aligned}$$

Finally,

$$c\bar{a}_{56}^{(T)} = 50,000$$
$$c = \underline{\underline{9102}}$$

10–22.

Dealing only with Employee A, and realizing that there are only two possible years of withdrawal, we have

$$9478.49 = 45,000\left[\frac{400}{D_{58}^{(T)}}(1.05)^{1/2} + \frac{500}{D_{58}^{(T)}}(1.05)^{3/2}\right].$$

Solving, $D_{58}^{(T)} = 4500$.

Finally, considering Employee B, we have as the required actuarial present value

$$40,000\left[\frac{400}{4500}(1.04)^{1/2} + \frac{500}{4500}(1.04)^{3/2}\right] = \underline{\underline{8340}}$$

10–23.

Letting y represent the age at hire, the employee's salary at that time was

$$(AS)_{50} \cdot \frac{S_y}{S_{50}}.$$

Using the fact that $\bar{a}_{50}^{(T)} = \dfrac{1}{\mu^{(T)} + \delta} = 10$, we have

$$.03(AS)_{50} \cdot \frac{S_y}{S_{50}} \bar{a}_{50}^{(T)} = .20305(AS)_{50}.$$

Solving,

$$.3 \frac{S_y}{S_{50}} = .20305$$

$$\frac{S_{50}}{S_y} = 1.4775 = (1.05)^{50-y}$$

From interest tables, we have $y = \underline{\underline{42}}$.

10–24.

The salary scales may be represented as

$$^A S_x = (1.05)^{x-50}$$
$$^B S_x = 1 + .05(x - 50) = .05x - 1.5.$$

Expressing the question symbolically, we have

$$\frac{40{,}000 \, {}^A_{10}Z_{65}}{K \cdot {}^B_{10}Z_{65}} = 1.4626$$

where K is B's current salary. Now, using familiar relationships for these salary scales, we have

$$\frac{40{,}000(\frac{1}{20})^A S_{65}(\ddot{a}_{\overline{10|}} + a_{\overline{10|}})}{K(1.5)} = 1.4626.$$

Using interest tables at 5%, $K = \underline{\underline{30{,}000}}$.

10–25.

This problem merely requires reading, understanding of the commutation symbols, and enumeration of cases. Thus,

$$380 = \frac{K}{D_{66}^{(T)}}({}^a\bar{C}_{68}^{\, r} + 2\,{}^a\bar{C}_{69}^{\, r} + 3\,{}^a\bar{C}_{70}^{\, r})$$

$$= \frac{K}{100}(380)$$

Thus, $K = \underline{\underline{100}}$.

10–26.

Key Concept: Salary scale functions are usually step functions, changing only once per year. Here, the salary scale is continuous. Thus, $_{10}Z_{50}$, usually defined as

$$\frac{1}{20}(S_{50} + 2S_{49} + 2S_{48} + \cdots + 2S_{41} + S_{40}),$$

must be defined here as

$$\frac{1}{10} \int_{40.5}^{50.5} S_y \, dy.$$

Integrating, we have

$$\frac{1}{10} \int_{40.5}^{50.5} (1 + 2y) \, dy = \underline{\underline{92}}.$$

10–27.

In the year of age from 60 to 61, this employee's annual salary is expected to be $\$15,000(8) = \$120,000$. Thus,

$$R(25, 5, 30\tfrac{1}{2}) = [(.01)(20,000) + (.02)(100,000)](35.5)$$
$$= \underline{\underline{78,100}}$$

10–28.

Key Concept: With a salary scale function defined at every half-age, the definition of $_4Z_{60}$ must be modified, i.e.,

$$_4Z_{60} = \frac{1}{8}[S_{60} + S_{59\frac{1}{2}} + S_{59} + \cdots + S_{56\frac{1}{2}}].$$

Thus,

$$\frac{_4Z_{60}}{S_{56}} = \frac{1}{8}[(1.04)^8 + (1.04)^7 + (1.04)^6 + \cdots + (1.04)]$$

$$= \underline{\underline{\frac{\ddot{s}_{\overline{8}|.04}}{8}}}$$

10–29.

The required actuarial present value is

$$1000[v^{1/2} \,_{1/2}p_{60}^{(T)} + v^{3/2}(1.03)^2 \,_{3/2}p_{60}^{(T)} + \cdots + v^{9/2}(1.03)^8 \,_{9/2}p_{60}^{(T)}]$$

$$= 1000v^{1/2}[\,_{1/2}p_{60}^{(T)} + \,_{3/2}p_{60}^{(T)} + \cdots + \,_{9/2}p_{60}^{(T)}]$$

$$= \frac{1000}{1.03}\left(\frac{95 + 85 + 75 + 65 + 55}{100}\right)$$

$$= \underline{\underline{3641}}$$

10-30.

In the year of age from $50+k$ to $51+k$, the anticipated contribution is given by

$$1000(1.04)^k.$$

Thus the actuarial present value of all contributions is given by

$$1000 \sum_{k=0}^{\infty} (1.04)^k (1.06)^{-k-1/2} \, {}_{k+1/2}p_{50}^{(T)}$$

$$= \frac{1000}{(1.04)^{1/2}} \sum_{k=0}^{\infty} \left(\frac{1.04}{1.06}\right)^{k+1/2} {}_{k+1/2}p_{50}^{(T)}$$

$$= 980.58 \sum_{k=0}^{\infty} \frac{\overline{D}_{50+k}^{(T)}}{D_{50}^{(T)}}, \text{ where } v = \frac{1.04}{1.06}$$

$$= 980.58 \frac{\overline{N}_{50}^{(T)}}{D_{50}^{(T)}}, \text{ where } 1+i = \frac{106}{104}$$

$$\therefore i = \underline{\underline{\frac{1}{52}}}$$

10-31.

Key Concept: The only quantity needed to complete this problem is the probability that (35) will ultimately exit the multiple-decrement table via withdrawal, i.e., ${}_{\infty}q_{35}^{(w)}$.

Since $\mu_x^{(T)} = \sum_k \mu_x^{(k)}$, we have

$$\mu_{35+t}^{(w)} \left[\frac{1}{3} + \frac{2}{3} + 1 + \frac{4}{3} \right] = \mu_{35+t}^{(T)}$$

$$\therefore \mu_{35+t}^{(w)} = \frac{3}{10} \mu_{35+t}^{(T)}.$$

Thus,

$$_{\infty}q_{35}^{(w)} = \int_0^{\infty} {}_tp_{35}^{(T)} \mu_{35+t}^{(w)} \, dt$$

$$= \frac{3}{10} \int_0^{\infty} {}_tp_{35}^{(T)} \mu_{35+t}^{(T)} \, dt$$

$$= \frac{3}{10}.$$

Finally, the desired actuarial present value is

$$50,000 \left(\frac{3}{10} \right) = \underline{\underline{15,000}}.$$

10–32.

Key Approach: It is necessary to determine the expected average annual salary between ages 60 and 65.

Thus, we have

$$20,000 \int_{15}^{20} \frac{S_{45+t}}{5 \cdot S_{45}} \, dt$$
$$= 50 \int_{15}^{20} (80 + 7t + 2t^2) \, dt$$
$$= 204,791.67$$

Finally, multiplying by .3 and discounting back to age 45, we have

$$\underline{\underline{61,437.50}} \; {}_{20}E_{45}^{(T)} \, \ddot{a}_{65}^{r}.$$

10–33.

Key Approach: This problem involves careful reading, analysis of the three years under consideration, and summing of the three actuarial present values.

Employee Contributions:

Age 62–63: $(.10)(25,000 - 23,000) = 200$

Age 63–64: $(.10)(27,500 - 25,300) = 220$

Age 64–65: $(.10)(30,000 - 27,600) = 240$

Thus, considering the tax factor, the after-tax contributions for the three years are 200, 210, and 220, respectively.

Employer Contributions:

Age 62–63: $(.01)(0) = 0$

Age 63–64: $(.01)(27,500 - 27,300) = 2$

Age 64–65: $(.01)(30,000 - 28,700) = 13$

Finally, we must discount the three contributions, now seen to be 200, 212, and 233, respectively.

Accordingly, the actuarial present value is

$$200(.97)(.9) + 212(.91)(.8) + 233(.86)(.7) = \underline{\underline{469.20}}.$$

10-34.

Assume that (50) retires at exact age $35 + t$. The size of his pension is given by

$$f(t) = (.6)(35,000 + 1500t) - (.02)(35,000 + 1500t)(.2t + 15)$$
$$= 10,500 + 310t - 6t^2.$$

Maximizing through differentiation, we have

$$310 - 2t = 0$$
$$\text{and } t = 25.8\dot{3},$$

representing retirement at exact age $60.8\dot{3}$.

Finally,

$$f(25.8\dot{3}) = \underline{\underline{14,504.17}}$$

NOTE: Retirement at exact age 60 (duration 25) produces a pension of $14,500, while retirement at exact age 61 produces a pension of $14,504.

10-35.

Key Approach:

It is required to determine the numerical values of the quantities denoted in the question by i) and ii).

i)

$$.0175 \left[40,000 \left(\frac{S_{62} + 2S_{63} + 2S_{64} + S_{65}}{6S_{55}} \right) - 50,000 \right]$$

$$= .0175 \left[40,000 \left(\frac{1}{6} \right) ((1.05)^7 + 2(1.05)^8 + 2(1.05)^9 + (1.05)^{10}) - 50,000 \right]$$

$$= 185.92$$

ii)

$$.0125 \left[40,000 \frac{S_{65}}{S_{55}} - 50,000 \right]$$

$$= .0125[40,000(1.05)^{10} - 50,000]$$

$$= 189.45.$$

Finally, according to the verbal description of the benefit, we have

$$(10\tfrac{1}{2})(.02)(50,000) + 10(189.45) \doteq \underline{\underline{12,394}}.$$

10-36.

Key Concept:

It is required to determine the value of k for which the values of $R(50,0,10)$ are equal under the two plans. In each case, a unit starting salary is assumed.

Under Employer A's plan,

$$R(50,0,10) = 800 \left(\frac{S_{50} + S_{51} + \cdots + S_{59}}{S_{50}} \right)$$

$$= \frac{800}{20}(20 + 20.1 + \cdots + 20.9)$$

$$= 8180$$

Under Employer B's plan,

$$R(50,0,10) = .01k(40,000)(10) \left(\frac{S_{55} + S_{56} + \cdots + S_{59}}{5 \cdot S_{50}} \right)$$

$$= 800k[(1.05)^5 + (1.05)^6 + \cdots + (1.05)^9]$$

$$= 5641.809k$$

Finally,

$$5641.809k = 8180$$

$$\therefore k = \underline{1.45}$$

10-37.

Since $^A S_x = (1.05)^x$ and

$^B S_x = 1 + .05(x - 20)$,

Joe's total retirement pension based upon retirement at age $20 + k + \frac{1}{2}$ would be

$$(.4)(20,000)((1.05)^k + 1 + .05k)$$

$$= 8000((1.05)^k + 1 + .05k) \geq 30,000$$

$$\therefore (1.05)^k + .05k \geq 2.75$$

Finally, using trial and error,

$$(1.05)^{14} + (.05)(14) = 2.68$$

$$(1.05)^{15} + (.05)(15) = 2.83$$

Thus, $\underline{k = 15}$.

10-38.

Key Approach: Assume that retirement, if it occurs, will occur at exact age $25 + t$. Note that the salary scale function is continuous, and that it can be represented for our purposes by

$$S_x = e^{.1x}$$

since the constant $625e^{.1025}$ is immaterial.

$$APV = \int_{20}^{40} v^t \, {}_tp_{25}^{(T)} \mu_{25+t}^{(r)} \frac{S_{25+t}}{S_{25}} (.02t) \bar{a}_{25+t}^r \, dt$$

$$= .02 \int_{20}^{40} e^{-.05t} e^{-.01t} e^{-.04t} \cdot \frac{40-t}{40} \cdot \frac{1}{20} \cdot t e^{.1t} \cdot 4 \, dt$$

since

$$_tp_{25}^{(T)} \mu_{25+t}^{(r)} = {}_tp_{25}^{\prime(i)} \, {}_tp_{25}^{\prime(d)} \, {}_tp_{25}^{\prime(w)} \, {}_tp_{25}^{\prime(r)} \mu_{25+t}^{(r)}$$

$$= e^{-.01t} e^{-.04t} \cdot \frac{40-t}{40} \cdot \frac{1}{20},$$

$$\text{and } \bar{a}_{25+t}^{(r)} = \frac{1}{\mu^{(r)} + \delta} = \frac{1}{.25} = 4. \qquad (CF)$$

Finally,

$$APV = \frac{.02}{200} \int_{20}^{40} t(40-t) \, dt$$

$$= \underline{\underline{.5\dot{3}}}$$

10-39.

Key Concept: The contribution to be made at age $40+t$ is $.02(40,000) \cdot \frac{40+t}{40}$, and it will be made for at most 30 years as long as the employee remains in service.

$$APV = \sum_{t=0}^{29} 20(40+t) \, {}_tE_{40}^{(T)}$$

$$= 20 \sum_{t=0}^{29} (40+t) v_{.05}^t$$

$$= 20 \left[40 \ddot{a}_{\overline{30}|.05} + (Ia)_{\overline{29}|.05} \right]$$

$$= 800 \ddot{a}_{\overline{30}|.05} + 400 \left[\ddot{a}_{\overline{29}|.05} - 29v_{.05}^{29} \right]$$

$$= 800 \ddot{a}_{\overline{30}|.05} + 400 [\ddot{a}_{\overline{30}|.05} - 30v_{.05}^{29}]$$

$$= \underline{\underline{1200(\ddot{a}_{\overline{30}|.05} - 10v_{.05}^{29})}}$$

10-40.

Key Approach: This problem requires only careful reading followed by an enumeration of the six components of the actuarial present value.

Withdrawal Benefit:

$$APV = 25(37)q_{57}^{(w)}v + 25(38)p_{57}^{(T)}q_{58}^{(w)}v^2 + 25(39) \, {}_2p_{57}^{(T)}q_{59}^{(w)}v^3$$

$$= 36.21$$

Death Benefit:

$$APV = 250[q_{57}^{(d)}v + p_{57}^{(T)}q_{58}^{(d)}v^2 + {}_2p_{57}^{(T)}q_{59}^{(d)}v^3]$$
$$= 11.78$$
$$\therefore \text{ Total } APV = \underline{47.99}$$

10–41.

Key Formula: Since total decrement is given to be independent of age, we have

$$\ddot{a}_y^{(T)} = \frac{1+i}{q^{(T)}+i} = 5.5, \text{ for all } y$$

Assuming that this employee, now aged y, was hired at age x, we have

$$.1(AS)_x \sum_0^\infty v^t \, {}_tp_y^{(T)} = .125(AS)_y$$

$$\therefore .55(AS)_x = .125(AS)_y$$

$$\therefore \frac{(AS)_y}{(AS)_x} = 4.4 = (1.1)^{y-x}$$

Solving algebraically, using the given values of the logarithms, we have

$$y - x = \frac{ln4.4}{ln1.1} = \frac{ln4 + ln1.1}{ln1.1} \doteq 15.59$$

Accordingly, past service is approximately $\underline{16}$ years.

10–42.

Key Concept: Since salary increases occur other than annually or continuously, the definition of ${}_2Z_{60}$ must be modified. Note that he will have had 17 salary increases before age $58\frac{1}{2}$.

Accordingly, here we have

$$\frac{{}_2Z_{60}}{S_{50}} = \frac{1}{2}\left[\frac{1}{6}(1.05)^{17} + \frac{2}{3}(1.05)^{18} + \frac{1}{3}(1.05)^{19} + \frac{2}{3}(1.05)^{20} + \frac{1}{6}(1.05)^{21}\right]$$

$$\doteq 2.531$$

Finally,

$$R(30,20,10\tfrac{1}{2}) = (.02)(AS)_{50}\frac{{}_2Z_{61}}{S_{50}}(30.5)$$

$$\doteq \underline{38,598}$$

10–43.

Key Approach: In order to obtain an expression for $R(30,10,20)$, we need to find the appropriate three-year final average salary and the career average salary.

a) Three-year final average:

$$\frac{(AS)_{40}}{S_{40}} \int_{17}^{20} \frac{S_{40+t}}{3}\, dt$$

$$= \frac{1}{60}(AS)_{40} \int_{17}^{20} (t+20)\, dt = 1.925(AS)_{40}$$

b) Career average:

$$\frac{(AS)_{40}}{S_{40}} \int_{-10}^{20} \frac{S_{40+t}}{30}\, dt$$

$$= \frac{1}{600}(AS)_{40} \int_{-10}^{20} (t+20)\, dt = 1.25(AS)_{40}$$

Finally,

$$.01r(1.925)(AS)_{40} + .2(1.25)(AS)_{40} = 1.02(AS)_{40}$$
$$\therefore r = \underline{\underline{40}}$$

10–44.

Key Fact: At age 44, the employee is contributing only on the first

$$\frac{2000}{.05} = 40{,}000$$

of this salary. Accordingly, $(WB)_{44} = 40{,}000$.

Key Approach: Since annual contributions are based upon both projected salary and projected wage base, we have as the anticipated contribution for the $(k+1)$ st year

$$.05[70{,}000(1.0608)^k - 40{,}000(1.04)^k].$$

Accordingly, the actuarial present value of employee contributions is

$$.05 \sum_{k=0}^{20} [70,000(1.0608)^k - 40,000(1.04)^k]v_{.04}^{k+1/2}$$

$$= \frac{500}{(1.04)^{1/2}} \sum_{k=0}^{20} [7(1.02)^k - 4]$$

$$= \frac{500}{(1.04)^{1/2}} [7s_{\overline{21}|.02} - 84]$$

$$\doteq \underline{\underline{47,304}}$$

Chapter Fourteen

Glossary of Notation

In order to permit the demonstration of certain accounting relationships in symbolic form, a set of useful (but non-standard) notation has been devised:

$(NI)_k$:   net income for policy year k

P_k :   premium income for policy year k

$(II)_k$:   investment income for policy year k

C_k :   claims for policy year k

E_k :   expenses for policy year k

$_kA$:   assets at the end of policy year k

$_kL$:   liabilities at the end of policy year k

$_kS$:   surplus at the end of policy year k

$_kV$:   policy reserves (benefit reserves or total reserves, as appropriate) at the end of policy year k

Supplementary Concepts

1.   An insurer's net income for a block of business, on an *annual* basis, may be significantly affected by the criteria chosen for the determination of liabilities. This is due to the "increase in reserves" component of net income. Over the *entire life* of a block of business, however, total net income is independent of the pattern through which the reserve at duration zero grades into the reserve at the duration at which the block of business is closed. This assertion may be substantiated, beginning with the net income equation for policy year k, i.e.,

$$(NI)_k = (P + II - E - C)_k - \Delta(_{k-1}V).$$

Assuming a maximum duration of n policy years, and summing, we have

$$\sum_{k=1}^{n}(NI)_k = \sum_{k=1}^{n}(P + II - E - C)_k - ({}_nV - {}_0V).$$

Thus, it is seen that the *progression* of liabilities is of no relevance in the determination of *total* net income.

Accordingly, for business such as term insurance for which ultimate and initial liabilities are equal total net income is simply the algebraic sum of premium income, investment income, expenses, and claims over the entire lifetime of the business.

2. Illustrative income statements and balance sheets, prepared at the inception of the existence of a block of business, are necessarily based on the premise that all actuarial assumptions will be precisely borne out as experience unfolds. It must be kept in mind that it is extremely unlikely for any single assumption, much less the totality of assumptions, to be realized without variation. For example, exact determination of investment income or claims for a future policy year falls into the category of wishful thinking; construction of such an income statement should never be allowed to cloud that fact.

3. If all assumptions are precisely realized, it is logical that neither gain nor loss would emerge throughout the lifetime of the block of business on account of mortality, interest, or expense. Accordingly, *total* net income is attributable to only two sources—interest earnings on initial surplus, if any, and accumulation of net profit loadings built into the premium structure.

An even more powerful statement may be made where the basis for liabilities is total reserves, i.e., benefit plus expense reserves. Where this is the case, net income for *each individual year* may be found simply as that year's net profit loadings plus interest on both the net profit loadings and the insurer's surplus at the beginning of the year. Specifically, increases or decreases in liabilities may be ignored because the assumed incidence of both claims and expenses is reflected in the year-end total reserve.

Where the basis for liabilities is benefit reserves only, such an annual projection of net income may not be determined in this same manner. This is explained by the fact that year-end liabilities, defined only by claim and not expense assumptions, do not afford the flexibility required to reflect the incidence of expenses on a year-by-year basis.

It is of extreme importance that the student verify the validity of these concepts through an analysis of the comprehensive illustration of the first few pages of Chapter 14 in *Actuarial Mathematics*.

4. The following income statement and balance sheet relationships should be used and thoroughly understood:

$$(NI)_k = (P + II - E - C)_k - \Delta({}_{k-1}V) = \Delta({}_{k-1}S)$$
$$\Delta({}_{k-1}A) = (P + II - E - C)_k = (NI)_k + \Delta({}_{k-1}V)$$
$${}_kS = {}_kA - {}_kL$$
$$\Delta({}_{k-1}S) = \Delta({}_{k-1}A) - \Delta({}_{k-1}L) = (NI)_k$$

$$(II)_k = i(\,_{k-1}A + P_k - E_k)$$

Perhaps both the most vital and the most elusive concept related to these formulas is that the calculation of net income requires an adjustment term for change in reserves while the calculation of change in assets does not. Suppose, for example, a block of business requires a $1000 increase in reserves for a given policy year. Since monies placed in reserves may still be invested by the insurer, the insurer's year-end assets are not affected by the $1000 accounting entry. Yet the $1000, theoretically set aside to pay future claims (or expenses), cannot be included in net income. It represents an increased liability, thus affecting surplus and, in turn, net income, but not assets.

5.   A policy fee is an amount added to a net premium solely to provide for the payment of per policy expenses. In determination of a policy fee, it must be remembered that the policy fee *itself* is subject to those expenses which are expressed as a percentage of the premium.

Specifically, a $100 policy fee is not sufficient to provide for a $100 per policy expense. Such an extra $100 premium is subject to sales commissions and premium tax, for example.

In the case of the unrealistic and unusual assumption that the per policy expense is the same for each policy year, say $100, let us assume a 20% charge against each premium. Thus, the appropriate policy fee would be $125, of which $25 is immediately allocated to "percentage of premium" rather than "per policy" expense. The remaining $100 is available for per policy expense, as required.

6.   The band method for the handling of per policy expenses can probably best be understood with the help of an oversimplified numerical example.

Suppose that $R(b)$, the premium rate for a policy of face amount b, and $G(b)$, the expense-loaded premium for a policy of face amount b, are given as follows for a premium scale with three bands:

$$\left.\begin{array}{l} R(b) = .05 + \dfrac{50}{10,000} = .0550 \\[2ex] G(b) = .0550b \end{array}\right\}, \quad 1,000 \le b \le 25,000$$

$$\left.\begin{array}{l} R(b) = .05 + \dfrac{50}{50,000} = .0510 \\[2ex] G(b) = .0510b \end{array}\right\}, \quad 25,000 < b \le 75,000$$

$$\left.\begin{array}{l} R(b) = .05 + \dfrac{50}{125,000} = .0504 \\[2ex] G(b) = .0504b \end{array}\right\}, \quad 75,000 < b$$

It should be noted from the form of $R(b)$ that, under the policy fee method, the policy fee would be $50. In addition, the cost of insurance in the absence of per policy expenses is $50 per thousand.

Considering the expense-loaded premiums for certain face amounts within the first and second bands, we obtain

$$G(1000) = 55 \qquad\qquad G(25,000.01) \doteq 1275$$
$$G(5000) = 275 \qquad\qquad G(40,000) = 2040$$
$$G(10,000) = 550 \qquad\qquad G(50,000) = 2550$$
$$G(20,000) = 1100 \qquad\qquad G(60,000) = 3060$$
$$G(25,000) = 1375 \qquad\qquad G(75,000) = 3825$$

The following observations should be clear from the calculated values:

a) Within any given band, expense-loaded premiums are directly proportional to the face amount.

b) The actual charge for per policy expense increases as face amounts increase within a given band. In the second band, for example, per policy charges grow from $25 to $75 as face amounts grow from the minimum to the maximum.

c) Within any given band, the per policy charge relative to the face amount is constant. In the first two bands, for example, the per policy charges are 0.5% and 0.1% of the face amounts, respectively.

d) A discontinuity in the expense-loaded premiums appears at the end points of each band. Thus, where possible, policyholders would be well advised to purchase face amounts at the lower end of the next larger band. This rationale for policyholders to purchase higher amounts of insurance is the primary reason that insurers adopt the band method.

e) For huge face amounts within the highest band, per policy charges are extremely large. For example, a policy with a $1,000,000 face amount would include a per policy expense charge of $400, compared with the $50 which would be charged under the policy fee method.

f) For policies with face amounts equal to that upon which the expense-loaded premium rate is based ($10,000, $50,000, and $125,000 in this example), the premiums are equal under the policy fee and band methods.

7.   The formula

$$_hp_x u(h) = \sum_{j=1}^{h}(1 + i)^{h-j+1} \; _{j-1}p_x(c - e_{j-1})$$

produces the expected surplus at duration h *per initial insured*. An equally useful formula, producing the expected surplus at duration h *per surviving insured*, is found by dividing the formula above by $_hp_x$. Thus we have

$$u(h) = \frac{1}{_hE_x} \sum_{j=1}^{h} {_{j-1}E_x}(c - e_{j-1})$$

or the actuarial accumulated value (share *per survivor*) of the excesses of loadings over expenses.

The difference in the concepts of "share per initial insured" and "share per survivor", illustrated above mathematically, is perhaps more easily understood with a simple example. Suppose there are 100 initial insureds, 75 of whom persist to duration h. If the actual fund value at duration h is \$7500, the share per initial insured is

$$_hp_xu(h) = \frac{7500}{100} = 75,$$

while the share per survivor is

$$u(h) = \frac{7500}{75} = 100.$$

The latter form is probably of greater actuarial significance because of its relationship to the reserve concept.

8. Reserves on policies issued on the Full Preliminary Term (FPT) basis may easily be expressed in terms of net level reserves. This results from the requirement that FPT reserves at duration one are zero and that, at least in theory, a "new" policy is issued at duration one, as no values were available at that time under the "old" policy. For example,

$$\begin{aligned}
_{10}V_x^{FPT} &= A_{x+10} - \beta\ddot{a}_{x+10} \\
&= A_{x+10} - P_{x+1}\ddot{a}_{x+10} \\
&= {}_9V_{x+1}
\end{aligned}$$

$$\text{and}$$

$$\begin{aligned}
_{10}^{15}V_{x:\,\overline{20|}}^{FPT} &= A_{x+10:\,\overline{10|}} - \beta\ddot{a}_{x+10:\,\overline{5|}} \\
&= A_{x+10:\,\overline{10|}} - {}_{14}P_{x+1:\,\overline{19|}}\ddot{a}_{x+10:\,\overline{10|}} \\
&= {}_9^{14}V_{x+1:\,\overline{19|}}.
\end{aligned}$$

9. In the determination and analysis of modified reserves, it is often helpful to consider the *difference* between reserves on two different bases. Often the simplest approach involves the prospective difference. Since the actuarial present value of future benefits is not a function of the reserve basis, this difference is entirely attributable to the actuarial present value of future net premiums.

Accordingly, the excess of a reserve on basis A over that on basis B is the excess of the actuarial present value of future net premiums on basis B over that on basis A.

For example,

$$\begin{aligned}
_{10}V_x - {}_{10}V_x^{FPT} &= (P_{x+1} - P_x)\ddot{a}_{x+10} \\
\text{and}
\end{aligned}$$

$$\begin{aligned}
_{10}^{20}V_x - {}_{10}^{20}V_x^{MOD} &= (\beta - {}_{20}P_x)\ddot{a}_{x+10:\,\overline{10|}} \qquad (j = 20) \\
&= (\beta - {}_{20}P_x)\ddot{a}_{x+10:\,\overline{5|}} \qquad (j = 15)
\end{aligned}$$

Note that, in the last example, the two values of β are unequal. Finally, in the second case, it should be observed that it is being assumed that the net premium reverts to the net level premium after the 15 year modification period expires.

Exercises

14–1   A first-year income statement, based upon net level reserves as liabilities for a block of $1000 fully discrete life insurance policies, shows the following:

Premiums:	$3500
Investment Income:	$450
Net Income:	−$100
Claims:	One
Initial Surplus:	$1000
Effective interest rate:	12%

A second, identical, block of policies, with the same experienced results, has an income statement based upon benefit plus expense reserves as liabilities. Aggregate reserves after the first year are, accordingly, $400 less than in the first statement. The net income is shown to be $420. What initial surplus was held for the second block of business?

A) $1000   B) $1500   C) $2000   D) $2500   E) $3000

14–2   A $10,000 fully discrete whole life policy to (x) is priced according to the following expense assumptions:

i)   1% of face amount as a one-time sales commission
ii) $61.75 start-up charge
iii) $20 per year for maintenance
iv)   10% of each premium for taxes and other expenses.

There is an initial fund of $992.75. If $A_x = .25$, $i = .05$, and, $_1V_x = .006734$, find the expected net income per policy for the first year.

A) −$109.42   B) −$99.33   C) −$10.09   D) $10.09   E) $89.24

14–3   A three-year, $1000 fully discrete endowment policy is issued to each of 500 lives aged x. The initial surplus fund of $150,000 is expected to grow to $176,506.26 by the end of the three-year period. Each premium contains $10 for profit and contingencies. The expected annual interest rates are 4%, 6%, and 5%, respectively. The percent of premium expense is expected to be 90%, 50%, and 40%, respectively. If $p_x = .6$, find p_{x+1}.

A) .20   B) .33   C) .35   D) .65   E) .66

14-4 The expense-loaded annual premium for a $1000 fully discrete, three-pay whole life policy to (30) is $275.70. The anticipated expense in the first year is 18% of the total premium plus $10. The anticipated interest rate is 12%; 20% of policyholders are expected to die in their first policy year. The required reserve after one year is $210.75 per policy. An initial surplus of $1500 is available.

Ten such policies are sold, and the insurer decides to add C to the premium for each policy for contingencies and profit. If the first year net loss is $856.37, find C.

A) $24.90   B) $25.00   C) $25.90   D) $26.10   E) $26.20

14-5 An insurance company sells ten $5000 fully discrete whole life insurance policies to lives aged 20, each with an annual premium of $375. First year expenses are 10% of the annual premium plus $50; subsequent year expenses are 2% of the annual premium. An initial fund of $10,000 is available. The following reserves per thousand are known:

Duration t	Benefit Reserve	Expense Reserve
1	60.00	−40.50
2	110.00	−30.20
3	165.00	−20.00

Assume $q_{20} = \frac{1}{10}$, $q_{21} = \frac{1}{3}$, and $q_{22} = \frac{1}{4}$.

Find the increase in total net income for the first three policy years if reserves are based upon benefit plus expense reserves instead of net premium reserves.

A) $350   B) $450   C) $500   D) $550   E) $650

14-6 A single premium whole life insurance policy to (x), with claims paid at the end of the year of death, is priced on the following assumptions:

    i) $A_x = .50$; $A_{x+3} = .55$
    ii) $_3q_x = .05 = d$
    iii) 21% of the premium is required for expenses
    iv) Per policy expense is $2 per year for the first three years, and $1 per year thereafter.

Calculate the policy fee.

A) $16.00   B) $16.04   C) $16.08   D) $16.12   E) $16.16

14-7   An insurer determines that it incurs a $75 expense each year that a policy is in force, regardless of the policy size. In addition, there is a 10% expense charge associated with each annual premium.

The gross annual premium for a $10,000 fully discrete whole life policy to Jones is $500. What *net* annual premium is implicitly being assumed?

A) $375   B) $400   C) $425   D) $450   E) $475

14-8   Rework Question 14-7 if, in addition to an annual expense charge of 10% of the premium, there is a settlement charge of 10% of the face amount.

A) $341   B) $351   C) $361   D) $371   E) $381

14-9   An insurer issued 100 fully discrete $1000 four-year endowment policies to lives aged x, charging an expense-loaded annual premium which is also loaded for contingencies and profit. The insurer's net income in the first year, based upon recognizing benefit plus expense reserves as liabilities, was $1338. There was an initial surplus of $1500. Expense assumptions include 10% of premium in the first year and 5% in renewal years; $i = .10$.

If $q_{x+k} = .10 + .05k$, $k = 0, 1, 2, 3$, find the expected net income in the third year.

A) $1234.35   B) $1243.11   C) $1250.55   D) $1384.35   E) $1393.11

14-10   A three-year $10,000 fully discrete endowment insurance policy issued to (x) has its annual premiums loaded as follows:

    i)   Percent of Premium: Year 1: 10%
                               Year 2: 9%
                               Year 3: 8%
    ii) Profit/Contingency Loading: $200
    iii) Per Policy: $100

In addition, it is assumed that $q_x = .05$, $_2q_x = .107$, and $i = .10$. If there is an initial fund of $500 per policy, and if the average of benefit and expense reserves is reported each year as liabilities, find the total expected net income over the three-year period generated by a single policy.

A) $790   B) $795   C) $800   D) $805   E) $810

14-11   The density function for the amount of insurance for individual policies of a certain type is $f(b) = 200b^{-3}$, $b \geq 10$, where b is measured in thousands. The insurer determines its premium *rate* for all face amounts by assuming that all policies have a face amount $\bar{b}$.

If $a = 25$, $f = .20$, and $R(\bar{b}) = 32$, find the amount by which each premium of the purchaser of a $10,000 policy underpays his justifiable share of expense.

A) $3.75   B) $7.50   C) $11.25   D) $15.00   E) $18.75

14-12   Ten single premium $10,000 whole life policies are issued to lives aged x. The expense assumptions are 20% of the premium plus $60 per policy per year. Each net single premium is $3000, based upon $d = .07$. If the insurer's funds earn 10% per year, and if the first-year investment income is $4000, find the amount of the initial surplus.

A) $4000   B) $4200   C) $4400   D) $4600   E) $4800

14-13   A single premium whole life policy is being developed by an actuary. Expenses are assumed to be 20% of the premium in addition to per policy expense of $30 in the first year and $5 in subsequent years. A band approach is incorporated as follows:

For policies with face amounts smaller than $55,000, the rate per dollar is based upon an average policy size of $50,000. For policies with face amounts larger than $55,000, the rate per dollar is based upon an average policy size of $100,000.

Let A equal the charge for per policy costs incorporated in a $50,000 policy, and B the charge for per policy costs incorporated in a $60,000 policy.

If $A_x = .4$ and $d = .06$, find $\frac{B}{A}$.

A) .6   B) .7   C) .8   D) .9   E) 1.0

14-14   An insurance company uses the band method for handling per policy expenses. Its bands are $250,000 wide, i.e., the first is $0–$250,000, the second is $250,000–$500,000, and so on. For the purpose of determining the premium rate per unit, the face amount within any band is taken to be the average of the upper and lower bounds for that band.

Each policy has a true insurance cost of $90 per thousand; expenses are determined to be 10% of each premium plus $45 per policy.

For a $400,000 policy, find the excess of the charge for per policy expenses over that which would be obtained through the use of a single policy fee for all policies.

A) 0   B) $1.67   C) $3.33   D) $5.00   E) $6.67

14–15   How many of the following statements with regard to the handling of per policy expenses are true?

    I.   All policyholders within a given band are paying identical per policy charges as a percentage of the face amount.

    II.   Under the single policy fee system, the charge for per policy expenses increases as the face amount increases.

    III.   The smaller policies within any band are bearing an inequitably large portion of per policy expenses.

    IV.   The per policy charges as a percentage of the face amount are larger for policyholders with small policies than for those whose face amounts fall in a higher band.

A) 0   B) 1   C) 2   D) 3   E) 4

14–16   Fully discrete \$1000 whole life policies are issued to lives aged 75, with the assumption that $i = 0$ and $\mu_{75+t} = \frac{1}{25-t}$, $0 \le t < 25$. Expenses are assumed to be \$25 at issue and \$15 in renewal years. The expected surplus per initial insured after two years is \$20.

Find the gross annual premium to the nearest dime.

A) \$105.90   B) \$106.90   C) \$107.20   D) \$110.50   E) \$111.40

14–17   A fully discrete whole life policy is issued to (x) and has reserves according to the Canadian method. The actuarial acquisition expenses are \$200, and the actuarial present value of expenses which are recoverable in the second and later years while still providing for administrative expenses and policyholder dividends is \$300.

If $\alpha^{CAN} = \$80$, find the face amount of the policy, given that $\ddot{a}_x = 10$ and $d = .03$. Assume the equivalence principle.

A) \$4000   B) \$5000   C) \$6000   D) \$8000   E) \$10,000

14–18   Given: $\ddot{a}_{25} = 16$

$$A_{30} = .25$$
$$d = .05$$
$$\alpha^{CAN} = -\frac{1}{2}P_{25}$$

Find $_5V_{25}^{CAN}$.

A) $\dfrac{17}{400}$ B) $\dfrac{23}{512}$ C) $\dfrac{7}{160}$ D) $\dfrac{9}{160}$ E) Invalid question because α can never be negative.

14-19 A special three-year fully discrete endowment policy to (50) has death protection of $25, $50, and $75, for the three years, respectively, in addition to a $100 pure endowment at age 53. De Moivre's Law is assumed; $\omega = 90$. If the ELRA is $60, find the interest rate.

A) 5% B) 10% C) 20% D) 25% E) 50%

14-20 A block of $1000 fully discrete whole life policies was issued to lives aged x. The expected first year loss with respect to each policy was $8.20; the accumulated loss per initial policy at the end of the second policy year was expected to be $7.28. The excess of the gross premium over actual expenses for the second year was assumed to be $1.25. If $p_x = .96$ and $p_{x+1} = .92$, find the interest rate.

A) 3% B) 4% C) $7\frac{1}{2}$% D) 18% E) 21%

14-21 A modified reserve method for a fully discrete whole life policy to (x) provides for a net premium of α for each of the first 10 policy years and a net premium of β for each year thereafter. If $A_x = .35$, $A^1_{x:\overline{10|}} = .15$, and $A_{x:\overline{10|}} = .60$, evaluate

$$\frac{\beta - P_x}{P_x - \alpha}$$

A) $\frac{1}{4}$ B) $\frac{3}{8}$ C) $\frac{1}{2}$ D) $\frac{5}{8}$ E) $\frac{3}{4}$

14-22 Based upon the Commissioners Method and the following values, find the first-year net premium for a $1000 fully discrete 20-pay life policy to (20).

Given: $\beta = .055$

$_{20}P_{20} = .050$

$_1E_{20} = .860$

$\ddot{a}_{21:\overline{19|}} = 6.28$

A) $20.00 B) $23.00 C) $23.50 D) $24.00 E) $25.00

14-23 On a fully discrete $1000 h-pay whole life policy to (x), the actual acquisition expense equals $60\,\theta$. The actuarial present value of expenses which are recoverable in the second and later years while still providing for administrative expenses and dividends is $80. The value of β^{CAN} is 60θ. Find θ, given $A_x = .85$ and $a_{x:\overline{h-1|}} = 16$.

A) .8$\dot{8}$ B) .91 C) 1.00 D) 1.25 E) 1.3$\dot{3}$

14-24   The gross annual premium for a $1000 fully discrete whole life policy to (x) is $119.09. Find the surplus per survivor at the end of the second policy year.

Given: $q_x = .12$ for all x

$i = .10$

$e_0 = 11$

$e_1 = 9.35$

A) $-$.75   B) $-$.58   C) $-$.41   D) $-$.17   E) $0

14-25   Five single premium $100,000 two-year term policies, payable at the end of the year of death, are issued on January 1, 1990. Assume the company set aside $5000 as an initial fund to offset the effects of possible unfavorable mortality on this block of business. Also assume $q_x = .01$ for all x, $i = .06$, and expenses are incurred as follows:

Acquisition Expense   = 15% of expense-loaded premium

Maintenance Expense   = $40 per policy, each year

Settlement Expense   = $10 plus $.50 per 1000 face amount

Which of the following would be closest to the *expected* (at issue) 1991 investment income for this block of business?

A) $500   B) $550   C) $600   D) $650   E) $700

14-26   Five persons, each aged 40, purchase $10,000 fully discrete three-year term insurance policies. The expense-loaded annual premium is $1070, of which $287.50 is designated for expenses in the first year. An initial surplus of $10,000 is available to protect against adverse experience. The net level annual premium is $913.87.

Assuming $i = .20$ and de Moivre's Law with $\omega = 50$, how much is expected in the surplus fund at the end of one year? (Answer to nearest $100)

A) $10,200   B) $10,700   C) $11,200   D) $11,700   E) $12,200

14-27   Which of the following represents the expected increase in surplus, for each initial insured, during the fifth policy year?

A) $_4p_x[u(4)\cdot i + (c - e_4)(1 + i)]$ B) $_5p_x[u(4)\cdot i + (c - e_4)(1 + i)]$

C) $_4p_x[u(4) + (c - e_4)](1 + i)$ D) $_5p_x[u(4) + (c - e_4)](1 + i)$

E) None of these

14-28   The expense assumptions used for calculating level expense-loaded premiums for n-year endowment insurance policies reflect an anticipated decreasing incidence of actual expenses. Which of the following statements is/are true? Assume the equivalence principle.

    I. $E[_tL] \geq E[_tL_e]$, $t = 1, 2, \ldots, n$
    II. $\sigma[_tL] \geq \sigma[_tL_e]$, $t = 1, 2, \ldots, n$
    III. Expense reserves are always nonpositive.
    IV. In the first policy year, expected net income is greater when benefit plus expense reserves are used as liabilities than when benefit reserves are used.

    A) All   B) All but I   C) All but II   D) All but III   E) All but IV

14-29   Consider the following information regarding the ABC Insurance Company:

    a)   Premium income for 1990 was $41,535.
    b)   Assets at the end of 1990 were $11,375.
    c)   Premium income for 1991 was $46,535.
    d)   Expenses of 1991 were $37,910.
    e)   Investment income for 1991 was $500.
    f)   Assets at the end of 1991 were $13,875.

If expenses are incurred at the beginning of the year, what effective rate of interest did ABC earn during 1991?

    A) .25%   B) 2.2%   C) 2.5%   D) 3%   E) 3.3%

14-30   If $_{16}V_{24}^{FPT} = .6$ and $_6V_{34}^{FPT} = .5$, find $_{11}V_{24}^{FPT}$.

    A) .1   B) .2   C) .3   D) .4   E) .5

14-31   Which of the following is/are true for fully discrete whole life policies?

    I.   If the force of mortality is constant, $\beta^{FPT} > \alpha^{FPT}$.
    II.   If the force of mortality is constant, $_kV_x > {_kV_x^{FPT}}$, $k = 1, 2, \ldots$
    III. $_kV_x^{COM} > {_kV_x^{FPT}}$, $k = 1, 2, \ldots$

    A) All   B) All but I   C) All but II   D) III only   E) Some other
                                                                                    combination

14-32   The expense-loaded premium for a $1000 fully discrete policy is $40 more than the net level premium. Actual expenses in the first policy year are $45, decreasing by 10% each year.

Find the expected surplus per survivor at the end of three policy years.

Given: $q_x = .05$ for all x, and $i = .05$.

    A) −$3.44   B) −$2.95   C) $0   D) $2.95   E) $11.29

14-33   The net level premium for a $1000 20-year endowment policy to (y) is $80; the modified net renewal premium is $100. Based upon the following values, find the modified first year net premium. The modification period is 20 years.

Age x	N_x
y	$72,650$
$y+1$	$64,350$
$\vdots$	$\vdots$
$y+20$	$47,335$

A) $39   B) $41   C) $50   D) $59   E) $61

14-34   An insurer makes the following assumptions in pricing a fully discrete $1000 whole life policy to (20):

   i)   Acquisition expense of $105
   ii) Recurring annual expenses of $4, plus 14% of expense-loaded premium
   iii) $i = .10$; $q_x = .10$ for all x

In determining the expense-loaded premium of $150, a profit margin was included.

What would the expense-loaded premium be if the insurer wishes to increase its profit margin, as a percent of premium, by 10%?

A) $151.00   B) $151.50   C) $152.00   D) $152.50   E) $153.00

14-35   A $1000 fully discrete 20-year endowment policy is issued to (30). Find the excess of the net level reserve over the modified reserve at the end of the tenth policy year.

Given: $A_{30:\,\overline{20|}} = .40$

$\ddot{a}_{40:\,\overline{10|}} = 8$

$\alpha = 10$

$d = .06$

A) $24   B) $25   C) $26   D) $27   E) $28

14–36   A \$1000 fully discrete whole life policy is issued to (95). Find the greatest difference between the net level and full preliminary term terminal reserves at any duration of the policy.

Given: $A_{95} = .842$

$A_{96} = .851$

$A_{97} = .858$

$A_{98} = .866$

$A_{99} = .873$

A) \$55   B) \$57   C) \$60   D) \$63   E) \$65

14–37   Simplify: $\dfrac{\beta^{CAN} - \alpha^{CAN} - E^{CAN}}{E^{CAN}}$ for a fully discrete whole life policy.

A) P_x B) $\beta^{CAN} - P_x$ C) β^{CAN} D) a_x E) None of these

14–38   Simplify $\left(\dfrac{P_{23:\,\overline{7}|} - P_{21:\,\overline{9}|}}{P_{23:\,\overline{7}|} - P_{20:\,\overline{10}|}} \right)$.

A) $_2V_{21:\,\overline{9}|}$ B) $_3V_{20:\,\overline{10}|}$ C) $\dfrac{_3V^{FPT}_{20:\,\overline{10}|}}{_3V_{20:\,\overline{10}|}}$ D) $\dfrac{_3V_{20:\,\overline{10}|}}{_3V^{FPT}_{20:\,\overline{10}|}}$ E) None of these

14–39   A fully discrete \$10,000 whole life policy is issued to (35). First-year expenses are assumed to be 50% of the gross premium, plus \$50. Renewal-year expenses are assumed to be 10% of the gross premium, plus \$10.

Find the first-year expense reserve, given $A_{35} = .25$, $\ddot{a}_{35} = 25$, and $q_{35} = .01$.

(Answer to nearest .10.)

A) −\$87.40   B) −\$89.60   C) −\$90.50   D) −\$91.30   E) −\$92.10

14–40   Ten \$1500 fully discrete three-year term policies are issued to lives aged 80. The first year gross premium is \$350 per policy.

From the following facts, determine the expected net income for the three-year period.

   i)   Expenses are 10% of each premium
   ii)   First-year expected net income is \$700
   iii)   Expected surplus after three years is \$2000
   iv) $q_{80} = .20$
   v) $i = \frac{1}{9}$
   vi) $_1V = 0$

A) \$100   B) \$150   C) \$200   D) \$250   E) \$300

14–41 Fully discrete $1000 whole life policies are issued to two lives aged 98. Find the expected total net income over the lifetime of the policies, given:

  i) $l_x = 100 - x$, $98 \le x \le 100$
  ii) $i = .05$
  iii) Expenses are expected to be 30% of each premium, plus $30.
  iv) Profit/contingency loading is $50 per year per policy.
  v) There is an initial surplus fund of $500.
  vi) All interest income is taxed at 20%.

A) $141   B) $144   C) $147   D) $150   E) $153

14–42 A ten-year fully discrete 10-pay life insurance policy is issued to (70) with an annual premium of $250. Budgeted expenses are $45 in the first year and $25 in renewal years. Expense loading is 20% of each premium. Find the expected surplus per initial policyholder at the end of the tenth policy year.

Given: $\ddot{a}_{70:\overline{10|}} = 8$

$\ddot{s}_{70:\overline{10|}} = 14$

$(1 + i)^{10} = 1.4$

A) $225   B) $252   C) $281   D) $315   E) $336

14–43 A $1000 fully discrete, nonparticipating, 20-year endowment policy to (x) is valued by the Canadian method. The acquisition expenses of $25 were half of the net annual premium. If $\beta^{CAN} - \alpha^{CAN} = 25$, find the actuarial present value of expenses recoverable in the second and later years while still providing for administrative expenses.

Given: $\ddot{a}_{x:\overline{20|}} = 10$

A) $20.00   B) $22.50   C) $23.50   D) $25.00   E) Cannot be
                                                                                       determined

14–44 A $5000 fully discrete 30-year endowment policy is issued to (x). Find the excess of the second net level terminal reserve over the second Canadian reserve.

Given:

  i) The net level premium is $100.
  ii) Loading is 40% of the net premium.
  iii) Policyholder dividends are $5 per year.
  iv) Renewal administrative expenses are 30% of the net premium.
  v) Actual acquisition expenses are 70% of the first-year gross premium.
  vi) $\ddot{a}_{x+2:\overline{28|}} = 16$

A) $78   B) $80   C) $82   D) $84   E) $86

14–45 A three-year fully discrete endowment policy to (25) provides death protection of $5000 and $10,000 in the first two policy years. If the ELRA is $16,600, find the face amount for the third policy year.

Given: $A^1_{26:\overline{1}|} = .09$

$A^1_{26:\overline{2}|} = .20$

$v = .90$

A) $21,000   B) $21,250   C) $21,500   D) $21,750   E) $22,000

Answers to Chapter Fourteen Exercises

14–1	C.	14–16	C.	14–31	E.
14–2	A.	14–17	A.	14–32	A.
14–3	B.	14–18	C.	14–33	A.
14–4	B.	14–19	E.	14–34	C.
14–5	B.	14–20	B.	14–35	D.
14–6	B.	14–21	D.	14–36	B.
14–7	A.	14–22	B.	14–37	E.
14–8	A.	14–23	A.	14–38	C.
14–9	D.	14–24	A.	14–39	C.
14–10	B.	14–25	C.	14–40	C.
14–11	B.	14–26	C.	14–41	E.
14–12	D.	14–27	A.	14–42	B.
14–13	A.	14–28	C.	14–43	B.
14–14	C.	14–29	C.	14–44	B.
14–15	C.	14–30	B.	14–45	E.

Solutions

14–1.

Method One

Key Formulas:

$$(II)_1 = i({}_0S + P_1 - E_1)$$
$$(NI)_1 = (P + II - E - C)_1 - {}_1V$$

Solving for E_1, we have

$$450 = .12(1000 + 3500 - E_1)$$
$$\therefore E_1 = 750$$

Now, solving for ${}_1V$, we have

$$-100 = 3500 + 450 - 750 - 1000 - {}_1V$$
$$\therefore {}_1V = 2300$$

Thus, for the second block of policies, ${}_1V = 1900$. Solving for investment income $(II)_1$, we have

$$420 = 3500 + (II)_1 - 750 - 1000 - 1900$$
$$\therefore (II)_1 = 570$$

Finally, solving for $_0S$ for the second block of business,

$$570 = .12(_0S + 3500 - 750)$$
$$\therefore {}_0S = \underline{\underline{2000}}$$

Method Two

A logical approach here is preferable. The second block of business requires \$400 less in reserves, and thus has first-year net income which is \$400 higher on that account. Yet, the difference in the two net incomes is \$520, leaving \$120 to be accounted for. It can only be generated by interest on the *additional* initial surplus. Thus,

$$.12(\text{additional initial surplus}) = 120.$$

As the additional initial surplus is thus seen to be \$1000, the actual initial surplus for the second block is $\underline{\$2000}$.

14-2.

Key Approach:

In order to determine expected net income, the premium income must first be found.

Letting G represent the annual expense-loaded premium, we have

$$G\ddot{a}_x = 10\,,000A_x + 100 + 61.75 + 20\ddot{a}_x + .10G\ddot{a}_x.$$

Since $\ddot{a}_x = \dfrac{1 - A_x}{d} = 15.75$, we obtain

$$G = 210.$$

Thus, for one policy, the expected components of the first year's income statement are:

$$P_1 = 210$$
$$E_1 = 100 + 61.75 + 20 + 21 = 202.75$$
$$\therefore (II)_1 = .05(992.75 + 210 - 202.75) = 50.00$$
$$C_1 = 10\,,000q_x$$
$$_1V = \Delta(_0V) = 67.34(1 - q_x)$$

Then,

$$(NI)_1 = 210 - 202.75 + 50 - 10\,,000q_x - 67.34 + 67.34q_x$$
$$= -10.09 - 9932.66q_x.$$

Now, we determine q_x as follows:

$$P_x = \frac{dA_x}{1 - A_x} = \frac{1}{63}$$
$$P_x(1 + i) = q_x + (1 - q_x)\,_1V_x$$
$$\therefore q_x = .01$$

Finally,

$$(NI)_1 \doteq -10.09 - 99.33 = \underline{\underline{-109.42}}$$

14–3.

Key Concept: The expected net income is entirely attributable to net loadings plus interest, and interest on the initial surplus.

Since the total net income is $176,506.26 - 150,000 = 26,506.26$, we have

$$26,506.26 = 500(10)(.10)(1.04)(1.06)(1.05)$$
$$+ 500(6)(.5)(1.06)(1.05)$$
$$+ 500(6)p_{x+1}(.6)(1.05)$$
$$+ 150,000[(1.04)(1.06)(1.05) - 1].$$

Solving,

$$p_{x+1} = \underline{\underline{\frac{1}{3}}}$$

14–4.

Key Formula: $$(NI)_1 = (P + II - E - C)_1 - {}_1V$$

Necessary input is as follows:

$$P_1 = 10(275.70 + C) = 2757 + 10C$$
$$E_1 = 1.8(275.70 + C) + 10(10) = 596.26 + 1.8C$$
$$(II)_1 = .12(1500 + 2757 + 10C - 596.26 - 1.8C)$$
$$= 439.29 + .984C$$
$$C_1 = 2000$$
$$\Delta({}_0V) = 8(210.75) = 1686$$

Thus,

$$-856.37 = 2757 + 10C + 439.29 + .984C - 596.26$$
$$- 1.8C - 2000 - 1686$$
$$\therefore C = \underline{\underline{25}}$$

14–5.

Key Concept: The difference in the total net income, on the two liability bases, for the first three years is totally attributable to the excess of the benefit reserve ($165 per thousand) over the total reserve ($145 per thousand) at duration three. Thus much of the given data is useless.

Thus the required quantity equals $20 times the expected face amount (in thousands) in force of duration three. Accordingly, we have

$$(20)(50) \, {}_3p_{20}$$
$$= 1000 \left(\frac{9}{10} \right) \left(\frac{2}{3} \right) \left(\frac{3}{4} \right)$$
$$= \underline{450}$$

14–6.

Key Concept: The *single* policy fee must provide for all per policy expenses in addition to the percentage of premium expense which it generates.

Thus,

$$g = \ddot{a}_x + \ddot{a}_{x:\overline{3}|} + .21g$$
$$\therefore g = \frac{\ddot{a}_x + \ddot{a}_{x:\overline{3}|}}{.79}$$

The required annuity values are found as follows:

$$\ddot{a}_x = \frac{1 - A_x}{d} = 10; \quad \ddot{a}_{x+3} = \frac{1 - A_{x+3}}{d} = 9$$
$$\ddot{a}_x = \ddot{a}_{x:\overline{3}|} + v^3 \, {}_3p_x \ddot{a}_{x+3}$$
$$\therefore 10 = \ddot{a}_{x:\overline{3}|} + (.95)^3(.95)9$$
$$\therefore \ddot{a}_{x:\overline{3}|} \doteq 2.669$$

Finally,

$$g = \frac{12.669}{.79} = \underline{16.04}$$

Note that the policy fee, as should be the case, is independent of policy size.

14–7.

The expense-loaded premium equation is

$$G\ddot{a}_x = 10{,}000A_x + 75\ddot{a}_x + .1G\ddot{a}_x.$$

Letting $G = 500$, we have

$$375\ddot{a}_x = 10{,}000A_x$$
$$\therefore 10{,}000P_x = \underline{\underline{375}}$$

14–8.

The expense-loaded premium equation is

$$G\ddot{a}_x = 11{,}000A_x + 75\ddot{a}_x + .1G\ddot{a}_x$$

Letting $G = 500$, we have

$$375\ddot{a}_x = 11{,}000A_x$$
$$\therefore 10{,}000P_x = \frac{10}{11}(375) \doteq \underline{\underline{341}}$$

NOTE: Since the fixed \$500 premium could have only purchased $\frac{10}{11}$ as much insurance as in the previous question, it is logical that the net premium here would be $\frac{10}{11}$ of that of Problem 14-7.

14–9.

Key Concepts:

In order to analyze net income for the third policy year, the second policy year must be analyzed as well.

Since liabilities are defined as benefit *plus* expense reserves, each policy year's net income is solely attributable to net profit/contingency loadings plus interest and interest on surplus.

Thus, considering the first year, and letting L equal the profit/contingency loading, we have

$$1338 = .10(1500) + 100L(.9)(1.1)$$
$$\therefore L = 12.$$

Then,

$$(NI)_2 = .10(1500 + 1338) + 100(12)p_x(.95)(1.1)$$
$$= 1412.40$$

Finally,

$$(NI)_3 = .10(1500 + 1338 + 1442.40) + 100(12)p_x p_{x+1}(.95)(1.1)$$
$$= \underline{\underline{1384.35}}$$

14–10.

Key Concept: Since the net income is required over *all* durations of the block of business, the liability basis is irrelevant. The required quantity is simply net profit/contingency loadings with interest in addition to interest on initial surplus.

Accordingly,

$$\sum_{k=1}^{3}(NI)_k = 200(.9)(1.1)^3 + 200(.95)(.91)(1.1)^2$$
$$+ 200(.893)(.92)(1.1)$$
$$+ 500[(1.1)^3 - 1]$$
$$= \underline{\underline{795.03}}$$

14–11.

Key Formula: $$R(b) = \frac{a}{1-f} + \frac{c}{b(1-f)}$$

We must first determine the mean face amount, i.e., $E[B] = \bar{b}$.

$$\bar{b} = \int_{10}^{\infty} b(200b^{-3})\,db$$
$$= 200\int_{10}^{\infty} b^{-2}\,db$$
$$= 20.$$

Now,

$$R(\bar{b}) = \frac{25}{.8} + \frac{c}{20(.8)} = 32$$
$$\therefore c = 12$$
$$\therefore R(b) = \frac{25}{.8} + \frac{12}{b(.8)} = 31.25 + \frac{15}{b}.$$
$$\therefore G(b) = 31.25b + 15$$

Thus, the theoretical premium for a $10,000 policy is

$$G(10) = 327.50$$

while the premium actually charged is

$$10R(\bar{b}) = 320.00.$$

The required quantity is therefore $\underline{\underline{\$7.50}}$.

14–12.

Key Concept: In order to determine investment income, the amount of the single premium must be ascertained.

Thus,

$$G = 10,000A_x + .2G + 60\ddot{a}_x.$$

Since $A_x = .3$ and $d = .07$, we have

$$\ddot{a}_x = 10.$$

Then,

$$.8G = 3000 + 600$$
$$\therefore G = 4500.$$

Using $P_1 = 45,000$ and

$$E_1 = .2(45,000) + 10(60) = 9600,$$

we have

$$(II)_1 = .10[45,000 - 9600 + {}_0S] = 4000$$
$$\therefore {}_0S = \underline{\underline{4600}}$$

14–13.

Key Approach: In order to determine premiums by the band method, $R(b)$ must be obtained.

Thus,

$$G(b) = bA_x + .2G(b) + 5\ddot{a}_x + 25.$$

Since $\ddot{a}_x = \dfrac{1 - A_x}{d} = 10$, we have

$$.8G(b) = .4b + 75$$
$$\therefore G(b) = \frac{1}{2}b + \frac{75}{.8}$$
$$\therefore R(b) = \frac{1}{2} + \frac{75}{.8b}$$

Thus, for band one,

$$R(b) = \frac{1}{2} + \frac{75}{.8(50,000)}, \qquad b \le 55,000$$

and, for band two,

$$R(b) = \frac{1}{2} + \frac{75}{.8(100,000)}, \qquad b > 55,000$$

Finally,

$$G(50,000) = 50,000R(50,000) = 25,093.75$$

and

$$G(60,000) = 60,000R(60,000) = 30,056.25$$

Since the per policy costs are represented by the second component of the expressions for $R(b)$, the per policy charges are $93.75 and $56.25, respectively.

Thus, $\dfrac{56.25}{93.75} = \underline{\underline{.6}}$.

14–14.

Key Formula:
$$R(b) = \frac{a}{1-f} + \frac{c}{b(1-f)}$$

Thus,

$$R(b) = \frac{.09}{1-.10} + \frac{45}{b(.9)} = .1 + \frac{50}{b}$$

and

$$R(400,000) = .1 + \frac{50}{375,000},$$

where 375,000 is the average of 250,000 and 500,000, the end points of the band in which 400,000 falls.

Thus the actual premium for a $400,000 policy is

$$400,000\left(.1 + \frac{50}{375,000}\right) = 40,053.33,$$

of which 53.33 represents the per policy expense charge.

The single policy fee would be

$$\frac{c}{1-f} = \frac{45}{.9} = 50.$$

Thus, $53.33 - 50.00 = \underline{\underline{3.33}}$.

14–15.

Discussion of the band method earlier in this chapter, supplemented by Figure 14.1 in *Actuarial Mathematics*, should make it clear that only Statements <u>I and IV are true</u>.

14–16.

Key Formula:
$$_2p_x u(2) = (c - e_0)(1 + i) + p_x(c - e_1)(1 + i)^2$$

Thus,

$$20 = (c - 25) + \frac{24}{25}(c - 15)$$
$$\therefore c \doteq 30.31$$

Since $G = P + c$, we need only find the net annual premium P.

$$1000P_{75} = 1000\left(\frac{1}{\ddot{a}_{75}}\right) = \frac{1000}{1 + e_{75}}.$$

Under de Moivre's Law with $\omega = 100$,

$$e_{75} = 12.$$

Finally,

$$1000P_{75} = \frac{1000}{13}$$

and

$$1000G = \frac{1000}{13} + 30.31$$
$$= \underline{107.23}$$

14–17.

Key Formula:
$$E^{CAN} = P - \alpha^{CAN}$$

Thus,

$$E^{CAN} = \min\begin{pmatrix} 1.5P \\ 200 \\ 300 \end{pmatrix} = P - 80$$

Assume that $1.5P < 200$.

Then $1.5P = P - 80$, an obvious absurdity. Thus we know that $1.5P > 200$.

Now,

$$200 = P - 80$$
$$P = 280.$$

Letting F equal the required face amount, and using $P_x = \frac{1}{\ddot{a}_x} - d = .07$, we have

$$280 = FP_x = .07F$$
$$\therefore F = \underline{4000}$$

14–18.

Key Formulas:
$$\beta_x^{CAN} = P_x + \frac{P_x - \alpha^{CAN}}{a_x}$$

$$_nV_x^{CAN} = A_{x+n} - \beta^{CAN}\ddot{a}_{x+n}$$

Thus,

$$\beta_{25}^{CAN} = P_{25} + \frac{\frac{3}{2}P_{25}}{a_{25}} = 1.1P_{25}$$

and

$$
\begin{aligned}
_5V_{25}^{CAN} &= A_{30} - \beta_{25}^{CAN}\ddot{a}_{30} \\
&= A_{30} - 1.1P_{25}\frac{1 - A_{30}}{d} \\
&= A_{30} - 1.1\left(\frac{1}{\ddot{a}_{25}} - d\right)\frac{1 - A_{30}}{d} \\
&= .04375 = \underline{\underline{\frac{7}{160}}}
\end{aligned}
$$

14–19.

Key Concept: Since ELRA stands for equivalent level *renewal* amount, the face amount for policy year 1 is irrelevant, as in the pure endowment component.

$$
\begin{aligned}
ELRA &= \frac{50vq_{51} + 75v^2\,_{1|}q_{51}}{vq_{51} + v^2\,_{1|}q_{51}} \\
&= \frac{50(1+i) + 75}{1 + i + 1} \qquad \text{Note: } q_{51} = \,_{1|}q_{51} \quad \text{(DML)} \\
&= \frac{125 + 50i}{2 + i} = 60 \\
\therefore i &= \underline{\underline{.50}}
\end{aligned}
$$

14–20.

It is given that

$$(c - e_0)(1 + i) = -8.20.$$

Since

$$_2p_xu(2) = (c - e_0)(1 + i)^2 + (c - e_1)p_x(1 + i),$$

we have

$$_2p_x u(2) = (-8.20)(1 + i) + (1.25)(.96)(1 + i)$$
$$= -7(1 + i) = -7.28$$
$$\therefore i = \underline{\underline{.04}}$$

14–21.

Key Approach: Although there are *ten* net premiums α rather than the traditional *one*, the question is still approached by equating the actuarial present values of the net level premiums and the modified premiums.

Thus,

$$\alpha \ddot{a}_{x:\overline{10|}} + \beta \,_{10|}\ddot{a}_x = P_x \cdot \ddot{a}_{x:\overline{10|}} + P_x \cdot \,_{10|}\ddot{a}_x$$
$$\therefore \frac{\beta - P_x}{P_x - \alpha} = \frac{\ddot{a}_{x:\overline{10|}}}{A_{x:\overline{10|}}^{\,1} \cdot \ddot{a}_{x+10}}$$
$$= \frac{1 - A_{x:\overline{10|}}}{A_{x:\overline{10|}}^{\,1}(1 - A_{x+10})}$$

We need A_{x+10}.

$$A_x - A_{x:\overline{10|}}^{1} = A_{x:\overline{10|}}^{\,1} A_{x+10}$$
$$\therefore A_{x+10} = \frac{1}{3}.$$

Finally,

$$\frac{\beta - P_x}{P_x - \alpha} = \frac{.25}{(.60)(\frac{2}{3})} = \underline{\underline{\frac{5}{8}}}$$

14–22.

Key Formula:

$$\beta^{COM} - P = \frac{\beta^{COM} - \alpha^{COM}}{\ddot{a}_{x:\overline{h|}}}$$

We need $\ddot{a}_{20:\overline{20|}}$.

$$\ddot{a}_{20:\overline{20|}} = 1 + \,_1E_{20}\ddot{a}_{21:\overline{19|}}$$
$$= 6.4008$$

Thus,

$$.055 - .050 = \frac{.055 - \alpha^{COM}}{6.4008}$$
$$\therefore \alpha^{COM} = .022996$$
$$\therefore 1000(\alpha^{COM}) \doteq \underline{\underline{23.00}}$$

14–23.

Key Formula:

$$\beta^{CAN} = P + \frac{E^{CAN}}{a_{x:\overline{h-1|}}}$$

Thus,

$$60\theta = 1000\,{}_hP_x + \frac{E^{CAN}}{a_{x:\overline{h-1|}}}.$$

Since ${}_hP_x = \dfrac{A_x}{\ddot{a}_{x:\overline{h|}}} = .05$, we have

$$60\theta = 50 + \frac{1}{16}\min\binom{1.5(50)}{60\theta}.$$

It is unclear whether 60θ is greater or smaller than 75. Trial and error is recommended.

Assume $60\theta > 75$

$$\therefore 60\theta = 50 + \frac{1}{16}(75)$$
$$\therefore \theta \doteq .91, \text{ contradicting the assumption.}$$

Thus, $60\theta < 75$, and

$$60\theta = 50 + \frac{1}{16}(60\theta)$$
$$\therefore \theta = \underline{\underline{.8\dot{8}}}$$

14–24.

Key Formula:

$$u(2) = (c - e_0)\frac{(1+i)^2}{{}_2p_x} + (c - e_1)\frac{(1+i)}{p_{x+1}}$$

The only unknown is $c = G - P$. Since

$$P_x = vq_x, \qquad \text{(geometric distribution)}$$
$$= \frac{.12}{1.1},$$

we have

$$c = 119.09 - \frac{120}{1.1}$$
$$\doteq 10.00$$

Finally,

$$u(2) = (-1)\frac{1.21}{(.88)^2} + (.65)\frac{1.1}{(.88)}$$
$$= \underline{\underline{-.75}}$$

NOTE: The student should verify the following values as an alternative solution. Assume *one* initial policyholder.

$$P_1 = 119.09 \qquad\qquad P_2 = 104.80$$
$$(II)_1 = 10.81 \qquad\qquad (II)_2 = 9.55$$
$$E_1 = 11.00 \qquad\qquad E_2 = 8.23$$
$$C_1 = 120 \qquad\qquad C_2 = 105.60$$
$$\Delta(_0V) = 0 \qquad\qquad \Delta(_1V) = 0$$
$$\therefore (NI)_1 = -1.10 \qquad\qquad \therefore (NI)_2 = .52$$

Thus, the net income per survivor is

$$\frac{-1.10 + .52}{(.88)^2} = \underline{\underline{-.75}}$$

14–25.

Method One

The "brute force" method, not recommended here, is instructive nevertheless. It *is* recommended, however, that the following values be verified and the procedure understood.

$$G \doteq 2238.76 \qquad \text{per } \$100,000 \text{ policy}$$
$$_1V \doteq 943.40$$
$$P_1 = 11,193.80$$
$$(II)_1 = 853.88$$
$$E_1 = 1879.07$$
$$C_1 = 5003.00$$
$$\Delta(_0V) = 4669.83$$
$$\therefore (NI)_1 = 500.78$$
$$E_2 = 198.00$$
$$\therefore (II)_2 = .06(5500.78 + 4669.83 - 198) = \underline{\underline{598.36}}$$

Method Two

The funds expected to be on hand as the second contract year ends are the accumulated value of the initial surplus plus expected death claims for the second policy year, i.e.,

$$5000(1.06)^2 + 5(100,060)p_x q_{x+1} = 10,570.97.$$

Thus, the investment income for the second policy year must satisfy the equation

$$(II)_2 = d(10,570.97)$$
$$\therefore (II)_2 = \underline{\underline{598.36}}$$

14–26.

Method One

$$P_1 = 5(1070) = 5350$$

$$E_1 = 5(287.50) = 1437.50$$

$$(II)_1 = (.20)(5350 - 1437.50 + 10,000) = 2782.50$$

$$C_1 = \frac{1}{10}(5)(10,000) = 5000$$

$$\Delta(_0V) = {}_1V = 5[913.87(1 + i) - 10,000q_{40}]$$

$$= 483.22$$

$$\therefore (NI)_1 = 1211.78$$

$$\therefore {}_1S = {}_0S + (NI)_1 = \underline{\underline{11,211.78}}$$

Method Two

Ignoring interest on the initial surplus, the net income per initial insured, at duration one, equals

$$p_{40}u(1) = (c - e_0)(1 + i)$$

$$= (1070 - 913.87 - 287.50)(1.2)$$

$$= -157.644$$

$$\therefore (NI)_1 = 5(-157.644) + .2(10,000)$$

$$= 1211.78$$

$$\therefore {}_1S = \underline{\underline{11,211.78}}$$

14–27.

Key Formula:
$$[u(h) + \overset{\circ}{c} - e_h](1 + i) = p_{x+h}u(h + 1)$$

Thus,

$$[u(4) + c - e_4](1 + i) = p_{x+4}u(5)$$

$$\therefore {}_4p_x[u(4) + c - e_4](1 + i) = {}_5p_xu(5)$$

Finally, since the desired quantity is ${}_5p_xu(5) - {}_4p_xu(4)$, we solve algebraically and obtain

$${}_5p_xu(5) - {}_4p_xu(4) = \underline{\underline{{}_4p_x[u(4)i + (c - e_4)(1 + i)]}}$$

14–28.

Key Concept: Where the incidence of expenses is represented by an increasing function, and expense loading is constant, expense reserves must be negative and increasing. Further, total reserves are less than benefit reserves.

From these considerations, it is clear that Statements I, III, and IV are true.

Statement II is shown to be false in Tables 14.2 and 14.4 of *Actuarial Mathematics*. This may have been seen logically by realizing that the introduction of the expense factor into the reserve concept simply brings in another area of uncertainty.

14–29.

Key Formula:

$$(II)_h = i[\,_{h-1}A + P_h - E_h]$$

Thus,

$$i = \frac{500}{11,375 + 46,535 - 37,910}$$
$$= \underline{.025}$$

14–30.

Key Formulas:

$$_nV_x^{FPT} = {}_{n-1}V_{x+1}$$
$$_{m+n}V_x = 1 - (1 - {}_mV_x)(1 - {}_nV_{x+m})$$

Thus,

$$_{15}V_{25} = .6\,,$$
$$_5V_{35} = .5\,,$$
$$\text{and}$$
$$_{15}V_{25} = 1(1 - {}_{10}V_{25})(1 - {}_5V_{35})\,.$$
$$\therefore\ {}_{10}V_{25} = {}_{11}V_{24}^{FPT} = \underline{\underline{.2}}$$

14–31.

Key Concept: Under a constant force of mortality, $\alpha^{FPT} = vq_x = P_x = P_{x+1} = \beta^{FPT}$. Further, whole life terminal reserves, FPT or otherwise, equal zero under constant force. Finally, for whole life policies with more than 20 premiums, Commissioners' reserves equal FPT reserves.

Thus all three statements are <u>false</u>.

14–32.

Key Formula:
$$u(3) = (c - e_0)\frac{(1 + i)^3}{_3p_x} + (c - e_1)\frac{(1 + i)^2}{_2p_{x+1}} + (c - e_2)\frac{(1 + i)}{p_{x+2}}$$
Since we are given $c = 40$, $e_0 = 45$, $e_1 = 45(.9) = 40.50$ and $e_2 = 45(.9)^2 = 36.45$, we have

$$u(3) = -5\frac{(1.05)^3}{(.95)^3} - .50\frac{(1.05)^2}{(.95)^2} + 3.55\frac{1.05}{.95}$$
$$= \underline{\underline{-3.44}}$$

Note that the expected surplus *per initial insured* is
$$(.95)^3(-3.44) = -2.95$$

14–33.

Key Formula:
$$\beta - P = \frac{P - \alpha}{a_{x:\overline{j-1}|}}$$

Thus, since $a_{y:\overline{19}|} = \frac{N_{y+1} - N_{y+20}}{D_y} = 2.05$, we have

$$100 - 80 = \frac{80 - \alpha}{2.05}$$
$$\therefore \alpha = \underline{\underline{39}}$$

14–34.

Letting K represent the profit margin, and realizing that $A_x = \frac{q}{q + i} = \frac{1}{2}$ and $\ddot{a}_x = \frac{1 - A_x}{d} = 5.5$, we have the following gross premium equation:

$$G\ddot{a}_{20} = 1000A_{20} + 105 + 4\ddot{a}_{20} + .14G\ddot{a}_{20} + K\ddot{a}_{20}$$
$$\therefore K = 15$$

Thus the profit loading is 10% of the gross premium. We wish to increase it to 11% of the gross premium.

Thus,

$$G'(5.5) = 500 + 105 + 22 + .14G'(5.5) + .11G'(5.5)$$
$$\therefore G' = \underline{152}$$

14–35.

Key Formula:

$$_{10}V_{30:\,\overline{20}|} - {}_{10}V_{30:\,\overline{20}|}^{MOD} = (\beta - P_{30:\,\overline{20}|})\ddot{a}_{40:\,\overline{10}|}$$
$$= \frac{(P_{30:\,\overline{20}|} - \alpha)}{a_{30:\,\overline{19}|}}\ddot{a}_{40:\,\overline{10}|}$$

Required values are

$$P_{30:\,\overline{20}|} = \frac{A_{30:\,\overline{20}|}}{\ddot{a}_{30:\,\overline{20}|}} = \frac{dA_{30:\,\overline{20}|}}{1 - A_{30:\,\overline{20}|}} = .04$$

and

$$a_{30:\,\overline{19}|} = \ddot{a}_{30:\,\overline{20}|} - 1 = 9.$$

Finally, the required reserve difference is

$$\frac{(.04 - .01)}{9}(8) = .02\dot{6}$$

for a \$1 policy. Accordingly, the result is $\underline{26.67}$ for a \$1000 policy.

14–36.

Key Concept:

The difference between full preliminary term and net level reserves is greatest at duration one.

Thus, we need

$$_{1}V_{95} - {}_{1}V_{95}^{FPT}$$

But this is simply

$$_{1}V_{95} = \frac{A_{96} - A_{95}}{1 - A_{95}}$$
$$\doteq .057$$

Thus, for a \$1000 policy, the required reserve is approximately $\underline{\$57}$.

14–37.

Since

$$E^{CAN} = P - \alpha^{CAN},$$

we have

$$\frac{\beta^{CAN} - \alpha^{CAN} - E^{CAN}}{E^{CAN}} = \frac{\beta^{CAN} - P}{P - \alpha^{CAN}}$$

$$= \frac{\dfrac{P - \alpha^{CAN}}{a_x}}{P - \alpha^{CAN}} = \underline{\underline{\frac{1}{a_x}}}$$

14–38.

Since $P_{x:\overline{n}|} = \dfrac{1}{\ddot{a}_{x:\overline{n}|}} - d$, we have

$$\frac{P_{25:\overline{7}|} - P_{21:\overline{9}|}}{P_{23:\overline{7}|} - P_{20:\overline{10}|}} = \frac{\dfrac{1}{\ddot{a}_{23:\overline{7}|}} - \dfrac{1}{\ddot{a}_{21:\overline{9}|}}}{\dfrac{1}{\ddot{a}_{23:\overline{7}|}} - \dfrac{1}{\ddot{a}_{20:\overline{10}|}}}$$

$$= \frac{1 - \dfrac{\ddot{a}_{23:\overline{7}|}}{a_{21:\overline{9}|}}}{1 - \dfrac{\ddot{a}_{23:\overline{7}|}}{\ddot{a}_{20:\overline{10}|}}}$$

$$= \frac{{}_2V_{21:\overline{9}|}}{{}_3V_{20:\overline{10}|}}$$

$$= \underline{\underline{\frac{{}_3V^{FPT}_{20:\overline{10}|}}{{}_3V_{20:\overline{10}|}}}}$$

14–39.

Key Concept: In order to find the expense reserve at the end of the first year, we must have both the amount of the premium allocated for expenses and the amount of first-year expense contemplated by the premium structure.

The gross premium equation is given by

$$G\ddot{a}_{35} = 10,000A_{35} + .4G + .1G\ddot{a}_{35} + 40 + 10\ddot{a}_{35}$$
$$\therefore G \doteq 126.24$$
$$\therefore c = G - P \doteq 126.24 - 100 = 26.24$$
$$e_0 = .5G + 50 \doteq 113.12$$

Thus, the first expense reserve is

$$(c - e_0)\frac{1+i}{p_{35}} \doteq (-86.88)\left(\frac{1}{.97}\right)\left(\frac{1}{.99}\right) \quad \text{since } d = \frac{1}{\ddot{a}_{35}} - P_{25} = .03$$

$$= \underline{\underline{-90.47}}$$

14–40.

Key Concepts:

It is not possible to approach this question from the traditional year-by-year approach, because neither premiums nor mortality rates are known beyond the first policy year.

Since the expected surplus after three years is known, and the required quantity is the three-year net income, we must find the initial surplus $_0S$.

$$P_1 = 10(350) = 3500$$
$$\therefore E_1 = 350$$
$$C_1 = 10(1500)q_{80} = 3000$$
$$(II)_1 = \frac{1}{9}(_0S + 3500 - 350) = \frac{1}{9}(_0S) + 350$$
$$\Delta(_0V) = 0$$
$$\therefore (NI)_1 = 3500 - 350 - 3000 + \frac{1}{9}(_0S) + 350 = 700$$
$$\therefore {_0S} = 1800$$
$$\therefore {_3S} - {_0S} = 2000 - 1800 = \underline{\underline{200}}$$

14–41.

Key Concepts:

The total net income is totally attributable to net profit/contingency loadings plus interest and interest on the initial surplus.

The effective rate at which funds are invested, after taxes, is 4%.

Thus, interest on initial surplus is

$$500((1.04)^2 - 1) = 40.80$$

and net income due to net profit/contingency loadings plus interest is

$$2(50)(.7)(1.04)^2 + 50(.7)(1.04) = 112.11.$$

Summing, the total expected net income is

$$40.80 + 112.11 = \underline{\underline{152.91}}$$

14-42.

Key Concept:

Since the contributions to surplus are equal for each policy year after the first, it is easier to determine surplus per *surviving* policyholder.

The loading in each premium is $50, leaving a $5 surplus contribution in year one and a $25 surplus contribution in renewal years. Thus,

$$u(10) = 25\ddot{s}_{70:\overline{10}|} - 20\frac{1}{_{10}E_{70}}$$

$$= 25(14) - 20\left(\frac{14}{8}\right)$$

$$= 315$$

Finally, the required quantity is

$$_{10}p_{70}u(10) = \frac{\ddot{a}_{70:\overline{10}|}}{\ddot{s}_{70:\overline{10}|}}(1+i)^{10}u(10)$$

$$= \underline{\underline{252}}$$

14-43.

Key Formula:

$$\beta^{CAN} - P = \frac{P - \alpha^{CAN}}{a_{x:\overline{19}|}}$$

Since $P = 50$ and $a_{x:\overline{19}|} = 9$, we have

$$9(\beta - 50) = 50 - \alpha$$

$$\therefore \alpha + 9\beta = 500$$

As we are given

$$\beta - \alpha = 25,$$

it is easily determined that

$$\alpha = 27.50 \quad \text{and}$$

$$\beta = 52.50.$$

Finally, letting K represent the desired quantity, we have

$$E^{CAN} = P - \alpha^{CAN} = (52.50 - 50.00)9 = 22.50$$

$$= \min\begin{pmatrix} 25 \\ 75 \\ K \end{pmatrix}$$

Thus $K = \underline{\underline{22.50}}$.

14–44.

Key Formula:

$$_2V - {_2V}^{CAN} = (\beta^{CAN} - P)\ddot{a}_{x+2:\,\overline{28|}}$$
$$= \frac{P - \alpha^{CAN}}{a_{x:\,\overline{29|}}}\ddot{a}_{x+2:\,\overline{28|}}$$

Now,

$$E^{CAN} = P - \alpha^{CAN} = \min\begin{pmatrix} 150 \\ 98 \\ 5a_{x:\,\overline{29|}} \end{pmatrix}$$

since \$5 is available each year over and above the funds required for dividends and administrative expense.

It must now be determined whether 98 or $5a_{x:\,\overline{29|}}$ is the smaller quantity:

$$a_{x:\,\overline{29|}} = vp_x + v^2\,{_2}p_x\,\ddot{a}_{x+2:\,\overline{28|}}$$
$$= vp_x + 16v^2\,{_2}p_x < 17.$$

Thus $5a_{x:\,\overline{29|}} < 98$, and we have

$$_2V - {_2V}^{CAN} = \frac{5a_{x:\,\overline{29|}}}{a_{x:\,\overline{29|}}}\ddot{a}_{x+2:\,\overline{28|}} = \underline{\underline{80}}$$

14–45.

Key Formula:

$$ELRA = \frac{10,000A^1_{26:\,\overline{1|}} + K(A^1_{26:\,\overline{2|}} - A^1_{26:\,\overline{1|}})}{A^1_{26:\,\overline{2|}}}$$

Note that the formula was written in a manner designed to use the given data without modification.

Letting K represent the desired face amount,

$$ELRA = \frac{900 + .11K}{.20} = 16,600$$
$$\therefore K = \underline{\underline{22,000}}$$

Further note that the value of v could have been used to determine the input for the more traditional formula for $ELRA$, i.e.,

$$ELRA = \frac{10,000vq_{26} + Kv^2p_{26}q_{27}}{vq_{26} + v^2p_{26}q_{27}}$$

but this would have substantially overcomplicated the problem.

Chapter Fifteen

Supplementary Concepts

1. The term *adjusted premium* was created in order that statutory minimum cash values could reflect the traditionally heavy front-end load associated with life insurance products. It is best comprehended by comparing it with net premiums P and gross premium G, i.e.,

$$P\ddot{a} = A$$
$$P^a\ddot{a} = A + E_1$$
$$G\ddot{a} = A + E_1 + E\ddot{a}.$$

This indicates that the discounted value of adjusted premiums is sufficient to fund the extra first year expense E_1 but not the level annual expense E. Accordingly, the actuarial present value of the excesses of P^a over P equals E_1, i.e.,

$$(P^A - P)\ddot{a} = E_1.$$

Since net level reserves are based upon net level premiums and minimum cash values are based upon adjusted premiums, it is convenient to calculate minimum cash values by considering the difference

$$_kV - {_kCV} = (P^a - P)\ddot{a}(k).$$

Specifically, since

$$_kV_x - {_kCV_x} = (P^a_x - P_x)\ddot{a}_{x+k}$$
$$= \frac{E_1}{\ddot{a}_x}\ddot{a}_{x+k}$$

it is easily seen that this excess reflects the unamortized value of the extra first year expense E_1.

Where the premium-paying period is limited, it is observed that the minimum cash values grade into the net level reserve at the time of the last premium payment. At that time, of course, the entire value of E_1 has been amortized. For example,

$$_k^{10}V_x - {_k^{10}CV_x} = \frac{E_1}{\ddot{a}_{x:\overline{10|}}}\ddot{a}_{x+k:\overline{10-k|}}, \quad k = 1, 2, 3, \ldots, 10.$$

Actual values of E_1 are determined legislatively, as in the 1941 Report and the 1980 Law. In turn, adjusted premiums and then minimum cash values are mechanically determined.

321

2.   If the value of E_1 under the 1980 Law is written

$$E_1 = 1.25 \left\{ \frac{P}{.04} \right\} + .01$$

where the bracket indicates that the smaller of the included quantities is to be chosen, it is easy to produce the analogous formula for the case of nonlevel benefit amounts and/or nonlevel gross premiums. Specifically,

$$E_1 = 1.25 \left\{ \frac{P}{.04(\text{AAI})} \right\} + .01(\text{AAI}).$$

The value of P in this second form is the fictitious level premium whose actuarial present value is sufficient to fund the contractual benefit.

3.   Consideration of the specified expressions for E_1 under the 1941 Report and the 1980 Law, respectively, shows that the maximum values are \$46 per thousand and \$60 per thousand, respectively. The student may carelessly infer that the 1980 Law is the more liberal and thus generates smaller minimum cash values in all cases. This is incorrect; no simple generalization may be made as to which formula produces smaller values.

4.   The amount of insurance available under the reduced paid-up nonforfeiture option is determined as the quotient of the available policy value divided by the net single premium for a unit of insurance at the attained age. When the benefit may be purchased by applying the full net level reserve, the symbol W is used to represent the paid-up face amount. In addition to the standard formulas such as

$$_kW_x = 1 - \frac{P_x}{P_{x+k}}$$

and

$$_kW_{x:\overline{n}|} = 1 - \frac{P_{x:\overline{n}|}}{P_{x+k:\overline{n-k}|}},$$

the following relationships are useful:

$$_kW_x = 1 - (1 - {_mW_x})(1 - {_{k-m}W_{x+m}})$$

and

$$_kW_{x:\overline{n}|} = 1 - (1 - {_mW_{x:\overline{n}|}})(1 - {_{k-m}W_{x+m:\overline{n-m}|}}).$$

Variations such as

$$_{30}W_{10} = 1 - (1 - {_{12}W_{10}})(1 - {_{18}W_{22}})$$
$$= 1 - (1 - {_1W_{10}})(1 - {_1W_{11}})(1 - {_1W_{12}}) \cdots (1 - {_1W_{39}})$$

should be recognized.

Similar formulas exist where the funds available to purchase reduced paid-up coverage are defined to be the statutory minimum cash values. Although the symbol W is no longer appropriate, the formula

$$b_k = 1 - \frac{P^a}{P(k)}$$

is clearly analogous to

$$_kW = 1 - \frac{P}{P(k)}.$$

Specifically, for fully discrete whole life insurance to (x), the paid-up coverage which may be funded by minimum cash values is given by

$$b_k = 1 - \frac{P_x^a}{P_{x+k}}.$$

Similar results hold for endowment and limited-pay life policies.

Likewise, where modified reserves are used to fund reduced paid-up insurance, and where the modification period equals the premium-payment period, we have

$$b_k = 1 - \frac{\beta}{P_{x+k}},$$

$$b_k = 1 - \frac{\beta}{{}_{n-k}P_{x+k}},$$

and

$$b_k = 1 - \frac{\beta}{P_{x+k:\overline{n-k|}}}$$

for whole life, n-pay life, and n-year endowments, respectively.

5. Reserves and asset shares represent quite different measures of policy values, as the former generally reflect statutory assumptions while the latter reflect assumptions which are substantially more realistic. It is important to note, however, that the *form* of asset share formulas are quite reminiscent of those for reserves. Accordingly, the following formulas for asset shares should be seen as only slight modifications of their reserve counterparts:

$$_nAS = \sum_{k=0}^{n-1} \frac{G(1-c_k) - e_k - vq_{x+k}^{(1)} - vq_{x+k}^{(2)} \cdot {}_{k+1}CV}{{}_{n-k}E_{x+k}^{(T)}}$$

$$_{k+1}AS = \frac{{}_kAS + G(1-c_k) - e_k - vq_{x+k}^{(1)} - vq_{x+k}^{(2)} \cdot {}_{k+1}CV}{{}_1E_{x+k}^{(T)}}$$

While these formulas incorporate the double decrement model and the withdrawal benefit, along with gross premiums and expense assumptions—none of which are components of reserve calculations—the similarities to the retrospective and recursive reserve formulas are clear.

6. In the adjustment of the initially projected asset shares to reflect evolving experience, the following formula is recommended:

$$_{k+1}\widehat{AS} = \frac{{}_kAS + G(1-\hat{c}_k) - \hat{e}_k - \hat{v}\hat{q}_{x+k}^{(1)} - \hat{v}\hat{q}_{x+k}^{(2)} \cdot {}_{k+1}CV}{{}_1\hat{E}_{x+k}^{(T)}}$$

Note particularly that the $(k+1)^{st}$ *experience* asset share is derived from the kth *expected* asset share. Further note that every other component of the right hand side of the equation is based upon the experience of the $(k+1)^{st}$ policy year *except* those which are cast in stone at the policy's inception, i.e., the gross premium and the tabular cash values.

7.   It cannot be denied that Lidstone's Theorem is of substantial theoretical interest. How-
        ever, it should be emphasized that, unless the critical function c_h is constant or strictly
        monotonic, its value may be more apparent than real. While classroom or textbook prob-
        lems may be easily derived in which the critical function may be analyzed, and Lidstone's
        results applied, such is not often the situation in the real world.

        In the present-day environment of electronic computing, the relationship between reserves
        under different sets of actuarial assumptions may more readily be determined by calcu-
        lation and analysis of annuity values. If, for example, the value of $\frac{\ddot{a}_{x+t}}{\ddot{a}_x}$ is greater under
        a "primed" mortality/interest basis than under a standard basis, the elementary reserve
        formula

        $$_tV_x = 1 - \frac{\ddot{a}_{x+t}}{\ddot{a}_x}$$

        may be used to conclude whether reserves are greater under the primed or the standard
        basis.

Exercises

15–1   A fully discrete $1,000 whole life policy is issued to (x). After ten years, the policy is
        lapsed and the net level reserve used to purchase reduced paid-up insurance.

        The variance of the future loss immediately after the change is 81% of the variance of
        the loss immediately before the change.

        Evaluate $\dfrac{A_{x+10}}{A_x}$.

        A) 8   B) 9   C) 10   D) 11   E) 12

15–2   On a fully discrete $1000 whole life policy to (x), the additional first year expense
        allowance is the absolute maximum permitted by the 1980 Law. If the fifth net level
        terminal reserve is $300, find the fifth year minimum cash value.

        A) $258.00   B) $267.80   C) $272.00   D) $282.00   E) $300.00

15–3   If $_5V_{30:\,\overline{10|}} = .40$ and the corresponding minimum cash value equals .37, find E_1 .

        A) .020   B) .030   C) .046   D) .050   E) .060

15–4   Simplify $\dfrac{A_y - A_x}{A_y - A_x A_y}$ $(x < y)$.

        A) $_yW_x$ B) $_yV_x$ C) $_{y-x}W_x$ D) $_{y-x}V_x$ E) None of these

15-5   If $_{30}W_{40} = \left(_{10}W_{40}\right)^{1/2}$ and $2P_{70} = 3P_{50}$, evaluate $_{10}W_{40}$.

A) $\frac{1}{5}$ B) $\frac{1}{4}$ C) $\frac{1}{3}$ D) $\frac{1}{2}$ E) $\frac{2}{3}$

15-6   A decreasing endowment insurance, whose net single premium is represented by $(DA)_{x:\,\overline{12}|}$, is issued to (x) with a net level annual premium of .55. Find the level adjusted premium according to the 1980 Law, if $\ddot{a}_{x:\,\overline{12}|} = 9$ and $r_N = .96$.

A) .575   B) .600   C) .625   D) .650   E) .675

15-7   Jones, ceasing premium payments on a fully discrete whole life policy at age 60, elects the extended term option. His cash value, which is 15% of his original face amount, is sufficient to extend his policy for n complete years and m days.

Assuming $v = .95$ and de Moivre's Law with $\omega = 80$, find m to the nearest day.

A) 130   B) 150   C) 170   D) 190   E) 210

15-8   Using the 1980 Law, find $P^a_{30:\,\overline{10}|}$, given $a_{30:\,\overline{9}|} = 7$ and $d = .08$.

A) .0525   B) .0533   C) .0538   D) .0542   E) .0550

15-9   A fully discrete increasing life insurance policy with level annual premiums is issued to (30), with annual insurance coverages following the pattern $1000, $3000, $5000, $7000, $\cdots$. Assuming $i = 0$ and using the 1980 Law, find the extra first year expense allowance E_1.

A) $300   B) $400   C) $500   D) $600   E) There is insufficient information given

15-10   A fully continuous $1000 whole life policy to (20) was placed on the extended term option at the end of the 10th policy year, at which time the tabular cash value was $240. The extended term coverage period is determined to be 20 years. Find the amount of policy indebtedness at the time of lapse if $\bar{a}_{30:\,\overline{20}|} = 15$, $_{20}E_{30} = .5$, and $\delta = .03$.

A) $100   B) $125   C) $150   D) $190   E) $200

15-11   Given: $\dfrac{^{1941}P_x^a}{^{1980}P_x^a} = .9$

$P_x \geq .04$

$q_x = .08$ for all x

Find i.

A) 2.0%   B) 8.0%   C) 9.2%   D) 20.0%   E) 92.0%

15-12   If $i' = (1+i)^2 - 1$, $i > 0$, $\Delta q_x > 0$, and $q'_h = q_h + k$, $k > 0$, $h = 0, 1, 2, \ldots, n-1$, which of the following is the strongest statement that can be made about $_hV'_{x:\overline{n}|} - {_hV_{x:\overline{n}|}}$, $h = 1, 2, 3, \ldots, n-1$?

A) It is positive for all h.
B) It is positive for some h.
C) It is negative for all h.
D) It is negative for some h.
E) Nothing is certain but death, taxes, and actuarial examinations.

15-13   The adjusted premium P_x^a is determined to have the same value under both the 1941 Report and the 1980 Law. Given that $d = .25$ and $P_x^a > .04$, find P_x^a.

A) .0402   B) .0410   C) .0416   D) .0422   E) .0460

15-14   A fully discrete 10-year endowment insurance policy to (x) has an initial face amount of $4,000, increasing by $1,000 at the end of every two-year period. In addition, a $5,000 lump sum benefit is contingent upon survival of the 10-year period. The present value of all benefits at issue is $2,195.

If $A_{x:\overline{10}|} = .763$ and $i = .035$, find the additional first year expense allowance provided for in the 1980 Law.

A) $340   B) $345   C) $350   D) $355   E) $360

15-15   Seven years after the insurance of a $1 10-year fully discrete endowment policy to (x), the policy is placed on the extended term option. Find the face amount of the pure endowment, if any, which may be purchased.

Given: $P_{x:\overline{10}|}^a = .08$

$\ddot{a}_{x+7:\overline{3}|} = 2.50$

$_3E_{x+7} = .90$

A) 0   B) $\frac{1}{3}$ C) $\frac{4}{9}$ D) $\frac{2}{3}$ E) $\frac{7}{9}$

15-16   A $1,000 fully discrete whole life policy, issued to (35) and with annual premiums based upon the equivalence principle, is placed on the reduced paid-up option after 20 policy years. To discourage the insured from withdrawing his cash value, the insurer allows a paid-up face amount which is $K\%$ greater than would normally be available.

The variance of the future loss to the insurer immediately before the change equals that immediately after the change.

Find K.

Given: $\ddot{a}_{55} = 10$; $\ddot{a}_{45} = 15$; $\ddot{a}_{35} = 20$; $i = .05$

A) 5   B) 10   C) 15   D) 20   E) 21

15-17   For a block of $1,000 fully discrete whole life policies, asset shares are projected based on expected expense factors, investment experience, mortality rates, and lapse rates. For the sixth policy year, all projections were precisely realized except for the mortality experience.

If $q^{(d)}_{x+5} = .010$, $\hat{q}^{(d)}_{x+5} = .012$, and $_6AS = \$75$, find $_6\widehat{AS}$.

A) $71.39   B) $73.13   C) $75.00   D) $77.17   E) Cannot be determined

15-18   The gross annual premium for a fully discrete whole life policy to (35) is $12.50; the 20th asset share is projected to be $400. It is desired to generate a 20th asset share of $600 by raising the annual premium. Ten percent of each gross premium is allocated to expenses.

Find the adjusted gross premium, given: $N^{(T)}_{35} = 73,300$, $N^{(T)}_{55} = 24,000$, and $N^{(T)}_{56} = 22,360$.

A) $19.81   B) $19.89   C) $19.93   D) $20.01   E) $20.14

15-19   Given: $_{10}W_x = \frac{2}{5}$
$_{15}W_x = \frac{8}{15}$
$_{10}V_x = \frac{4}{15}$

Find $_{15}V_x$.

A) .384   B) .400   C) .430   D) .500   E) .545

15-20   Modified reserves on a 10-year endowment policy to (x) are defined such that $\beta = P^a_{x:\overline{10|}}$ under the 1980 Law, with $j = 10$. If $\ddot{a}_{x:\overline{10|}} = 5$ and $d = .1$, find α.

A) −.008   B) 0   C) .052   D) .060   E) .100

15–21   Simplify: $\dfrac{_aV_bA_b + A_{a+b} - A_b}{A_{a+b}}$

A) $_aV_b$ B) $_aW_b$ C) $_{a-b}V_b$ D) $_{a-b}W_b$ E) P_b

15–22   Ten years after (40) purchased a $10,000 fully discrete whole life policy, he began to have his $250 annual premiums paid through his automatic premium loan provision. At age 56, there are insufficient values to provide another year's insurance. Find the termination cash value available to the insured at that time. (Answer to the nearest $5.)

Given: $P_{40}^a = .015$, $A_{56} = .38$, $i = .05$.

A) $55   B) $60   C) $140   D) $145   E) $150

15–23   Given: $_{10}^{15}W_{20} = .20$
                        $_5P_{30} = .20$
                        $_{10}P_{25} = .18$

Find $_5^{15}W_{20}$.

A) $\frac{1}{6}$ B) $\frac{1}{7}$ C) $\frac{1}{8}$ D) $\frac{1}{9}$ E) $\frac{1}{10}$

15–24   The asset share per policy at the end of the kth policy year was $140; the $(k+1)^{\text{st}}$ asset share was then projected. The experience results were identical to those projected, except that an additional $\frac{1}{2}$ of 1% was earned on invested funds. Accordingly, the experience asset share was $1 greater than projected. Find the projected probability of death in the multiple-decrement model for the $(k+1)^{\text{st}}$ policy year.

Given: $G = 60$; $c_k = .1$; $e_k = 14$; $q_{x+k}^{(d)} = \frac{2}{3}q_{x+k}^{(w)}$.

A) .02   B) .03   C) .04   D) .05   E) .06

15–25   Two sets of actuarial assumptions are being analyzed to compare their effects on policy reserves. It is known that, at all ages, q_h' is less than q_h but that q_h' is increasing more rapidly than q_h. According to Lidstone's Theorem, which of the following statements is/are true?

    I. If $i' < i$ and reserves increase with duration, then $_kV' > _kV$ for integral values of k between 0 and m.

    II. If $i' > i$ and reserves decrease with duration, S_h is an increasing function.

    III. If $i' > i$ and reserves increase with duration, then $_kV' < _kV$ for integral values of k between 0 and m.

A) None   B) I only   C) II only   D) III only   E) More than
                                                                                    one

15–26   A $1000 5-year endowment policy was issued to (30) with net annual premiums of $175. Based on the 1941 Report, E_1 is determined to be $45.

Find $1000 \cdot {}_5V_{30}$, to the nearest dollar, given:

$$d = .075; \quad {}_5p_{30} = .9.$$

A) $55   B) $57   C) $60   D) $63   E) $65

15–27   Find the minimum cash value at the end of the tenth policy year for a $1,000 25-pay whole life policy issued to (40). Assume the 1941 Report and the following values:

$$A_{40} = .1975 \qquad \ddot{a}_{40} = 16.30$$
$$A_{50} = .3300 \qquad \ddot{a}_{50:\overline{15|}} = 10.00$$
$$P^a_{40} = .0140 \qquad \ddot{a}_{40:\overline{25|}} = 13.40$$

A) $150   B) $152   C) $155   D) $158   E) $160

15–28   For a fully discrete whole life policy to (x), both the 1941 Report and the 1980 Law generate a value of E_1 which is 4.275% of the face amount. Find d.

A) .170   B) .172   C) .175   D) .178   E) .180

15–29   The "1988 Rule" defines adjusted premiums to be sufficient to provide all contractual benefits in addition to 1% of the face amount plus the smallest of

    i)   3% of the face amount
   ii)   the adjusted premium
  iii)   125% of the net level premium

For a $10,000 fully discrete whole life policy to (30), determine the adjusted premium to the nearest dollar, given:

$$\ddot{a}_{30} = 20.6; \quad i = .03.$$

A) $209   B) $210   C) $211   D) $212   E) $213

15–30   Given: $P_{30} = .04$; $P_{40} = .06$.

If adjusted premiums are 20% greater than net level premiums, what fraction of the net level reserve is the cash value at the end of the tenth policy year of a fully discrete whole life policy to (30)?

A) 50%   B) 60%   C) 70%   D) 80%   E) 90%

15-31   You are given the following data for a fully discrete whole life policy to (30):

  i) $_{10}AS = 100 = {}_{11}CV + 100$
  ii) $_{11}AS = 986.45$
  iii) $q_{40}^{(w)} = 9 \cdot q_{40}^{(d)} = .18$
  iv) $e_{10} = .0004$
  v) $c_{10} = .1$
  vi) $i = .06$
  vii) The gross premium is one cent per dollar of face amount.

Find the face amount.

A) $1000   B) $1500   C) $10,000   D) $10,400   E) $15,000

15-32   A fully discrete life insurance policy to (x) would be expected to produce a $400 asset share at the end of the third policy year if the gross annual premium were to be $250. If the insurer wishes the third asset share to be 25% larger, by what percentage must the gross premium be increased?

Given:

k	c_k	e_k	$D_{x+k}^{(T)}$
0	.5	10	100,000
1	.4	9	95,000
2	.2	8	85,000
3	.1	7	70,000

A) 16%   B) 18%   C) 20%   D) 25%   E) 28%

15-33   For a $10,000 fully discrete whole life policy to (x), find the absolute difference between the adjusted premium based upon the 1941 Report and that based upon the 1980 Law.

Given: $A_x = .36$, $d = .064$.

A) $0   B) $5   C) $6   D) $9   E) $14

15-34   The net annual premium for a $10,000 fully discrete whole life policy to (60) is $580. If the adjusted premium based on the 1941 Report is 96% of that based on the 1980 Law, find the absolute difference in the adjusted premiums generated by the two statutes.

A) $20   B) $22   C) $24   D) $26   E) $28

15–35 A $1000 fully discrete whole life policy, issued to (20), is placed on the reduced paid up option at the end of the tenth policy year; the resulting face amount is $105.

Given the following values, what was the basis of the determination of the reduced paid up face amount?

x	P_x	P_x^a
20	.0450	.0537
30	.0600	.0660

$d = .10$

A) Net Level Reserve

B) 40% of Net Level Reserve

C) Minimum Cash Value; 1941 Report

D) Minimum Cash Value; 1980 Law

E) None of these

15–36 A $1000 fully discrete whole life policy was issued to (20). After 10 years, a $100 policy loan was effected. The policy loan accrued interest at $i = .05$ for 20 years, at which time the policy was placed on the extended term option. The tabular cash value at age 50 is $500.

Assuming de Moivre's Law with $\omega = 95$, at what age (to the nearest integer) does the term insurance expire?

A) 76　　　　B) 77　　　　C) 78　　　　D) 79　　　　E) 80

15–37 The adjusted premium for a $1000 fully discrete 30-year endowment policy to (30) is 120% of the net level premium. How much reduced paid-up insurance is available at the end of the 15th policy year if the minimum cash value may be applied toward its purchase?

Given: $_{10}W_{30:\overline{30|}} = .45$
$_{5}W_{40:\overline{20|}} = .20$

A) $440　　　　B) $472　　　　C) $500　　　　D) $528　　　　E) $560

15-38   Jones and Brown, each aged 60, lapse their $1000 fully discrete whole life policies and purchase reduced paid up insurance with their net level reserves. Since Jones' policy was issued at age 40, and Brown's at age 55, Jones' paid up face amount is 3.4 times that of Brown.

Smith, who bought an identical policy at the same age as Jones, received a $600 paid-up policy when he lapsed at age 55.

Find the face amount of Brown's paid up policy.

A) $105   B) $200   C) $250   D) $295   E) $357

15-39   If the values of P_x are in geometric progression for $x = 0, 1, 2, \cdots$, and $_{40}W_{20} = .5904$, find $_{30}W_{25}$.

A) .360   B) .488   C) .500   D) .512   E) .640

15-40   A fully discrete $1000 whole life policy to (40) is placed on the automatic premium loan provision at age 50. The gross annual premium is $20. The loan interest rate is $8\frac{1}{2}\%$ and the valuation interest rate is 6%.

If cash values equal full net level reserves after the tenth policy anniversary, how many more full years of coverage will be provided?

Given:

x	A_x	n	$s_{\overline{n}.085}$
40	.343	1	1.000
45	.356	2	2.085
50	.369	3	3.262
51	.383	4	4.540
52	.397	5	5.925
53	.411	6	7.429
54	.425	7	9.060
55	.440	8	10.831
56	.455	9	12.751
57	.469	10	14.835
58	.485		
59	.500		
60	.515		

A) 4   B) 5   C) 6   D) 7   E) 8

15–41 A $1000 fully discrete whole life policy is issued to (x) with a gross annual premium of $200. Expense assumptions are 15% of each gross premium plus $4 per policy per year. The fourth asset share is $65.

Find the fifth tabular cash value, given:

a) The asset share increased by $15 in the fifth policy year.
b) $q_{x+4}^{(d)} = .18$; $q_{x+4}^{(w)} = .20$; $i = .05$.

A) $64.75   B) $65.75   C) $66.75   D) $67.75   E) $68.75

Answers to Chapter Fifteen Exercises

15–1	C.		15–15	E.		15–29	A.
15–2	A.		15–16	B.		15–30	B.
15–3	D.		15–17	E.		15–31	C.
15–4	C.		15–18	B.		15–32	A.
15–5	B.		15–19	A.		15–33	D.
15–6	B.		15–20	C.		15–34	E.
15–7	A.		15–21	B.		15–35	D.
15–8	A.		15–22	B.		15–36	A.
15–9	D.		15–23	D.		15–37	B.
15–10	E.		15–24	C.		15–38	B.
15–11	E.		15–25	B.		15–39	B.
15–12	C.		15–26	B.		15–40	A.
15–13	C.		15–27	E.		15–41	A.
15–14	E.		15–28	E.			

Solutions

15–1.

First, consider the variance of the loss random variable L_1 just *after* the change:

$$L_1 = {}_{10}W_x v^{K+1} - {}_{10}V_x, \quad K = 0, 1, 2, \cdots$$
$$E[L_1] = {}_{10}W_x A_{x+10} - {}_{10}V_x = 0$$
$$E[(L_1)^2] = \text{VAR}[L_1] = ({}_{10}W_x)^2 ({}^2 A_{x+10} - A_{x+10}^2)$$

Next, recall that the variance of the loss random variable L_2 just *before* the change is

$$\text{VAR}[L_2] = \frac{{}^2 A_{x+10} - A_{x+10}^2}{(1 - A_x)^2}.$$

Thus,

$$\frac{\text{VAR}[L_1]}{\text{VAR}[L_2]} = (_{10}W_x)^2(1 - A_x)^2 = .81$$

$$\therefore \, _{10}W_x(1 - A_x) = \frac{_{10}V_x(1 - A_x)}{A_{x+10}} = \frac{A_{x+10} - A_x}{A_{x+10}} = .9$$

$$\therefore \frac{A_x}{A_{x+10}} = .1, \text{ and } \frac{A_{x+10}}{A_x} = \underline{\underline{10}}.$$

15–2.

Key Fact: The absolute maximum value of E_1 permitted by the 1980 Law is $60 per thousand.

Since $_5V_x - {}_5CV_x = (P_x^a - P_x)\ddot{a}_{x+5}$, we have

$$1000(_5V_x - {}_5CV_x) = \frac{60}{\ddot{a}_x}\ddot{a}_{x+5} = 60(1 - {}_5V_x)$$

$$\therefore 300 - 1000\,{}_5CV_x = 60 - 18 = 42$$

$$\therefore 1000\,{}_5CV_x = \underline{\underline{258}}$$

15–3.

Key Formula: $$_5V_{30:\,\overline{10|}} - {}_5CV_{30:\,\overline{10|}} = (P^a_{30:\,\overline{10|}} - P_{30:\,\overline{10|}})\ddot{a}_{35:\,\overline{5|}}$$

$$= \frac{E_1}{\ddot{a}_{30:\,\overline{10|}}}\ddot{a}_{35:\,\overline{5|}}$$

$$= E_1(1 - {}_5V_{30:\,\overline{10|}})$$

Thus,

$$E_1 = \frac{.40 - .37}{1 - .40} = \underline{\underline{.05}}$$

15–4.

Key Formula: $$_nV_x = \frac{A_{x+n} - A_x}{1 - A_x}$$

Thus,

$$\frac{A_y - A_x}{A_y(1 - A_x)} = \frac{_{y-x}V_x}{A_y} = \underline{\underline{{}_{y-x}W_x}}$$

15–5.

Key Formulas:

$$_{30}W_{40} = 1 - (1 - {}_{10}W_{40})(1 - {}_{20}W_{50})$$

$$_{20}W_{50} = 1 - \frac{P_{50}}{P_{70}}$$

Thus,

$$1 - {}_{30}W_{40} = (1 - ({}_{30}W_{40})^2)(1 - {}_{20}W_{50})$$

$$= (1 - ({}_{30}W_{40})^2)\left(\frac{2}{3}\right)$$

$$= (1 - {}_{30}W_{40})(1 + {}_{30}W_{40})\left(\frac{2}{3}\right)$$

$$\therefore 1 = (1 + {}_{30}W_{40})\left(\frac{2}{3}\right)$$

$$\therefore {}_{30}W_{40} = \frac{1}{2}$$

$$\therefore {}_{10}W_{40} = \left(\frac{1}{2}\right)^2 = \underline{\underline{\frac{1}{4}}}$$

15–6.

Key Facts:

In the case of nonlevel premiums and/or benefit amounts, the adjusted premium for any year is the product of r_N and the gross premium for that year. When (as in this case) annual premiums are level, the level adjusted premium is $r_N \cdot G$.

According to the 1980 Law, if the net level premium P is greater than $.04(\text{AAI})$, then $E_1 = .06(\text{AAI})$.

The value of r_N is defined as follows:

$$r_N = \frac{E_1 + \text{actuarial present value of policy benefits}}{\text{actuarial present value of gross premiums}}$$

Since $\text{AAI} = \frac{1}{10}(12 + 11 + 10 + \cdots + 3) = 7.5$, and $P = .55$, it is seen that P is greater than $.04(\text{AAI})$. Thus $E_1 = .06(7.5) = .45$.

Thus,

$$r_N = .96 = \frac{.45 + (DA)_{x:\overline{12|}}}{G\ddot{a}_{x:\overline{12|}}}$$

Finally, the adjusted premium, $.96G$, equals $\dfrac{.45}{\ddot{a}_{x:\overline{12|}}} + P$, or

$$\frac{.45}{9} + .55 = \underline{\underline{.60}}.$$

15–7.

Key Concept: Assuming a unit face amount, it is first necessary to determine the number of *complete* years for which the full unit of insurance may be extended.

$$A_{60:\,\overline{1}|}^{1} = vq_{60} = .95\left(\frac{1}{20}\right) < .15$$

$$A_{60:\,\overline{2}|}^{1} = vq_{60} + v^2{}_{1|}q_{60} = [.95 + (.95)^2]\left(\frac{1}{20}\right) < .15$$

$$A_{60:\,\overline{3}|}^{1} = vq_{60} + v^2{}_{1|}q_{60} + v^3{}_{2|}q_{60} = [.95 + (.95)^2 + (.95)^3]\left(\frac{1}{20}\right) < .15$$

Since $A_{60:\,\overline{4}|}^{1} > .15$, the insurance is extended into the fourth year. The available funds are

$$.15 - A_{60:\,\overline{3}|}^{1} \doteq .0145.$$

The cost of the insurance for the *entire* fourth year would be

$$v^4{}_{3|}q_{60} = .0407.$$

Thus the desired fraction of a year is

$$\frac{.0145}{.0407} \doteq .356, \text{ or } \underline{\underline{130}} \text{ days.}$$

NOTE: More formally, we have

$$.15 = A_{60:\,\overline{3}|}^{1}$$
$$= A_{60:\,\overline{3}|}^{1} + v^4{}_3p_{60} \cdot {}_sq_{63}.$$

Solving, $s \doteq .356$, as before.

15–8.

Key Fact: Since $P_{30:\,\overline{10}|} = \frac{1}{\ddot{a}_{30:\,\overline{10}|}} - d = \frac{1}{8} - .08 > .04$, we know that $P^a > P > .04$. Thus E_1 assumes its maximum value under the 1980 Law, i.e., \$60 per thousand.

Since $P^a_{30:\,\overline{10}|} = P_{30:\,\overline{10}|} + \frac{E_1}{\ddot{a}_{30:\,\overline{10}|}}$, we have

$$P^a_{30:\,\overline{10}|} = \frac{1}{8} - .08 + \frac{.06}{8}$$
$$= \underline{.0525}$$

15–9.

Key Concept: Since the AAI is easily seen to equal \$10,000, it is necessary to determine whether the net annual premium P exceeds \$400. Clearly it does; in fact, it is easily seen to exceed \$1000. This is because (with $i = 0$) a succession of death benefits represented by \$1000, \$2000, \$3000, $\cdots$ would require a \$1000 annual net premium.

Thus,

$$E_1 = .01(\text{AAI}) + 1.25 \min \left\{ \begin{array}{c} P \\ .04(\text{AAI}) \end{array} \right\}$$
$$= 100 + 1.25(400)$$
$$= \underline{\underline{600}}$$

15–10.

Key Formula:
$$_{10}CV - L = (1000 - L)\overline{A}^{1}_{30:\,\overline{20|}}$$

Since $\overline{A}^{1}_{30:\,\overline{20|}} = 1 - \delta\bar{a}_{30:\,\overline{20|}} - {}_{20}E_{30}$
$$= .05,$$
we have

$$240 - L = (1000 - L)(.05),$$

and $L = \underline{\underline{200}}$.

15–11.

Key Fact: If $P_x \geq .04$, then $P_x^a > .04$ and, accordingly

$$^{1980}P_x^a = P_x + \frac{.06}{\ddot{a}_x} = \frac{A_x + .06}{\ddot{a}_x}$$

and

$$^{1941}P_x^a = P_x + \frac{.046}{\ddot{a}_x} = \frac{A_x + .046}{\ddot{a}_x}$$

Thus,

$$\frac{^{1944}P_x^a}{^{1980}P_x^a} = \frac{A_x + .046}{A_x + .06} = .9$$

Finally,

$$A_x = .08 = \frac{q}{q + i}$$

$\therefore$ Since $q = .08$, we have $i = \underline{\underline{.92}}$.

15–12.

Key Approach: In order to apply Lidstone's Theorem, the critical function

$$c_h = ({}_hV + P)(i' - i) - (q'_h - q_h)(1 - {}_{h+1}V)$$

must be analyzed.

Note that $i' - i = i + i^2$, a positive constant which we shall represent by m. Thus,

$$c_h = m({}_hV + P) - k(1 - {}_{h+1}V).$$

It is known that reserves increase with duration since mortality rates are monotonically increasing.

Finally, it is evident that $m({}_hV + P)$ is increasing, while $k(1 - {}_{h+1}V)$ is decreasing. However, the quantity $-k(1 - {}_{h+1}V)$ is increasing. Thus c_h increases for all h, $h = 1, 2, \ldots, n - 1$.

Thus,

$$_hV_{x:\overline{n}|} > {}_hV'_{x:\overline{n}|}$$

and

$$\underline{{}_hV'_{x:\overline{n}|} - {}_hV_{x:\overline{n}|} \text{ is negative.}}$$

NOTE: The reserves would be equal at duration zero and duration n.

15–13.

Key Concept: The value of P_x *must* be less than .04. If it were *greater* than .04, then the adjusted premiums under the 1941 Report and the 1980 Law could not be equal, because ${}^{1941}E_1$ would equal .046 and ${}^{1980}E_1$ would equal .060.

Since $P_x < .04 < P_x^a$,

$$^{1941}E_1 = .046 \text{ and}$$
$$^{1980}E_1 = .01 + 1.25P_x.$$

Thus

$$.046 = .01 + 1.25P_x, \text{ and}$$
$$P_x = .0288.$$

Finally,

$$P_x^a = P_x + \frac{E_1}{\ddot{a}_x} = P_x + E_1(P_x + d)$$
$$= .0288 + .046(.0288 + .25)$$
$$= \underline{.0416}$$

15–14.

Key Concept: Since $AAI = 6000$, the 1980 Law produces $E_1 = .06(6000) = 360$ if $P > .04(6000) = 240$. It must then be determined whether the level premium P exceeds 240.

$$P\ddot{a}_{x:\overline{10|}} = 2195$$
$$\therefore P = \frac{2195}{\ddot{a}_{x:\overline{10|}}} = \frac{2195d}{1 - A_{x:\overline{10|}}} = 313 > 240$$

Thus, $E_1 = \underline{360}$.

15–15.

Key Approach: At attained age $x + 7$, we equate the minimum cash value on the endowment policy to the present value of benefits purchased on the extended term option, letting K equal the face amount of the pure endowment.

$$A_{x+7:\overline{3|}} - P^a \ddot{a}_{x+7:\overline{3|}} = A\frac{1}{x+7:\overline{3|}} + K \cdot {}_3E_{x+7}$$

Thus

$${}_3E_{x+7} - P^a \ddot{a}_{x+7:\overline{3|}} = K {}_3E_{x+7},$$
$$\text{and}$$
$$K = \frac{.90 - (.08)(2.50)}{.90}$$
$$= \underline{\underline{7/9}}$$

15–16.

Key Approach: We must equate the variance of ${}_{20}L$ under the whole life policy to the variance of $Z = (1 + .01K)_{20}W_{35}v^{K+1}$, the present value random variable just after conversion to a paid-up plan.

Key Formula:

$$_nW_x = \frac{_nV_x}{A_{x+n}} = \frac{A_{x+n} - A_x}{A_{x+n}(1 - A_x)}$$

Thus,

$$\frac{^2A_{55} - A_{55}^2}{(1 - A_{35})^2} = (1 + .01K)^2 (_{20}W_{35})^2 (^2A_{55} - A_{55}^2)$$

$$\therefore 1 + .01K = \frac{1}{(1 - A_{35})(_{20}W_{35})} = \frac{A_{55}}{A_{55} - A_{35}}$$

Finally,

$$1 + .01K = \frac{A_{55}}{A_{55} - A_{35}} = \frac{1 - d\ddot{a}_{55}}{d(\ddot{a}_{35} - \ddot{a}_{55})} = 1.1$$

$$\therefore \underline{K = 10}$$

15–17.

Key Formula:

Since only *mortality* experience differed from expected results,

$$_{k+1}\widehat{AS} - _{k+1}AS = q_{x+k}^{(1)}(1000 - _{k+1}AS)$$
$$- \hat{q}_{x+k}^{(1)}(1000 - _{k+1}\widehat{AS})$$
$$+ q_{x+k}^{(2)}(_{k+1}\widehat{AS} - _{k+1}AS).$$

NOTE: Even though withdrawal experience equals that which was expected, an adjustment term involving the probability of withdrawal is required. This is because the "amount at risk" for withdrawals, $_{k+1}CV - _{k+1}AS$, changes as asset shares change.

Using the given formula,

$$_6\widehat{AS} = 75 + .01(925) - .012(1000 - _6\widehat{AS})$$
$$+ q_{x+5}^{(2)}(_6\widehat{AS} - 75).$$

Since there is no way to determine $q_{x+5}^{(2)}$, it is __impossible__ to find $_6\widehat{AS}$.

15–18.

Key Concept:

Of each dollar added to the gross premium, ninety cents are available for the purpose of increasing the subsequent asset shares. Thus, the increase in the 20th asset share generated by an extra dollar of premium is

$$.9\ddot{s}_{35:\overline{20}|} = .9\frac{N_{35}^{(T)} - N_{55}^{(T)}}{D_{55}^{(T)}} \doteq 27.055.$$

Thus, in order to generate an increase of $200 in the 20th asset share, a premium increase is required in the amount

$$\Delta G = \frac{200}{27.055} \doteq 7.39 \,,$$

and the resulting premium is $\underline{\$19.89}$.

NOTE: More formally, the formula

$$200 = \sum_{k=0}^{19} (G_2 - G_1)(.9) l_{35+k}^{(T)} (1+i)^{20-k} \left(\frac{1}{l_{55}^{(T)}} \right)$$

could be applied.

15–19.

Key Formulas:

$$_n V_x = \frac{A_{x+n} - A_x}{1 - A_x} = {_n}W_x A_{x+n}$$

Thus,

$$A_{x+10} = \frac{_{10}V_x}{_{10}W_x} = 2/3$$

$$_{10}V_x = \frac{2/3 - A_x}{1 - A_x} = 4/15$$

$$\therefore A_x = 6/11$$

$$_{15}V_x = \frac{A_{x+15} - 6/11}{1 - 6/11} = (8/15)A_{x+15}$$

$$\therefore A_{x+15} = 18/25$$

Finally, $_{15}V_x = \frac{8}{15} \cdot \frac{18}{25} = \frac{48}{125} = \underline{.384}$

15–20.

Key Fact:

Since $P_{x:\overline{10|}} = \frac{1}{\ddot{a}_{x:\overline{10|}}} - d = .1 > .04$, we know that

$$P_{x:\overline{10|}}^a = P_{x:\overline{10|}} + \frac{.06}{\ddot{a}_{x:\overline{10|}}} = .112.$$

Now,

$$\alpha + \beta a_{x:\overline{9|}} = A_{x:\overline{10|}} = \frac{1}{2}$$

$$\therefore \alpha = \frac{1}{2} - .112(4) = \underline{.052}$$

NOTE: It is possible to relate the concept of adjusted premiums to that of modified reserves by letting

$$\alpha = P^a - E_1 \text{ and}$$
$$\beta = P^a.$$

Thus, $\alpha = .112 - .06 = \underline{.052}$.

15–21.

Key Formula:

$$1 - {}_nV_x = \frac{1 - A_{x+n}}{1 - A_x}$$

Thus,

$$1 - \frac{A_b(1 - {}_aV_b)}{A_{a+b}} = 1 - \frac{A_b(1 - A_{a+b})}{A_{a+b}(1 - A_b)}$$
$$= 1 - \frac{A_b \cdot d\ddot{a}_{a+b}}{A_{a+b} \cdot d\ddot{a}_b}$$
$$= 1 - \frac{P_b}{P_{a+b}} = \underline{\underline{{}_aW_b}}$$

15–22.

Key Concept: The cash value remaining at age 56 is the tabular cash value reduced by the indebtedness generated by the automatic premium loans.

Thus,

$$\begin{aligned}
{}_{16}CV &= 10,000A_{56} - 10,000P_{40}^a\ddot{a}_{56} \\
&= 3800 - 150\frac{1 - A_{56}}{d} \\
&= 1847
\end{aligned}$$

The remaining cash value is

$$1847 - 250\ddot{s}_{\overline{6}|.05} \doteq \underline{61.50}$$

15–23.

Key Formula:

$$_{k}^{n}W_{x} = 1 - \frac{_{n}P_{x}}{_{n-k}P_{x+k}}$$

Thus,

$$.8 = \frac{_{15}P_{20}}{_{5}P_{30}}$$

$$\therefore _{15}P_{20} = .16$$

$$_{5}^{15}W_{20} = 1 - \frac{_{15}P_{20}}{_{10}P_{25}}$$

$$= 1 - \frac{.16}{.18} = \underline{\underline{1/9.}}$$

15–24.

Key Formulas

Assuming that only the interest rate varies from that which was projected,

$$[_{k}AS + G(1 - c_{k}) - e_{k}](1 + i) = p_{x+k}^{(T)}{}_{k+1}AS + q_{x+k}^{(1)} + q_{x+k}^{(2)} \cdot {}_{k+1}CV$$

$$[_{k}AS + G(1 - c_{k}) - e_{k}](1 + i') = p_{x+k}^{(T)}{}_{k+1}\widehat{AS} + q_{x+k}^{(1)} + q_{x+k}^{(2)} \cdot {}_{k+1}CV$$

Letting $i' = i + .005$, and subtracting,

$$(140 + 60(.9) - 14)(.005) = p_{x+k}^{(T)}(1)$$

$$\therefore p_{x+k}^{(T)} = .9$$

$$\therefore q_{x+k}^{(T)} = .1 = q_{x+k}^{(2)}(5/3)$$

$$\therefore q_{x+k}^{(2)} = .06$$

$$\therefore q_{x+k}^{(1)} = \underline{\underline{.04}}$$

15–25.

Key Approach:

In the analysis of Lidstone's critical function,

$$c_{h} = (_{h}V + P)(i' - i) + (q_{h} - q_{h}')(1 - {}_{h+1}V)$$

we must impose the hypothesis that $q_{h} - q_{h}'$ is a positive, decreasing function.

I.

Since $_{h}V + P$ is positive and increasing, and $i' - i$ is negative and constant, then $(_{h}V + P)(i' - i)$ is negative and decreasing.

Since $q_h - q_h'$ is positive and decreasing, and $(1 - _{h+1}V)$ is positive and decreasing, then $(q_h - q_h')(1 - _{h+1}V)$ is positive and decreasing.

Thus c_h is decreasing; I is true.

II. Since S_h equals c_h plus a constant, again it suffices to analyze c_h. But $q_h - q_h'$ is positive and decreasing while $(1 - _{h+1}V)$ is positive and increasing, it is impossible to determine whether their product is increasing or decreasing.

III. Since $_hV + P$ is positive and increasing, we see that $(_hV + P)(i' - i)$ is also positive and increasing. Since $q_h - q_h'$ and $(1 - _{h+1}V)$ are both positive and decreasing, we see that $(q_h - q_h')(1 - _{h+1}V)$ is positive and decreasing. Thus, it is impossible to determine whether c_h increases or decreases—it may well do neither over its entire range.

$\therefore$ $\underline{\underline{\text{I only}}}$.

15–26.

Key Concept: Since $^{1941}E_1$ is less than the \$46 maximum, we know that P_{30}^a must be less than .04.

$$\therefore E_1 = .02 + .4(.04) + .25P_{30}^a = .045$$
$$\therefore P_{30}^a = .036$$

For a whole life policy to (30),
$$P_{30}^a \ddot{a}_{30} = A_{30} + .02 + .65P_{30}^a$$
$$= 1 - .075\ddot{a}_{30} + .02 + .65P_{30}^a$$
$$\therefore \ddot{a}_{30} = 9.4$$
$$\ddot{a}_{30:\overline{5}|} = \frac{1}{P_{30:\overline{5}|} + d} = 4$$
$$\ddot{a}_{30} = \ddot{a}_{30:\overline{5}|} + v^5 {_5}p_{30}\ddot{a}_{35}$$
$$\therefore \ddot{a}_{35} = \frac{9.4 - 4}{(.925)^5(.9)} = 8.86$$

Finally,
$$1000 {_5}V_{30} = 1000\left(1 - \frac{\ddot{a}_{35}}{\ddot{a}_{30}}\right) = \underline{\underline{57}}$$

15-27.

Key Approach: The required cash value is represented by $A_{50} - P^a \ddot{a}_{50:\overline{15}|}$. Thus we only need P^a.

Knowing that $P^a_{40} < .04$, and assuming that $_{25}P^a_{40} < .04$, we have
$$_{25}P^a_{40} \cdot \ddot{a}_{40:\overline{25}|} = A_{40} + .02 + .4_{25}P^a_{40} + .25P^a_{40}.$$

Solving,
$$_{25}P^a_{40} = .017$$
(Thus the assumption on $_{25}P^a_{40}$ was correct.)

Finally,
$$_{10}CV = .33 - (.017)(10) = .16$$
$$\therefore 1000_{10}CV = \underline{160}$$

15-28.

The given fact states that
$$.04275 = .02 + .65^{1941}P^a_x = .01 + 1.25P_x,$$
since clearly both P^a_x and P_x are less than .04.

Thus $^{1941}P^a_x = .035$ and $P_x = .0262$.

Since
$$^{1941}P^a_x \cdot \ddot{a}_x = A_x + .04275,$$
we have $^{1941}P^a_x = P_x + .04275(P_x + d)$
$$\therefore d = \underline{.180}$$

15-29.

Key Approach: Based upon the "1988 Rule", we have
$$P^a_{30}\ddot{a}_{30} = A_{30} + .01 + \min \begin{pmatrix} .03 \\ P^a_{30} \\ 1.25\,P_{30} \end{pmatrix}.$$

We must, by trial and error, determine which of the three quantities in the above parentheses is the smallest.

Note that $A_{30} = 1 - \frac{3}{103}(20.6) = .4$ and that $P_{30} = \frac{.4}{20.6} = .01942$.
Thus .03 is clearly *not* the smallest of the three quantities in question.

Thus, we will assume that $P_{30}^a > 1.25 P_{30}$. Accordingly,

$$P_{30}^a(20.6) = .41 + 1.25(.01942).$$

Solving gives $P_{30}^a = .021$, a value less than $1.25\ P_{30}$. Our "trial and error" assumption, then, was erroneous.

Now, we are certain that $P_{30}^a < 1.25\ P_{30}$. Accordingly,

$$P_{30}^a(20.6) = .41 + P_{30}^a$$
$$\therefore P_{30}^a = .0209, \text{ and}$$
$$10,000 P_{30}^a = \underline{\underline{209}}.$$

15–30.

Key Formulas: The reduced paid-up insurance purchased by the net level reserve and the minimum cash value, respectively, at duration 10 on fully discrete whole life policies to (40) are

$$1 - \frac{P_{30}}{P_{40}} = \frac{_{10}V_{30}}{A_{40}}$$
$$\text{and}$$
$$1 - \frac{P_{30}^a}{P_{40}} = \frac{_{10}CV_{30}}{A_{40}}.$$

Thus, dividing produces

$$\frac{P_{40} - P_{30}}{P_{40} - P_{30}^a} = \frac{_{10}V_{30}}{_{10}CV_{30}}.$$

Finally,

$$\frac{_{10}V_{30}}{_{10}CV_{30}} = \frac{.06 - .04}{.06 - .04(1.2)} = 5/3,$$

and the required fraction is $\underline{\underline{.6}}$.

15–31.

Key Formula: $$_{11}AS = \frac{_{10}AS + G(1 - c_{10}) - e_{10} - vq_{x+10}^{(1)} - vq_{x+10}^{(2)} \cdot {}_{11}CV}{_{1}E_{x+10}^{(T)}}$$

Letting F represent the face amount, and inserting the given data, we have

$$986.45 = \frac{1000 + .01F(.9) - .0004F - \frac{F}{1.06}(.02) - \frac{1}{1.06}(.18)(90)}{\frac{1}{1.06}(.8)}$$

Solving, $F = \underline{\underline{10,000}}$.

15–32.

Key Concept: If the gross premium is increased by \$1, the funds available to generate a larger asset share at duration three are 50¢, 60¢, and 80¢, respectively, at the beginnings of the first three policy years.

Accumulating these excesses with interest and survivorship up to the end of the third policy year, we obtain

$$\frac{.5D_x^{(T)} + .6D_{x+1}^{(T)} + .8D_{x+2}^{(T)}}{D_{x+3}^{(T)}} = 2.5.$$

Thus, an extra dollar of annual premium increases the third asset share by \$2.50. Since we want the third asset share to be increased by \$100, the increment in the annual premium must be

$$\frac{100}{2.5}, \text{ or } \$40.$$

Finally the new gross premium becomes \$290, an increase of $\frac{40}{250}$, or <u>16%</u>.

NOTE: Whereas a substantially more sophisticated formula could be applied, the solution shown seems far more desirable because of its logical, intuitive nature.

15–33.

Key Formula:

$$^{1980}P_x^a - {}^{1941}P_x^a = ({}^{1980}P_x^a - P_x) - ({}^{1941}P_x^a - P_x)$$

$$= \frac{^{1980}E_1 - {}^{1941}E_1}{\ddot{a}_x}$$

It is clear that $^{1980}E_1 = .01 + 1.25P_x = .055$. Thus we only need $^{1941}E_1$.

Since $P_x = .036$, let us *assume* that $^{1941}P_x^a > .04$. Then $^{1941}E_1$ would equal .046. To verify the validity of this assumption, we must calculate $^{1941}P_x^a$.

$$^{1941}P_x^a = P_x + \frac{.046}{\ddot{a}_x} = .0406 > .04.$$

Thus the assumption was correct.

Finally,

$$^{1980}P_x^a - {}^{1941}P_x^a = \frac{.055 - .046}{10} = .0009$$

For a \$10,000 policy, the required difference is thus $\underline{\underline{\$9}}$.

NOTE: Had the assumption that $^{1941}P_x^a > .04$ proven to be incorrect, the problem would have entailed extra effort and somewhat more difficulty.

15–34.

Key Concept:

Since the net level premium exceeds \$40 per thousand, it is easily seen that the values of E_1 are \$460 and \$600, respectively, for the 1941 Report and the 1980 Law.

Key Formula:

$$^{1980}P_{60}^a - {}^{1941}P_{60}^a = \frac{^{1980}E_1 - {}^{1941}E_1}{\ddot{a}_{60}}$$

The problem, then, is to determine the value of $\ddot{a}_{60}$.

Using the given relationship between the adjusted premiums, we have

$$P_{60} + \frac{.046}{\ddot{a}_{60}} = (.96)\left(P_{60} + \frac{.060}{\ddot{a}_{60}}\right)$$

$$.058 + \frac{.046}{\ddot{a}_{60}} = (.96)\left(.058 + \frac{.060}{\ddot{a}_{60}}\right).$$

Solving, $\ddot{a}_{60} = 5$, and thus the required difference is

$$\frac{600 - 460}{5} = \underline{\underline{28}}.$$

15–35.

Key Approach:

Since the available nonforfeiture value equals

$$105A_{30} = 105\frac{P_{30}}{P_{30} + d} = 39.375,$$

it is necessary to determine which of the possible answers would generate a value of 39.375.

A) Net Level Reserve

$$1000\,_{10}V_{20} = 1000\frac{P_{30} - P_{20}}{P_{30} + d} = 93.75 \neq 39.375$$

B) 40% of Net Level Reserve

$$400\,_{10}V_{20} = 37.5 \neq 39.375$$

C) 1941 Report

$$P_{20}^a = P_{20} + \frac{.046}{\ddot{a}_{20}} = P_{20} + .046(P_{20} + d)$$

This equation is inconsistent with the given data.

D) 1980 Law

$$P_{20}^a = P_{20} + \frac{.060}{\ddot{a}_{20}} = P_{20} + .060(P_{20} + d)$$

This equation is consistent with the given data. Thus, the 1980 Law *may* be the correct basis.

As a check, the tenth minimum cash value under this basis is

$$_{10}CV = A_{30} - P_{20}^a \ddot{a}_{30}$$
$$= \frac{P_{30}}{P_{30} + d} - P_{20}^a \frac{1}{P_{30} + d}$$
$$= .039375, \text{ as desired.}$$

Thus, $\underline{D}$ is the correct basis.

15–36.

Key Concepts:

The fund available to purchase extended term at age 50 is the tabular cash value reduced by the outstanding loan balance, i.e.,

$$500 - 100(1.05)^{20} = 234.67.$$

The amount of extended term insurance which may be purchased is the original face amount less the loan balance.

Thus,

$$234.67 = (1000 - 265.33)A_{50:\overline{n}|}^1.$$

Under de Moivre's Law, we have

$$234.67 = 734.67\frac{a_{\overline{n}|}}{45}$$
$$\therefore a_{\overline{n}|} = 14.374$$

Using interest tables at $i = .05$, we obtain $n = 26$. Thus, the insurance expires at age $\underline{76}$.

15–37.

Key Formulas: The desired quantity is $1 - \dfrac{P^a_{30:\overline{30|}}}{P_{45:\overline{15|}}}$, or, in this case $1 - \dfrac{1.2P_{30:\overline{30|}}}{P_{45:\overline{15|}}}$.

Further, this equals $1 - 1.2(1 - {}_{15}W_{30:\overline{30|}})$. But

$$_{15}W_{30:\overline{30|}} = 1 - (1 - {}_{10}W_{30:\overline{30|}})(1 - {}_5W_{40:\overline{20|}}).$$

Thus, we need

$$1 - 1.2(1 - {}_{10}W_{30:\overline{30|}})(1 - {}_5W_{40:\overline{20|}}).$$

Applying the given data, the required value is

$$1 - 1.2(.55)(.80) = .472.$$

In a \$1000 policy, $\underline{\$472}$ of reduced paid-up insurance may be purchased.

15–38.

Given Facts:
$$_{20}W_{40} = 3.4\,{}_5W_{55}$$
$$_{15}W_{40} = .6$$

Key Formula:
$$_{20}W_{40} = 1 - (1 - {}_{15}W_{40})(1 - {}_5W_{55}).$$

Thus,

$$3.4\,{}_5W_{55} = 1 - (.4)(1 - {}_5W_{55})$$
$$\therefore {}_5W_{55} = .2$$

The face amount of Brown's paid-up policy is thus seen to be

$$1000(.2) = \underline{200}.$$

15–39.

Key Formula:
$$_nW_x = 1 - \frac{P_x}{P_{x+n}}$$

Since $P_t = P_0 \cdot r^t$, $t = 0, 1, 2, \cdots$, we have

$$_{40}W_{20} = 1 - \frac{P_{20}}{P_{60}} = 1 - \left(\frac{1}{r}\right)^{40} = .5904$$

$$\therefore \left(\frac{1}{r}\right)^{40} = .4096 = (.8)^4$$

$$\therefore \left(\frac{1}{r}\right)^{10} = .8$$

Finally,

$$_{30}W_{25} = 1 - \frac{P_{25}}{P_{55}} = 1 - \left(\frac{1}{r}\right)^{30} = 1 - (.8)^3 = \underline{\underline{.488}}$$

15–40.

Key Approach: We must find the value of t for which

$$20\ddot{s}_{\overline{7}|} \leq {}_{10+t}CV = {}_{10+t}V$$
$$\text{and}$$
$$20\ddot{s}_{\overline{t+1}|} > {}_{10+t}CV = {}_{10+t}V$$

We use a trial-and-error approach:

i) Let $t = 3$

$$_{13}V_{40} = \frac{A_{53} - A_{40}}{1 - A_{40}} = .1035$$
$$20\ddot{s}_{\overline{3}|} = 70.79$$
$$20\ddot{s}_{\overline{4}|} = 98.52 \quad \therefore t \neq 3$$

ii) Let $t = 4$

$$_{14}V_{40} = \frac{A_{54} - A_{40}}{1 - A_{40}} = .1248$$
$$20\ddot{s}_{\overline{4}|} = 98.52$$
$$20\ddot{s}_{\overline{5}|} = 128.57$$

This satisfies the given criterion, and thus <u>four</u> full years of coverage may be provided.

NOTE: If the policy were continued for the fifth year (age 54 to age 55), the loan balance would exceed the available funds ($_{14}V$) before year-end.

15–41.

Key Formula:

$$_5AS = \frac{_4AS + G(1 - c_4) - e_4 - vq_{x+4}^{(1)} - vq_{x+4}^{(2)} \cdot {}_5CV}{_1E_{x+4}^{(T)}}$$

Plugging in the given values, we have

$$80 = \frac{65 + 200(.85) - 4 - \frac{1000}{1.05}(.18) - \frac{1}{1.05}(.20)_5CV}{\frac{1}{1.05}(.62)}$$

Solving, $_5CV = \underline{64.75}$.